INTRODUCTION

TO

MECHANICS AND HEAT

INTRODUCTION
TO
MECHANICS AND HEAT

BY

NATHANIEL H. FRANK, Sc.D.

Associate Professor of Physics
Massachusetts Institute of Technology

SECOND EDITION
SECOND IMPRESSION

McGRAW-HILL BOOK COMPANY, Inc.

NEW YORK AND LONDON

1939

THE MAPLE PRESS COMPANY, YORK, PA.

PREFACE TO THE SECOND EDITION

During the four years that have elapsed since its initial appearance, this book has been subjected to the careful scrutiny of the members of the staff at the Massachusetts Institute of Technology engaged in teaching the elementary physics course and to the merciless criticism of the students using it as a text. It is gratifying that the scope of the book and the general order and treatment of the material have proved satisfactory and that a basic revision has not been found necessary. Hence in this second edition a number of topics have been rewritten in an attempt to improve the mode of exposition rather than to alter the original aims and material.

It seems advisable in a preface of this sort to list the more important revisions that have been made. First, Chap. II on linear kinematics has been completely reworked and expanded so as to lessen the difficulties that invariably confront the beginning student who is learning the elements of calculus at the same time. Enough detail has been included to make the subject matter in this chapter self-contained. A final section on some of the aspects of the kinematics of circular motion has been inserted to acquaint the student as early as possible with the concepts of angular velocity and angular acceleration, treating the motion as an example of a motion of one degree of freedom.

In Chap. III the geometrical proof of the radial acceleration in circular motion has been changed to bring out more clearly the concept of the rate of change of a rotating vector. In the chapter on plane dynamics a sharper distinction between constrained and non-constrained motion has been drawn and projectile motion is treated as an example of the latter type of motion rather than as a separate subject. The ever-troublesome subject of potential energy has been completely rewritten and the presentation of simple harmonic motion has been altered so that the kinematical aspects of the motion are discussed before the dynamics of the motion are studied. In addition, a section on resonance without friction is inserted at this point to avoid some of the difficulties that occur when the subject is deferred to the chapter on acoustics.   The discussion of angular momentum has been revised and that of gravitational potential expanded with an eye to the student's later study of electrostatics.   The chapter on static elasticity proved to be too concise and has now been completely rewritten and expanded.   In the chapter on dynamics of elasticity the treatment of wave motion has been changed, and throughout the chapters on heat many minor revisions and corrections have been incorporated.

A large number of new problems have been included, some of them of a very elementary nature, as well as a number of more difficult ones.   It is hoped that these additional problems will help to avoid too much duplication of assignments from year to year as well as provide a greater range in complexity.

It would be virtually impossible for me to express my thanks individually to all who have been kind enough to offer their aid in the form of suggestions and of criticisms.   These include both colleagues and students.   To all of them I wish to express my deepest gratitude.

N. H. FRANK.

CAMBRIDGE, MASS.,
March, 1939.

PREFACE TO THE FIRST EDITION

This book has its origin in the development of a course in physics. This course is the first of a sequence of two full years of physics at the Massachusetts Institute of Technology, a basic elementary course required for all but a few of the students at the Institute. In attempting to describe the nature and purpose of this course, it is, I believe, necessary to point out the sharp differences which exist between two types of elementary physics course taught in our universities and technical schools. On the one hand exists the general survey course studied by students who, in general, have no intention of pursuing scientific or technical careers. This type of course essentially minimizes the use of mathematical methods and necessarily is of a descriptive nature. On the other hand students intending to pursue scientific or engineering professions must be given a course in physics which is far more exacting and thorough, especially with respect to the use of mathematical methods, than the usual survey course. After all, physics is fundamental as a basis for all technical and engineering subjects. It is hoped that the present book will serve a purpose for this type of elementary or intermediate course in technical physics, where a thorough quantitative foundation is desired.

In the preparation of this book the guiding thought has been to develop a logical unified treatment of the subject matter, comprising the topics of mechanics, acoustics, and heat, so that the student may learn to appreciate and to utilize fundamental and general methods of attack on problems in all branches of physics. The attempt has been made to discourage the use of special formulas for special problems, unless the relation of such special formulas to general principles has been carefully expounded. It is clear that such a program can be successfully carried out only if elementary calculus is employed from the very outset; yet the subject matter is so arranged that a concurrent course in calculus may provide the student with all the necessary mathematical tools.

After an introduction to the kinematics of particle motion on a straight line and in a plane, a chapter has been inserted presenting Newton's laws and dealing with particle statics. The object in doing this is to allow the student to grasp the fundamental notion of force as a vector quantity before embarking into the realm of dynamics proper. Thus the troublesome question of units is separated from the study of forces as such. The discussion of planetary motion and of gravitation is placed after the chapters on rigid body statics and dynamics so as to serve as introduction to the general concept of force fields. Thus a smooth transition is made to the mechanics of continuous media. The latter subject is treated more extensively than in most elementary discussions so as to impress on the student that the general principles employed in particle and rigid body mechanics form the basis of this subject. In the last sections devoted to topics in heat, a close connection to mechanical principles is maintained by developing the elementary kinetic theory of gases. As already stated, every attempt has been made to develop the ideas as a single unified structure, each section building on the previously developed material.

It should be emphasized that the primary purpose of this book is definitely that of a guiding textbook, and, as such, it may advantageously be supplemented by laboratory work and more extensive descriptive material. The latter has been minimized for two principal reasons. In the first place, any attempt properly to introduce all the descriptive matter pertinent to the subjects treated would result in an unwieldy book. Second, too much descriptive physics interspersed with a logical systematic development of physical principles tends to hinder the student from grasping the well-ordered continuity of thought and method pervading the whole quantitative structure of physics. Thus the ratio of qualitative to quantitative material is smallest at the beginning, but of necessity increases in the later chapters where the properties of matter are introduced.

A number of sections have been set in smaller type than the main body of the text. These, and perhaps a few of the regular sections, may well be omitted in a first course. The primary purpose of these sections is that of completeness to the extent that no wide gaps be left between this book and those used in more advanced treatments of similar subjects. A number of problems have been included at the end of each chapter. I firmly believe that no adequate understanding of physical principles can be obtained without ample practice in applying these principles to many and varied problems. It is a common experience of teachers to hear students maintain that they understand the theory perfectly but are unable to solve problems. An attempt has been made to design the problems so that they will truly test the student's understanding of principles without leading to unnecessary mathematical complications.

I should like to express my thanks to several of my colleagues for many helpful suggestions, and especially to Dr. M. F. Manning, whose keen interest and constant criticism have done much toward giving this book its final form.

N. H. F.

CAMBRIDGE, MASS.,
August, 1934.

CONTENTS

PAGE

PREFACE TO THE SECOND EDITION. v

PREFACE TO THE FIRST EDITION. vii

CHAPTER I

FUNDAMENTAL DEFINITIONS

Introduction. 1
1. Divisions of Physics 1
2. Definition of Mechanics. 3
3. Definitions of Physical Quantities 4
4. The Measurement of Length. 4
5. The Measurement of Time 6
6. Material Bodies; Divisions of Mechanics 6

CHAPTER II

LINEAR KINEMATICS OF A MASS POINT

Introduction. 8
7. Reference Systems 8
8. Graphical Description of Linear Motion: Velocity 9
9. Acceleration in Straight-line Motion 14
10. Equations of Motion 17
11. Angular Motion 25
    Problems 27

CHAPTER III

PLANE KINEMATICS OF A MASS POINT

Introduction. 32
12. Vectors in a Plane 32
13. Velocity and Acceleration in a Plane; Circular Motion 37
14. Circular Motion with Variable Speed. 42
    Problems 44

CHAPTER IV

NEWTON'S LAWS: STATICS OF A PARTICLE

Introduction. 47
15. The Concept of Inertia 47
16. The Concept of Force. 48
17. The Concept of Mass; Momentum. 49
18. Forces Occur in Pairs. 51
19. Newton's Laws of Motion. 51
20. Examples. 52

PAGE

21. The Static Measure of Force. 53
22. Classification of Forces 54
23. Equilibrium of a Particle 55
    Problems 58

CHAPTER V

LINEAR AND PLANE DYNAMICS

Introduction. 61
24. Dynamical Measure of Force; Units 61
25. Freely Falling Bodies. 62
26. Application of Newton's Laws to Rectilinear Motion 63
27. Example 65
28. Newton's Laws for Plane Motion. 67
29. Constrained Motion 71
30. Conservation of Momentum for Rectilinear Motion. 75
31. Conservation of Momentum for Plane Motion. 76
32. Impulse-momentum Theorem 78
33. Application of the Impulse-momentum Theorem to Plane Motion 78
    Problems 80

CHAPTER VI

WORK AND ENERGY; POTENTIAL ENERGY

Introduction. 87
34. Fundamental Definitions; Motion in a Straight Line 87
35. Work-energy Theorem for Plane Motion 90
36. Potential Energy; Straight-line Motion 91
37. Potential Energy; General Case for Plane Motion 94
38. Example: Equipotential Surfaces. 95
39. Power 97
    Problems 98

CHAPTER VII

SPECIAL DYNAMICS OF A MASS POINT

Introduction. 104
40. The Ballistic Pendulum. 104
41. Collisions; Coefficient of Restitution 106
42. Periodic Motion; Kinematics of Simple Harmonic Motion. . . 110
42a. Initial Conditions for Simple Harmonic Motion. 113
43. Dynamics of Simple Harmonic Motion; Hooke's Law. 114
44. Forced Harmonic Motion; Resonance. 116
45. The Simple Pendulum 119
46. Lissajous Figures. 121
47. Effect of the Earth's Rotation on the Value of g 123
    Problems 125

CHAPTER VIII

DYNAMICS OF A SYSTEM OF PARTICLES

Introduction. 131
48. Motion of Two Particles; Center of Mass 131

PAGE

49. Center of Mass (*Continued*) 134
50. Examples. 136
51. Kinetic Energy of a System of Particles. 140
52. Work-energy Theorem for a System of Particles 142
   Problems 143

CHAPTER IX
STATICS OF RIGID BODIES

Introduction. 146
53. Plane Motion of a Rigid Body; Degrees of Freedom 146
54. Equilibrium Conditions for Rigid Bodies; Moments of Forces . . 147
55. Analytic Representation of Moments of Forces. 149
56. Equilibrium Equations 150
57. Examples. 152
   Problems 156

CHAPTER X
PLANE DYNAMICS OF RIGID BODIES

Introduction. 160
58. Translation of a Rigid Body. 160
59. Rotation of a Rigid Body about a Fixed Axis 162
60. Calculation of Moment of Inertia; Radius of Gyration 165
61. Relation of Moments of Inertia about Different Axes. 169
62. Energy Relations for Rotation. 172
63. Combined Translation and Rotation 175
64. Instantaneous Axis for Rolling Bodies. 177
65. Energy Relations for Combined Translation and Rotation. . . . 179
66. Rolling and Sliding. 183
   Problems 185

CHAPTER XI
SPECIAL RIGID-BODY MOTIONS

Introduction. 191
67. The Physical Pendulum. 191
68. Center of Oscillation 193
69. The Torsion Pendulum 193
70. Angular Velocity and Torque as Vectors 194
71. Angular Momentum and Its Conservation. 196
72. Angular Impulse-Angular Momentum Theorem 199
73. Center of Percussion 199
74. The Gyroscope; Precession 200
   Problems 203

CHAPTER XII
PLANETARY MOTION; GRAVITATION

Introduction. 206
75. Kepler's Laws 206
76. Field of Force; Gravitational Potential 208
77. The Potential of a Sphere. 211

PAGE
78. Variations of g with Altitude. 212
Problems 214

CHAPTER XIII
HYDROSTATICS
Introduction. 217
79. Pressure. 219
80. Law of Equilibrium. 220
81. Applications. 222
82. The Free Surface of a Liquid 224
83. Surface Tension 225
84. Coefficient of Surface Tension; Surface Energy. 226
85. Formation of Drops; Capillary Rise 228
86. Excess Pressure in Bubbles 230
Problems 231

CHAPTER XIV
FLUID DYNAMICS
Introduction. 235
87. Stationary Flow 236
88. Equation of Continuity. 237
89. Bernoulli's Principle 239
90. Applications of Bernoulli's Principle 241
91. Qualitative Examples. 244
92. Viscosity; Coefficient of Viscosity. 245
93. Laminar Flow in Cylindrical Pipes; Poiseuille's Law 246
94. Stokes's Law. 248
95. Pressure Changes Perpendicular to the Streamlines. 249
96. Turbulent Motion; Pressure Resistance; Reynolds Number . . . 251
97. Some Laws of Vortex Motion 253
Problems 253

CHAPTER XV
STATIC ELASTICITY
Introduction. 257
98. Stresses. 257
99. Stresses (Continued) 261
100. Strain. 264
101. The General Analysis of Strain. 266
102. Stress-strain Relations; Hooke's Law 268
103. Hooke's Law for Principal Axes 270
104. Compressibility; Compression Modulus. 270
105. Simple Torsion. 272
Problems 274

CHAPTER XVI
DYNAMICS OF ELASTICITY; ACOUSTICS
Introduction. 278
106. The Wave Equation 278

PAGE
107. Periodic and Simple Harmonic Waves; Superposition. 280
108. Velocity of Transverse Waves on a String. 283
109. Velocity of Acoustic (Longitudinal) Waves 285
110. Standing Waves 288
111. Phase Changes in Reflection; Organ Pipes. 290
112. Reflection and Transmission at a Boundary 292
113. Forced Vibrations and Resonance 294
114. Addition of Oscillations; Interference; Beats. 295
115. Doppler Effect. 297
116. Proper Frequencies; Proper Functions in General. 298
Problems 299

CHAPTER XVII

TEMPERATURE AND THERMOMETRY

Introduction. 305
117. Thermal Equilibrium; Concepts of Quantity of Heat and of
Temperature. 305
118. The Measurement of Temperature 306
119. Expansion of Gases; Absolute-temperature Scale. 308
120. Expansion of Liquids and Solids 313
121. Thermal Stresses. 314
122. Examples. 314
Problems 316

CHAPTER XVIII

THE FIRST LAW OF THERMODYNAMICS

Introduction. 320
123. The Macroscopic Method. . . . . , 320
124. The Atomic Method 321
125. The First Law of Thermodynamics. 323
126. Heat Capacity; Specific Heat Capacity 325
127. The Water Calorimeter; Determination of Specific Heats 327
Problems 328

CHAPTER XIX

HEAT CONDUCTION

Introduction. 330
128. Steady Heat Flow 330
129. Examples. 332
Problems 335

CHAPTER XX

THERMODYNAMICS AND KINETIC THEORY OF AN IDEAL GAS

Introduction. 337
130. Thermodynamic Definitions of an Ideal Gas. 337
131. Relation between C_p and C_v. 338
132. Isothermal Changes for Ideal Gases. 339

PAGE

133. Adiabatic Changes for Ideal Gases 340
134. Isothermal and Adiabatic Compressibilities; Velocity of Sound . 343
135. Kinetic Theory of an Ideal Gas 344
     Problems 349

CHAPTER XXI

THE PROPERTIES OF REAL GASES

Introduction. 353
136. Isotherms of a Real Gas. 353
137. Condensation Processes. 354
138. The Critical Point 356
139. Constant-volume Changes. 357
140. Kinetic Theory of Real Gases; Van der Waals' Equation 359
     Problems 361

CHAPTER XXII

THE SECOND LAW OF THERMODYNAMICS

Introduction. 364
141. Reversible and Irreversible Processes. 364
142. The Carnot Cycle 365
143. Entropy. 368
     Problems 370

APPENDIX (TABLES OF PHYSICAL CONSTANTS). 373

INDEX. 377

INTRODUCTION TO
MECHANICS AND HEAT

CHAPTER I

FUNDAMENTAL DEFINITIONS

Physics, in common with the other exact sciences, sets as its object the ability to predict the behavior of natural phenomena with the help of a system of laws which have been derived from observation and experience. To accomplish this, it has been necessary to build up a large number of concepts and to create a special vocabulary which give precision to our everyday mode of expression. In particular, these concepts and this vocabulary must be so chosen that they are amenable to the methods of mathematics; for physics is a quantitative science, and a qualitative prediction, although very helpful and necessary in the course of development of our knowledge, never forms a satisfactory answer to a physicist. Since the concepts of physics grow out of our naive sensations, we shall attempt to trace their development from the experiences of everyday life and then give them the precise form demanded by a science which eliminates as far as possible the vagueness common to all human endeavors. Physics lays the basis for most of our engineering achievements and, apart from its own inherent interest, must be conscientiously studied by those who wish to enter any engineering or scientific profession. We shall not be satisfied with a descriptive knowledge but will pursue the subject quantitatively, taking advantage of that tremendously powerful weapon, mathematical logic.

1. Divisions of Physics.—Physics divides itself very naturally into two great branches, experimental physics and theoretical physics. The former is the science of making observations and devising experiments which give us accurate knowledge of the actual behavior of natural systems. The accumulation of data alone, however, even with the help of the most careful and painstaking measurements, would result in no progress toward our goal were it not for the second great division which, on the basis of the experimental facts, builds up a system of quantitative relations among the measured quantities and formulates these relations into physical *laws*. The great theoretical structure of physics which has been erected reacts strongly on the experimentalist, who must use the experience of the past as expressed in these laws as a guide to his own work and who must plan decisive experiments to answer further questions proposed by the theory and thus break the ground for further advancement. Physics is fundamentally an experimental science, but it is not mere experimenting, and its fruitfulness lies largely in the theoretical structure it has reared. Experimental and theoretical physics must be pursued with equal zeal in a first course.

It may not be out of place to make a few remarks about the "truth" of a physical law. Every physical law is based on experiments and is devised to correlate and to describe accurately these experiments. The wider the range of experience covered by such a law, the more important it is. Since the knowledge which humans have is incomplete and very limited, it is obvious that there can be no such thing as a final, finished theory in physics. Furthermore one can never "overthrow" a theory of physics which has successfully described a certain range of experience. Every new theory must, in its field, explain at least as much as the theory it proposes to replace. Thus the history of physics brings with it an ever increasingly powerful theoretical structure and a highly developed experimental technique.

The subject matter of physics is usually divided into a number of branches: mechanics, acoustics, heat, electricity, magnetism, and optics. The cause of this type of division is to be sought in the historical development of the science and is easily understood if one remembers that the concepts of physics have always started with direct sense perceptions. From a more modern standpoint, this classical, customary mode of division of physics into compartments possesses certain serious disadvantages in that the fundamental interconnections among these branches remain hidden and hinder progress toward that unity of thought and method which is so important in understanding a science such as physics. For example, one may experience the sensation of warmth with the help of a hot stove in one of two ways, either by direct physical contact with the stove or by merely holding one's hand in the vicinity of the stove. According to our present viewpoint, these two processes of transferring heat from one body (the stove) to another body (the hand) are of quite different nature. In the first case, the nerve sensations in the skin are excited by certain mechanical vibrations of the material (more exactly, of the atoms) of which the stove is made. These vibrations are of a similar nature to those of very much lower frequency, *i.e.*, fewer vibrations per second, which affect another sense organ, the ear. Thus there exists an intimate interconnection between mechanics, acoustics, and heat. In the second case, however, the process is quite different. The nerves of the hand are excited largely by a radiation which emanates from the stove and is propagated throughout the room. This radiation turns out to be electromagnetic waves which are of a nature similar to radio waves and to those associated with visible light and X-rays. All these waves differ in but one fundamental property, their frequency. Thus we see common bonds between heat, electricity, magnetism, and optics.

In our treatment we shall not follow these classical divisions of physics but shall treat the two large divisions which have been exemplified above. Mechanics, acoustics, and certain appropriate topics in heat form our first division to which we devote our attention in this book, and perhaps we may use the word *mechanics* in a wider sense to denote these. The remaining topics can be rightly called *electromagnetic theory*, or *electrodynamics*.

2. Definition of Mechanics.—Mechanics, the oldest of all physical sciences, is defined in a specific sense as the study of the laws of motion of material bodies, *i.e.*, the relative changes of position of such bodies with time. The purpose of this study is to classify these motions and to describe them in a simple, logical manner. The mechanics which we shall study is based on a number of hypotheses, apart from those which we intuitively make, which are due largely to Newton, although the essence of them is to be found in the works of Galileo.

We place mechanics first in our study because this oldest branch of physics appeals so directly to our intuition, and hence the fundamental concepts in this field have been employed and generalized to help build up the rest of physics, so that a proper understanding of mechanics, apart from its desirability for its own sake, provides a sound foundation for all other work in physics and in its manifold applications.

3. Definitions of Physical Quantities.—In the preceding section we have defined mechanics as the study of the laws of motion of material bodies. Since the motion of a body is the change of its position in space with respect to time, it is essential at the outset to give definite and unique meanings to the words, *space* and *time*. We here meet one of the most fundamental characteristics of physics, or rather of all exact sciences, which makes it so enormously powerful compared to the other modes of investigating the world in which we live. We have already pointed out that in the last analysis all the results of physics depend on experiment and observation and that these become endowed with their greatest power when they deal with quantities described by numbers and measures. Two steps must be taken in defining a physical quantity. First, the idea or concept of the quantity must be specified. Unless a method of measurement is given, the quantity remains undefined and ambiguous from the standpoint of physics. How different from the usual definitions of words which we encounter in daily life! The ideas of distance and time are intuitive with all human beings. We must lay down methods for measuring them if they are to serve any purpose in physics, and the methods are arbitrary. The manner of measuring any fundamental quantity in physics is defined, never discovered, and the final results of any physical theory are (or should be) numbers which can be obtained by a measuring process.

4. The Measurement of Length.—We shall define the distance between any two points as the number of times a certain "unit" material body (a scale), or copy of it, can be fitted between the two points in question. This definition specifies a method of measuring a length, *viz.*, we count the number of times our unit scale can be placed in successive positions in the interval. The unit scale is arbitrary and we may choose it as we wish. Different peoples have introduced different units, but we shall be concerned with only two of them. For scientific purposes we ordinarily employ the arbitrarily accepted unit of length in the metric system, which is defined as the one-one-hundredth part of the distance between two scratches on a platinum-iridium bar, kept in Sèvres, near Paris, the bar being maintained at a temperature of 0°C. The distance between the scratches is called *one meter* and the unit is called *one centimeter*. In the metric system we commonly employ the terms *millimeter* for $\frac{1}{1000}$ meter, *decimeter* for $\frac{1}{10}$ meter, and *kilometer* for 1,000 meters. There are names for 10 and 100 meters, but, as they are seldom used, we omit them here.

In the English system of units, used almost exclusively in this country in engineering practice, the unit distance is defined as one-third the distance between two scratches on a metal bar kept in London and is called the *foot*. The common multiples of the foot are the *inch*, which is $\frac{1}{12}$ foot; the *yard*, which equals 3 feet; the *rod*, equaling $16\frac{1}{2}$ feet, and the *mile*, which is 5,280 feet. The relations between the units of the metric and English systems must be determined by experiment. A convenient relation to remember is that 2.54 centimeters very nearly equals 1 inch. From this fact a conversion table between lengths in the English and metric system can easily be constructed.

It is clear from the definition of distance that the position of a body is not an absolute quantity, but that it must be referred to some reference body. All we can determine is the distance between two bodies. We now call attention to two fundamentally different types of length measurement, the direct and the indirect. Every direct measurement of length depends on the actual use of a scale. This seems a rather trivial statement in the light of our definition, but its fundamental importance was not properly emphasized until 1905 (Einstein). It is clear that a

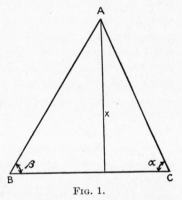

FIG. 1.

direct measurement of length is impossible in many cases of interest, *e.g.*, the distance between two mountain peaks or the distance between the earth and a star. Such measurements must be made by some indirect method, such as measuring a base line BC and the two angles α and β and then calculating the desired distance x (Fig. 1). This simple indirect method is not free from possible criticism. We must identify the paths of the rays of light from A to B and from A to C used in determining the angles with the straight lines of Euclidean geometry. In fact, every indirect measurement involves some hypotheses in the process of evaluation of the desired quantities; and the calculations may involve rather intricate theoretical knowledge as in the determination of the distance between two ions in a rock-salt crystal by means of X-rays. These points are brought to the reader's attention lest he proceed in his study without a proper appreciation of the possible intricacies in the determination of so apparently simple a thing as length.

5. The Measurement of Time.—The experimental basis for a measurement of time is a periodic motion of some sort. We choose the earth as the fundamental body for time measurement, making use of the fact that it rotates about its axis. The time of one rotation of the earth with respect to the fixed stars is employed as a unit of time in astronomical work and this time interval is called one *sidereal day*. The *sidereal second*, as it is called, is the 1/86,400 part of this day. The *mean solar second*, which is the unit used in most physical measurements, is obtained by multiplying the sidereal second by 366.25/365.25. The *mean solar day* is obtained by referring the rotation of the earth to the sun and averaging the result obtained over a year. There are 365.25 solar days and 366.25 sidereal days in a year. The slight difference in these units (remember that since the unit is arbitrary both kinds of second are equally justified) is due to the relative motions of sun, earth, and fixed stars. The most usual device for measuring time is a watch or clock which is referred to the mean solar second. Two common time intervals frequently used as units are the *hour* which is $\frac{1}{24}$ day, and the *minute*, which is 60 seconds.

It must not be thought that the necessity for a method of measuring time is not important. We all have the feeling that time elapses as we live, but the intuitive time "sense" which we possess must not be identified with the measured time of physics. How often does a day seem "long" or "short" to us!

6. Material Bodies; Divisions of Mechanics.—We now turn to a classification of material bodies for the purposes of mechanics. The simplest material body is a material, or mass point, sometimes called a *particle*. It is defined as a body whose linear dimensions are smaller than the experimental uncertainty in the length measurement which fixes its position. It is clear that every physical measurement involves some uncertainty. No matter how fine a measuring instrument is employed, no matter how carefully it is used, inevitable errors creep in and we cannot reduce the uncertainty of any measurement exactly to zero.

A body need not be "small" in the everyday sense of this word to be a material point. For example, if we consider the distance from the earth to the sun, then with respect to this measurement the earth may be considered a material point. However, if we consider the rotation of the earth on its axis, we can by no means deal with it as a material point. (Note the tremendous difference between this idea and that of a geometrical point as employed in mathematics.) If a body is too large to be considered a particle, we can always think of it as composed of a large number of particles.

If the distance between these particles remains unaltered (what are the restrictions on this statement?), we say the body is *rigid*. If not, we say the body is *deformable*. The same body may be considered rigid or deformable depending on the type of process considered. A bullet may well be considered a rigid body during its flight, but no one would ever say it was rigid when it hits a target and gets "squashed."

Finally, we shall divide mechanics itself into sections. First, the subject of kinematics, which classifies various types of motion and their characteristics without regard to the causes of the motions considered, and secondly, dynamics, the study of motions as related to their causes. Statics is to be considered a special case of dynamics.

CHAPTER II

LINEAR KINEMATICS OF A MASS POINT

In this chapter we shall devote our attention almost entirely to the kinematical description of the motion of a particle on a straight line. By thus restricting ourselves to rectilinear motion we introduce a minimum number of new concepts and definitions essential to a proper mathematical description of motion. This procedure allows us to divide our kinematical discussion into two parts, the first of which comprises the content of this chapter. We must start by formulating our problems so that quantitative as well as qualitative answers may be obtained.

7. Reference Systems.—We start our study of mechanics with the motion (change of position with time) of a single mass point. Since all points of space are identical and indistinguishable, it is impossible to fix the position of a mass point absolutely, but the position, and hence the motion, must always be specified relative to some other body. Thus we see that from a kinematical standpoint there is no such thing as absolute motion, all motion being relative. The body to which we refer the position of the mass point is known as a *reference body* and it provides an anchor for a frame of reference which we consider fixed. We choose some point of a rigid body as an origin of our reference system and discuss the motion relative to this frame of reference. If it requires only one number to specify the position of a mass point with respect to this origin, we say that the mass point has one degree of freedom. As an example, a mass point which can move along a straight line passing through the origin has but one degree of freedom. In this case the mass point performs linear motion. Another example of motion with one degree of freedom is that of a mass point in a circular path. If we choose our origin at the center of the circle and draw the radius from the origin to the mass point, the angle which this radius makes with a fixed straight line through the origin is sufficient to determine uniquely the position of the mass point. To specify the position of a mass point free to move in a plane (or on any surface), however, we need two numbers and we say that the mass point has two degrees of freedom. Finally, a mass point free to move throughout space has three degrees of freedom. In the following discussion we shall use the expressions position of a mass point, velocity, etc., but it must be remembered that these statements tacitly refer to a system of reference.

8. Graphical Description of Linear Motion: Velocity.—Suppose we consider the motion of an automobile along a straight road and inquire as to how we should set about describing its motion. Our first task is clearly that of adopting a method of specifying its position on the road. For this purpose we must first choose an origin of position, and we then can uniquely

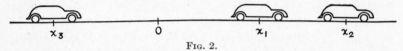

x_3 O x_1 x_2

FIG. 2.

specify the position of the automobile by giving its distance to the right or to the left of the origin O (Fig. 2).

We shall adopt the convention that distances to the right of O shall be specified by *positive* numbers and those to the left by *negative* numbers. Thus, if we say that the automobile is at the position x feet, we mean that it is x feet to the right of O if x is a positive number and x feet to the left of O if x is negative. In Fig. 2, x_1 and x_2 are positive, and x_3 is negative. The x's are called the *coordinates of the body*.

Suppose that the automobile is at the position x_1 at a certain instant of time and that it is later at the position x_2. We say that the automobile has undergone a *displacement* and define this displacement as the algebraic difference between its final and initial coordinates. Thus $x_2 - x_1$ represents the displacement of the car from the position x_1 to the position x_2 and is a positive displacement to the right. Similarly, $x_1 - x_2$ represents a displacement to the left from x_2 to x_1. It is important to note that not only the magnitude but also the direction of the displacement must be given.

The most direct mode of ascertaining the motion of a body consists of noting the position of the body at different instants of time. Suppose we have made such a series of observations in the automobile of the preceding discussion which we record in tabular form (see Table I). Our problem is to determine the details of the motion as far as possible from the observed data.

In the following table we have placed the origin of coordinates at the starting position of the automobile.

TABLE I

t (sec.)	0	1	2	3	4	5	6	7	8	9	10	11	12	13	14	15	16
x (ft.)	0	5	20	45	80	125	180	240	300	360	410	440	455	463	465	465	465

(all positive)

From this table we see that the automobile moves always in the same direction (to the right), and if we inspect the displacements occurring in successive seconds, we can say roughly that the car speeds up at the beginning, then later it slows down and eventually comes to rest. To make our conclusions more precise, we now introduce the concept of *average velocity* of the body during a specified time interval. We define *average velocity* as the displacement undergone by the body divided by the time interval during which the displacement occurs. Thus, if the body occupies the position x_1 at time t_1 and a position x_2 at a later instant of time t_2, its average velocity in the time interval $t_2 - t_1$ is given by the relation

$$\text{Average velocity} = \bar{v} = \frac{x_2 - x_1}{t_2 - t_1} \tag{1}$$

and is expressed in units of length/time such as cm./sec., ft./sec, miles/hr., etc.

Average velocity is a quantity possessing direction, its direction being that of the displacement $x_2 - x_1$, since the expression $t_2 - t_1$ is always positive. Now suppose we calculate the average velocity of the automobile during successive seconds of its motion. For the first second

$$\bar{v} = \frac{x_2 - x_1}{t_2 - t_1} = \frac{5 - 0}{1 - 0} = 5 \text{ ft./sec.}$$

For the second second

$$\bar{v} = \frac{x_2 - x_1}{t_2 - t_1} = \frac{20 - 5}{2 - 1} = 15 \text{ ft./sec.}$$

For the third second

$$\bar{v} = \frac{x_2 - x_1}{t_2 - t_1} = \frac{45 - 20}{3 - 2} = 25 \text{ ft./sec.}$$

From such a calculation we then can construct a table of average velocities for the corresponding time intervals as follows:

TABLE II

Time interval	1st sec.	2d sec.	3d sec.	4th sec.	5th sec.	6th sec.	7th sec.	8th sec.	9th sec.	10th sec.	11th sec.	12th sec.	13th sec.	14th sec.	15th sec.	16th sec.
$\bar{v}$ (ft./sec.)	5	15	25	35	45	55	60	60	60	50	30	15	8	2	0	0

The preceding table now allows a somewhat closer description of the actual motion. We see easily that the automobile is increasing its velocity (accelerating) for the first six seconds, from the seventh to ninth second it moves with constant velocity, then it loses velocity (decelerates), and, finally, it comes to rest about the fifteenth second.

We have now a rough idea of the motion, and if we wish to pursue our investigation further and obtain still more detailed information, we must adopt some scheme which allows us to obtain information as to position and velocity at all instants of time from 0 to 16 sec. and not merely at the relatively few instants of time provided by the table of observed data. For this purpose we construct a graph of the motion to show the relation between x and t geometrically. This is done as follows: We first construct two straight lines which intersect each other at right angles. Usually one line is drawn horizontally and the other vertically. The vertical line is known as the *axis of ordinates* and the horizontal one as the *axis of abscissas*. Along the axis of abscissas we mark off equal intervals of length, each interval representing some unit of time. Thus we may choose $\frac{1}{2}$ in. on this axis to represent a time interval of 1 sec. The relation between the time interval and the length interval on the abscissa is known as the *scale*, and the scale is arbitrarily chosen for convenience. The student must use his judgment in deciding on the proper scale. If the scale is too small, the graph becomes too small to show proper detail, and if too large, it limits the time during which the motion can be represented on a single plot. Similarly, we mark off equal length intervals on the axis of ordinates, each interval on the axis representing some length in the actual motion. The intersection of the axes is taken as the origin O, *i.e.*, it corresponds to both the origin of coordinates $x = 0$ and the origin of time $t = 0$ (Fig. 3).

We now choose some value of t, find the corresponding value of x, and, directly above or below this value of t on the horizontal axis, we place a fine dot at a vertical distance corresponding to the value of x. Repeating this process for a number of values of t (and x), we obtain a series of points whose horizontal distances from O represent values of t and whose vertical distances from O represent the corresponding values of x. Next we join these points by a *smooth* fine curve which provides us with a geometrical picture of the motion. The curve is called a *graph of the motion*. In constructing this curve, it is best first to sketch it lightly in pencil and to ink it in later.

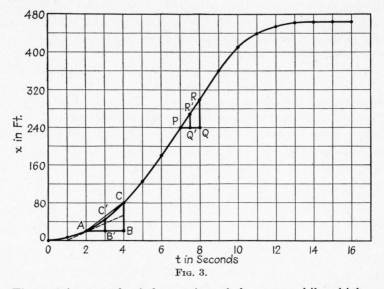

Fig. 3.

Figure 3 is a graph of the motion of the automobile which we have already discussed with the help of Tables I and II. The small circles are the points corresponding to the values given in Table I. One advantage of the graph over the table of values is immediately clear. We can now readily find the position of the automobile for instants of time not given directly in the table. Another becomes apparent when we inquire as to the graphical representation of the average velocity over different intervals of time.

Suppose we wish to calculate the average velocity of the automobile during the eighth second of its motion with the help of the graph. On the graph the point P represents the values $t = 7$ sec. and $x = 240$ ft.; and the point R represents the values $t = 8$ sec. and $x = 300$ ft. If we construct the horizontal line

PQ and the vertical line *QR*, as shown, it is clear from the figure that *QR* represents the displacement of the automobile during the eighth second and *PQ* represents the time interval of 1 sec. during which this displacement occurred.   Thus

$$\bar{v} = \frac{QR}{PQ}$$

and is the ratio of the side opposite the angle *RPQ* to the side adjacent in the right triangle *PQR*.   This suggests a close relation to the tangent of the angle *RPQ*, and indeed $\bar{v}$ would equal this tangent were it not for the fact that in the triangle *PQR* the sides have neither the same dimensions nor are they drawn to the same scale.   We shall, however, say that

$$\bar{v} = \tan \angle RPQ$$

remembering that we do not mean the geometrical tangent but the ratio of the opposite to adjacent sides with the proper dimensions.   Thus the geometrical tangent of the angle *RPQ* is $\frac{3}{2}$, but in our sense it is

$$\frac{60 \text{ ft.}}{1 \text{ sec.}} = 60 \text{ ft./sec.}$$

In order to proceed further in our description of the motion, we can now find the average velocity of the car over half-second intervals instead of over whole-second intervals as before.   It is clear that, as we lessen the time interval over which we average, we obtain an increasingly detailed description of the motion and that a complete description will be obtained only as we investigate what happens to the average velocities as the time interval is reduced indefinitely.   In general, as the time interval is decreased, the displacement occurring in that time interval is also decreased, but the ratio of displacement to time interval approaches a definite, limiting value which we call the *instantaneous velocity,* or simply the *velocity* of the body.   How may we carry out this process with the help of the graph?   Suppose we wish to calculate the average velocity in the half-second interval after the body reaches *P*.   This value is indicated on the graph as *Q'R'/PQ'*, and since the triangles *PQR* and *PQ'R'* are similar,

$$\frac{Q'R'}{PQ'} = \frac{QR}{PQ}$$

It is clear that this equality is due to the fact that during the eighth second the graph of the motion is a straight line. If we now proceed to average over shorter and shorter intervals of time, we should construct smaller and smaller right triangles, and, because of similar triangles, the angle at P and hence its tangent stay unchanged. Thus, in this simple case, we have shown that average velocity equals instantaneous velocity, and the velocity of the automobile 7 sec. after it starts is 60 ft./sec.

If we now wish to carry out the above process during a time interval when the graph is not a straight line, *e.g.*, from $t = 2$ sec. to $t = 4$ sec., we see in Fig. 3 that, in the right triangle ABC, $BC/AB = \tan \angle CAB$ equals the average velocity in this time interval. However, in this case the hypotenuse AC no longer coincides with the graph from A to C. We now average over a shorter time interval, from $t = 2$ sec. to $t = 3$ sec. and obtain as the average velocity for this time interval

$$\frac{C'B'}{AB'} = \tan \angle C'AB'$$

and this value is smaller than BC/AB since the straight line $C'A$ makes a smaller angle with the horizontal than the straight line CA. Now, as we take smaller and smaller time intervals, the angles between the hypotenuses of the right triangles and the horizontal get more and more nearly equal to a definite angle, the tangent of which is the velocity of the car at A. We may also describe this by saying that the directions of the straight lines AC, AC', etc., become more and more nearly alike and approach, as a limiting value, the direction of the dotted line through A in Fig. 3. The dotted line is called the *tangent line* to the curve at A, and the tangent of the angle between this line and the axis of abscissas is called the *slope* of the curve at A. We now have the important relation that the slope of the displacement-time curve at any point equals the velocity of the body at that point. We shall later learn an algebraic method of determining this slope if the equation of the graph is known.

9. Acceleration in Straight-line Motion.—We have just seen how to obtain the velocity of a body from the displacement-time graph of its motion. An inspection of Fig. 3 shows that the slope of the curve, which equals the velocity, increases steadily up to about 6 sec., then stays sensibly constant up to about 10 sec., and after that decreases, finally becoming zero at about

16 sec. Thus we see that the velocity of the automobile varies during the motion, and it becomes necessary to introduce a new concept to describe the changes in velocity—that of *acceleration*.

Suppose that we have determined the velocity of the automobile from Fig. 3 at different instants of time, let us say, at $t = 1, 2, 3, 4$ sec., etc. Or, perhaps, let us imagine that a passenger in the automobile records the speedometer reading at 1-sec. intervals. We can then construct a table of velocities and corresponding values of time as is done in Table III.

TABLE III

t (sec.)	0	1	2	3	4	5	6	7	8	9	10	11	12	13	14	15	16
v (ft./sec.)	0	10	20	30	40	49	57	60	60	60	45	20	10	5	2	1	0

If the velocity at time t_1 is v_1 and at a later time t_2 is v_2, we define the average acceleration ($\bar{a}$) during the time interval $t_2 - t_1$ by the relation

$$\bar{a} = \frac{v_2 - v_1}{t_2 - t_1} \tag{2}$$

and this is a vector quantity having the dimensions velocity/time or length/(time)^2. The average acceleration is positive or negative depending on whether $v_2 - v_1 > 0$ or $v_2 - v_1 < 0$, where we must remember that v_1 and v_2 are algebraic quantities. Thus, if v_2 is positive and larger numerically than v_1, which is also positive, $v_2 - v_1 > 0$, and the average acceleration is positive representing a speeding up to the right. Suppose, however, that v_2 is negative and that v_1 is also negative but larger numerically than v_2. Then $v_2 - v_1 > 0$, and the acceleration is still positive. In this case the body is moving to the left and slowing down. But slowing down during a motion to the left is exactly equivalent to speeding up during a motion to the right, as far as velocity changes are concerned, so that the acceleration is positive in both cases. The analysis of other possibilities is left as an exercise for the student.

We now construct a graph of velocity vs. time using the values tabulated in Table III and obtain the curve shown in Fig. 4. From this curve we can immediately obtain the average acceleration of the automobile over any desired interval of time, and hence, by taking successively smaller time intervals, we obtain the instantaneous acceleration of the car at any desired moment. Thus the average acceleration during the third second is equal to $BC/AC = 10$ ft./sec.^{2}, and since the graph is essentially a straight line from $t = 0$ to 4 sec., the average acceleration over any time interval in this range is equal to its value over any other time interval in this same range, no matter how small this latter time interval is chosen.   Thus this portion of the motion is one with constant acceleration.

It will further be noted from Fig. 4 that the velocities at $\frac{1}{2}$, $1\frac{1}{2}$, $2\frac{1}{2}$ sec., etc., coincide rather closely with the average velocities for the first, second, third seconds, etc., as shown in Table II.   The only exception is the point at $9\frac{1}{2}$ sec. where the actual velocity is about 55 ft./sec., whereas the average

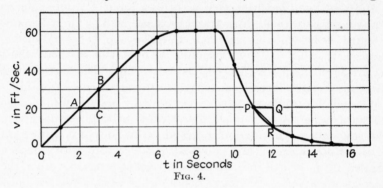

Fig. 4.

velocity for the tenth second is 50 ft./sec.   This is due to the fact that the velocity change from 9 to 10 sec. is not uniform and is comparatively large.   In general, if the velocity changes slowly, one can approximately obtain the velocity at instants halfway between two observed values of time by taking the average velocity.   It must be kept in mind, however, that this is only approximate and is of little use when the acceleration is non-uniform and large.

On the other hand, the average acceleration during the twelfth second is given by $QR/PQ = -10$ ft./sec.², but in order to obtain the acceleration at $t = 11$ sec., we must average over successively shorter time intervals and thus approach the tangent to the curve at the point P.   From the figure one sees that the acceleration at P is negative and greater numerically than the average acceleration from $t = 11$ to $t = 12$ sec.

With the help of the curve in Fig. 4, we now can give a detailed description of the motion.   The automobile starts from rest, speeds up at a constant rate of 10 ft./sec.² for the first 4 or 5 sec., and then picks up velocity less rapidly until at 7 sec. it has attained a maximum velocity of 60 ft./sec., which it holds for the next 2 sec. Then the brakes are applied causing a deceleration; first a large one and later a somewhat smaller one and, finally, the car comes to rest about 16 sec. after the beginning of the motion.

10. Equations of Motion.—We have seen that the motion of a particle on a straight line can be completely described if the position of the body, *i.e.*, the displacement of the body measured from an origin, is known for every value of the time. In the preceding discussion the relationship between the coordinate x and the time t has been expressed by a table of values such as Table I or, better still, by a graph such as Fig. 3. There remains a third very valuable method of expressing the relationship between x and t, *viz.*, by a formula. This latter method, which we are about to discuss, has decided advantages over the first two if we must make further calculations utilizing this relationship.

In such a formula we have the two quantities x and t, and the value of either is determined if the value of the other is given. We say that x is a function of t, and, conversely, t is a function of x. Both x and t are called *variables*, the quantity chosen arbitrarily is called the *independent variable* and the other the *dependent variable*. We may choose either variable as the independent variable, and, for reasons which will appear immediately, we shall choose the time t as the independent variable. This is a convenient but not necessary procedure. If we specify a given value of t and then determine the corresponding value of x, we find where the particle is at that instant of time. On the other hand, were we to specify a value of x (choosing it as the independent variable) and determine the corresponding value of t, we find the instant of time when the particle is situated at a given point of the line.

As an example of such a formula let us write

$$x = 5 - 10t \qquad (3)$$

where x is the coordinate of the body expressed in centimeters and t is the time in seconds. If any value of t is given, it is substituted in the above equation, and the corresponding value of x can be found. In this manner we may construct a table of values of x vs. t from which a graph may be constructed. The above equation connecting values of x with corresponding values of t is known as the *equation of motion* of the body. With the help of such an equation all questions concerning the position of the body at different instants of time may be answered. For example, we may ask, "When does the body pass through the origin of coordinates?" The answer is obtained by substituting $x = 0$ into the equation and solving for t. Thus we have

$$0 = 5 - 10t$$
$$t = \tfrac{1}{2} \text{ sec.}$$

so that, $\tfrac{1}{2}$ sec. after we start counting time, the body passes through the origin.

If we now inquire into the question of the velocity of the body whose motion is described by Eq. (3) at different instants of time, we start with the definition of average velocity as given by Eq. (1). Suppose we wish to calculate the velocity of the body when $t = 1$ sec. From Eq. (3) we find that the position at $t = 1$ sec. is

$$x_1 = 5 - 10 \cdot 1 = -5 \text{ cm.}$$

Let us first find the average velocity from $t = 1$ sec. to $t = 2$ sec. We then have $t_2 = 2$ sec.; $x_2 = 5 - 20 = -15$ cm.; and

$$\bar{v} = \frac{x_2 - x_1}{t_2 - t_1} = \frac{-15 + 5}{2 - 1} = -10 \text{ cm./sec.}$$

To obtain the velocity at $t = 1$ sec., we proceed to average over shorter and shorter time intervals.

Let $t_2 = 1.1$ sec. Then $x_2 = 5 - 11 = -6$ cm., and

$$\bar{v} = \frac{-6 + 5}{1.1 - 1} = -\frac{1}{0.1} = -10 \text{ cm./sec.}$$

so that the average velocity is the same for these two time intervals.

Now let $t_2 = 1.01$ sec. Then $x_2 = 5 - 10.1 = -5.1$ cm., and

$$\bar{v} = \frac{-5.1 + 5}{1.01 - 1} = -\frac{0.1}{0.01} = -10 \text{ cm./sec.}$$

We see that the average velocity stays unchanged as we change the time interval over which we average. A graph of Eq. (3) is a straight line. The slope of this graph (which, as we have seen, is the velocity) is constant, so that the velocity is constant throughout the motion and, hence, the average velocity over any time interval equals the constant value of the velocity through the motion. We can prove this from the formula [Eq. (3)] as follows:

The position of the body at time t is

$$x_1 = 5 - 10t$$

At a later time $t + h$, the position is

$$x_2 = 5 - 10(t + h) = 5 - 10t - 10h$$

so that the average velocity over the time interval h sec. is

$$\bar{v} = \frac{x_2 - x_1}{(t + h) - t} = \frac{(5 - 10t - 10h) - (5 - 10t)}{(t + h) - t} = -\frac{10h}{h} = -10 \text{ cm./sec.}$$

a constant value which does not depend on the time interval h. Thus Eq. (3) describes a motion which takes place with constant velocity, *i.e.*, uniform motion.

Now suppose we consider the motion of a particle on a straight line described by the equation

$$x = 10t^2 \tag{4}$$

where x is in centimeters and t in seconds. We wish to calculate the velocity of the body when it is 10 cm. to the right of the origin, *i.e.*, at $t = 1$ sec. Suppose we start by calculating the average velocity in the time interval from 1 to 2 sec. When $t_1 = 1$, $x_1 = 10$; and when $t_2 = 2$, $x_2 = 40$, so that

$$\bar{v} = \frac{40 - 10}{2 - 1} = 30 \text{ cm./sec.}$$

Now let us reduce this time interval, taking $t_2 = 1.1$ sec. In this case $x_2 = 12.1$ cm., and the average velocity for the $\frac{1}{10}$ sec. following $t = 1$ sec. is

$$\bar{v} = \frac{12.1 - 10}{1.1 - 1} = 21 \text{ cm./sec.}$$

not equal to the value previously found.

We now repeat this process, taking $t_2 = 1.01$ sec. and find $x_2 = 10.201$ cm., so that for $\frac{1}{100}$ sec. the average velocity is

$$\bar{v} = \frac{10.201 - 10}{1.01 - 1} = 20.1 \text{ cm./sec.}$$

Repeating this process for $t_2 = 1.001$ sec., we have

$$x_2 = 10.02001 \text{ cm.,}$$

and the average velocity for $\frac{1}{1000}$ sec. is

$$\bar{v} = \frac{10.02001 - 10}{1.001 - 1} = 20.01 \text{ cm./sec.}$$

Thus we see that as we average over shorter and shorter time intervals, the average velocity changes and gets nearer and nearer to a definite limiting value, in this case 20 cm./sec., which is defined as the velocity for $t = 1$ sec. The student should repeat this calculation for $t = 1.0001$ sec., and this should yield a value of $\bar{v} = 20.001$ cm./sec., indicating how $\bar{v}$ approaches the instantaneous value $\bar{v} = 20$ cm./sec. as the time interval approaches zero.

Now let us extend the above method to hold for any value of the time. At time t, the position is

$$x_1 = 10t^2$$

and at a later time $t + h$, the position is

$$x_2 = 10(t + h)^2 = 10t^2 + 20ht + 10h^2$$

The average velocity for the time interval h is

$$\bar{v} = \frac{x_2 - x_1}{(t + h) - t} = \frac{10t^2 + 20ht + 10h^2 - 10t^2}{h} = 20t + 10h$$

so that it will be different for different time intervals h.

To find the velocity at any definite instant of time t, we let t stay fixed in the above equation and let h get smaller and smaller. The term $20t$ does not change, but the term $(+10h)$ gets smaller and smaller as h approaches zero. Hence the limiting value of $\bar{v}$ is obtained by placing $h = 0$, and we find, for the velocity at any time t,

$$v = 20t \tag{5}$$

where v is, of course, expressed in centimeters per second and t in seconds. This formula now allows us to calculate the value of v for any value of time t, so that this algebraic method is more general than the arithmetic method previously given.

We can state the results of the above discussion by specifying that the velocity of a body is the limiting value of the ratio of displacement to time interval as the latter approaches zero. In symbols

$$v = \text{limit of } \frac{x_2 - x_1}{t_2 - t_1} \quad \text{as} \quad t_2 - t_1 \to 0$$

It is customary to write $t_2 - t_1$ as Δt (read delta t), and Δt is known as the increment of time. Similarly, we write

$$x_2 - x_1 = \Delta x,$$

where Δx is the corresponding increment in x. We may then write for our definition of velocity

$$v = \text{limit of } \frac{\Delta x}{\Delta t} \quad \text{as} \quad \Delta t \to 0 \tag{6}$$

Now let us apply the above methods to calculate the acceleration of the body from Eq. (5). At time t, the velocity is $v = 20t$, and at a later time $t + \Delta t$, the velocity is

$$v + \Delta v = 20(t + \Delta t)$$

so that the average acceleration is

$$\bar{a} = \frac{(v + \Delta v) - v}{(t + \Delta t) - t} = \frac{20t + 20(\Delta t) - 20t}{t + \Delta t - t} = 20 \text{ cm./sec.}^2$$

and is constant, so that the instantaneous acceleration at any instant of time is constant and has the value $+20$ cm./sec.^{2} Thus we see that Eqs. (4) and (5) describe a motion taking place with constant acceleration.

In general, we write as the definition of acceleration

$$a = \text{limit of } \frac{\Delta v}{\Delta t} \quad \text{as} \quad \Delta t \to 0 \tag{7}$$

Example.—We shall now illustrate in detail the methods which we have discussed, with the help of another example. Suppose a stone thrown into the air moves along a vertical straight line according to the equation

$$x = 4 + 32t - 16t^2 \tag{8}$$

where t is in seconds and x is in feet measured positively upward from an origin on the ground. First we note that *every term in a physical equation must have the same dimensions.* Thus the 4 means 4 ft., the 32 means 32 ft./sec. and is a velocity, the 16 means 16 ft./sec.^{2} and has the dimensions of an acceleration. Every term in Eq. (8) represents a displacement.

If we place $t = 0$ in Eq. (8), we find $x = 4$ ft., and this means that initially the stone is 4 ft. above the ground. Another way of stating this is that the initial position of the stone (denoted by x_0) is 4 ft. Let us obtain an expression for the velocity of the stone at any time t. At time t, the position is

$$x = 4 + 32t - 16t^2$$

At a later time, $t + \Delta t$, the stone is at $x + \Delta x$, where

$$x + \Delta x = 4 + 32(t + \Delta t) - 16(t + \Delta t)^2 =$$
$$4 + 32t + 32(\Delta t) - 16t^2 - 32t(\Delta t) - 16(\Delta t)^2$$

whence

$$\Delta x = 32(\Delta t) - 32t(\Delta t) - 16(\Delta t)^2$$

The average velocity over this time interval Δt is

$$\bar{v} = \frac{\Delta x}{\Delta t} = 32 - 32t - 16(\Delta t)$$

and if $\Delta t \to 0$, we obtain for the velocity, at any time t,

$$v = 32 - 32t \qquad (9)$$

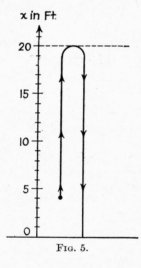

x in Ft.

If we place $t = 0$ in Eq. (9), we find $v = 32$ ft./sec., so that initially the stone is projected upward with a speed of 32 ft./sec. We shall denote the initial velocity by v_0. The values of x_0 and v_0 for any motion are called the initial conditions.

Finally, from Eq. (9) we find for the acceleration the constant value

$$a = -32 \text{ ft./sec.}^2 \qquad (10)$$

which represents a constantly decreasing velocity. We are now in possession of enough data to describe roughly the motion (Fig. 5). The stone starts upward from a point 4 ft. above the ground with an initial speed of 32 ft./sec., slows down, and turns around, falling with increasing speed (decreasing velocity!) until it hits the ground.

To find when and where the stone reverses the direction of motion, we note that previous to this instant of time the velocity is positive and after this instant of time it is negative.

Fig. 5.

Hence the velocity must be zero at the top point of the path where the reversal of direction takes place.

Placing $v = 0$ in Eq. (9), we find that for

$$32t - 32 = 0 \qquad \text{or} \qquad t = 1 \text{ sec.}$$

the stone reverses direction. At this instant of time we find the position of the stone by substituting this value of t in Eq. (8)

$$x_1 = 4 + 32 \cdot 1 - 16(1)^2 = 20 \text{ ft.}$$

so that the stone rises to a maximum height of 20 ft. above the earth.

If we inquire when the stone hits the ground, we place $x = 0$ in Eq. (8) and find

$$16t^2 - 32t - 4 = 0$$
$$t = 1 \pm \tfrac{1}{2}\sqrt{5}$$

whence

$$t = 2.12 \text{ sec.} \qquad \text{or} \qquad t = -0.12 \text{ sec.}$$

Since the second value corresponds to an instant of time before the motion starts, it is discarded, and the stone hits the ground 2.12 sec. after it starts.

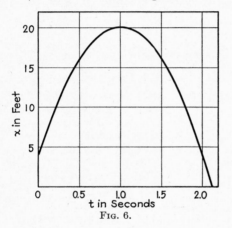

FIG. 6.

From Eq. (9) we find that the velocity of the stone is negative as it hits the ground and has the value

$$v = 32 - 32(2.12) = -32(-1 + 2.12) = -35.8 \text{ ft./sec.}$$

so that the speed of the stone at this time is 35.8 ft./sec.

It is instructive to express t in terms of x. We rewrite Eq. (8) in the form

$$16t^2 - 32t = 4 - x$$

and solving for t, we obtain

$$t = 1 \pm \tfrac{1}{4}\sqrt{(20 - x)}$$

For values of x greater than 20, *i.e.*, for heights above 20 ft., the quantity under the radical is negative, so that t is not real for these values of x. This means that the stone never reaches a height greater than 20 ft.

Thus we see that a large amount of physical information may be obtained from as simple an equation as Eq. (8). The physical interpretation of mathematical equations is all-important in the study of physics.

Figures 6 and 7 show the displacement-time and velocity-time graphs for this motion. The curve of Fig. 6 is known as a *parabola*. The straight-line plot of Fig. 7 shows clearly that the velocity decreases uniformly with the time and hence the acceleration is constant.

In conclusion, we will give general relations for the two simplest kinds of linear motion, *viz.*, (1) motion with constant velocity and (2) motion with constant acceleration. It must be kept in mind, however, that these are special cases and usually we must

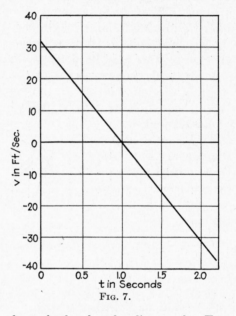

Fig. 7.

use the general methods already discussed. For motion with constant velocity the equation of motion is

$$x = x_0 + v_0 t \tag{11}$$

where x_0 is the initial position and v_0 the initial velocity. The velocity is constant and equal at all times to the initial value v_0. For motion with constant acceleration a, the equation of motion is

$$x = x_0 + v_0 t + \tfrac{1}{2}at^2 \tag{12}$$

where again x_0 and v_0 are the initial values of position and velocity. The velocity at any time t is given by

$$v = v_0 + at \tag{13}$$

and the acceleration is constant throughout the motion and equal to a.

In using these equations to solve problems one is at liberty to choose the origin of coordinates arbitrarily. Hence x_0 can be made zero by placing the origin at the starting point of the motion. However, if we are discussing the motion of two or more bodies simultaneously, we may make $x_0 = 0$ for one of the bodies but obviously not for all of them. In some problems one is confronted with a situation where two or more bodies start their motion at different instants of time (as well as different positions), and it is convenient to have a systematic method of handling such cases. This may be done as follows: In all our discussion we have started counting time at $t = 0$, *i.e.*, we have placed our origin of time at the start of the motion. Thus the t appearing in the equations of motion really means the time interval which has elapsed since the motion started. If now we call the instant of time at which the motion starts t_0 instead of 0, all our equations must be rewritten, so that in place of t we now have $(t - t_0)$. Thus Eq. (12) may equally well be written

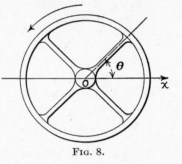

$$x = x_0 + v_0(t - t_0) + \tfrac{1}{2}a(t - t_0)^2$$

Fig. 8.

where x_0 and v_0 are as before the values of position and velocity at the start of the motion, *i.e.*, when $t = t_0$.

11. Angular Motion.—We shall digress in this section from the problem of rectilinear motion of a particle to discuss some aspects of another type of motion involving only *one* degree of freedom. Suppose we consider a wheel which is free to rotate about its axle. Such a motion can be described by a single coordinate, the angle θ which one spoke of the wheel makes with a fixed line (the x-axis) through the center of the wheel (Fig. 8). If the wheel rotates in a counterclockwise direction as indicated, we shall say that θ increases and if clockwise that θ decreases. The angle θ shall be specified in *radians*, not in degrees.

All the concepts we have introduced may now be taken over to describe this angular motion. Thus, if at an instant of time t_1 the angular position of the shaded spoke is θ_1 and at a later time

t_2 it is θ_2, we define the *average angular velocity* of the wheel by

$$\bar{\omega} = \frac{\theta_2 - \theta_1}{t_2 - t_1} \tag{14}$$

$\theta_2 - \theta_1$ is the angular displacement of the wheel in the time interval $t_2 - t_1$, and the average angular velocity $\bar{\omega}$ is measured in radians per second. The notion of instantaneous angular velocity immediately follows as the limiting value of the average angular velocity as the average is taken over shorter and shorter time intervals. Thus

$$\omega = \text{limit of } \frac{\Delta\theta}{\Delta t} \qquad \text{as} \qquad \Delta t \to 0$$

or, more concisely,

$$\omega = \frac{d\theta}{dt} \tag{15}$$

If we have a motion with constant angular velocity ω_0 then the relation between angular displacement and time is simply

$$\theta - \theta_0 = \omega_0 t \tag{16}$$

where θ_0 is the initial value of θ.

In general, the angular velocity of the wheel will not be constant but will keep changing during a motion. In such a case it is necessary to introduce the idea of *angular acceleration*. We define the *average angular acceleration* for a time interval $t_2 - t_1$ as

$$\bar{\alpha} = \frac{\omega_2 - \omega_1}{t_2 - t_1} \tag{17}$$

where ω_2 is the angular velocity at time t_2 and ω_1 the angular velocity at time t_1. From this we obtain the *instantaneous angular acceleration* α in the usual manner. Thus

$$\alpha = \text{limit of } \frac{\Delta\omega}{\Delta t} \qquad \text{as} \qquad \Delta t \to 0$$

or, again in calculus notation,

$$\alpha = \frac{d\omega}{dt} \tag{18}$$

Everything we have done for linear motion can be now done for angular motion, all the formulas remaining valid if we substitute angular coordinate θ for linear coordinate x, angular velocity ω for linear velocity v, and angular acceleration α for linear acceleration a. For example, the equations describing a motion with *constant* angular acceleration α take a form just like Eqs. (12) and (13). They are

$$\theta = \theta_0 + \omega_0 t + \tfrac{1}{2}\alpha t^2 \tag{19}$$

and

$$\omega = \omega_0 + \alpha t \tag{20}$$

Problems

1.

t (sec.)	0	1	2	3	4	5	6	7
x (cm.)	3	8	11	12	11	8	3	−4

The table above gives the coordinates of a moving body over an interval of 7 sec.

Make a graph of the table, plotting the coordinates of the body as ordinates (vertically) and the corresponding times as abscissas (horizontally). Use EE graph paper; let 20 small divisions equal 1 sec. and 10 small divisions equal 1 cm. The graph need not be drawn in ink.

a. Find the displacement of the body during the following intervals: 0 to 1 sec., 4 to 5 sec., 0 to 6 sec., 1 to 7 sec., 1.5 to 5.7 sec.

b. Calculate the average velocity during these same intervals.

c. Find the average velocity during the intervals from 1 to 3 sec., 1 to 2 sec., 1 to 1.5 sec. Then draw the tangent to the curve at the point $t = 1$ sec., and from this determine the instantaneous velocity at that point.

d. By drawing tangents, find the velocity at times $t = 2$ sec., $t = 3$ sec., $t = 4$ sec., $t = 5$ sec., $t = 6$ sec., and $t = 7$ sec. From these values construct a graph of velocity vs. time, including the value for $t = 1$ sec. obtained in Part *c.* Making allowance for possible errors in estimating the slope of the tangent lines, what sort of curve seems to fit the points best?

e. From the velocity graph find the average acceleration during the time intervals 1 to 3 sec., 4 to 6 sec., 0 to 7 sec., expressed in the proper units. What is the meaning of the sign of the acceleration?

2. The equation of motion of the body referred to in Prob. 1 is

$$x = 3 + 6t - t^2$$

a. Check this by computing the values of x from the equation for four values of t and comparing with the table in Prob. 1.

b. From the equation of motion compute the position of the body at times $t = 1.5$ sec. and $t = 5.7$ sec. Then calculate the average velocity during this time, and compare with the value found graphically in Prob. 1.

c. From the positions of the body at times $t = 1$ sec. and $t = 1.5$ sec., find the average velocity over the interval 1 to 1.5 sec. Repeat the process for the interval 1 to 1.1 sec., 1 to 1.01 sec., 1 to 1.001 sec. What limiting value do your results seem to be approaching? Compare with the value found graphically in Prob. 1. Which method do you think is more accurate?

d. Find the general expression for the velocity of this body at any time *t*; *i.e.*, find the expression giving its position at times *t* and *t* + *h*, find the average velocity during time *h*, and find the limiting value of the expression as *h* becomes zero.   Check your answer by using the expression which you obtain for *v*, to find the instantaneous velocity at time *t* = 1 sec.

e. Find the expression for the acceleration of this body, and compare with the result obtained in Prob. 1*e*.

f. Answer the following questions (let the quantity *x* refer to distances on a vertical line):

a. Where is the body initially?

b. At what time does it reverse its direction of motion?

c. What is the maximum height reached?

d. At what time does it reach the origin?

e. What is its velocity at this point?

3. A particle moving along a vertical line has the following positions at various instants of time:

$$t(\text{sec.}) = \quad 0 \quad\quad 1 \quad\quad 2 \quad\quad 3 \quad\quad 4 \quad\quad 5 \quad\quad 10$$
$$x(\text{cm.}) = +8.0 \quad +5.0 \quad +4.0 \quad +5.0 \quad +8.0 \quad +13.0 \quad +68.0$$

a. Make a plot of displacement from the origin vs. time.

b. Find the average velocity of the particle in the intervals 0 to 1 sec., 0 to 2 sec., 0 to 3 sec., 0 to 4 sec.

c. What is the displacement of the particle at the end of 3 sec.? at the end of 4 sec.?

d. Find the slope of the curve you have drawn at the points *t* = 1, 2, 3, 4, and 5 sec.

e. Plot these values of the slope (what units?) vs. time.

f. From this plot determine the acceleration of the particle for different values of *t*.

4. A particle moving along the *x*-axis obeys the following equation of motion:

$$x = 6t^2 - 2t^3$$

where *x* is in feet and *t* in seconds.

a. Find the velocity of the particle at *t* = 0, 1, 2, 3, and 4 sec.

b. Find the acceleration of the particle at *t* = 0, 1, 2, 3, and 4 sec.

5*a.* Make a graph of the equation of Prob. 4.

b. Make a graph of velocity vs. time.

c. Make a graph of the acceleration of the body vs. time.

d. Describe the motion in words.

6. The velocity of a body is 60 miles/hr.   Express this velocity in feet per hour, feet per minute, feet per second, centimeters per second, meters per minute, and kilometers per hour.

7. If a runner covers 100 yards in 10 sec., what is his average velocity in miles per hour?   What would be the time for 100 meters at the same average velocity?

8. The radius of the earth is about 4,000 miles, and it makes one revolution in 24 hr.   Find the speed of a point on the equator, due to the earth's rotation (*a*) in miles per hour; (*b*) in feet per second.

9. A body starts from rest and gains velocity at the rate of 2 ft./sec. every second. What is its velocity, in feet per second, at the end of 1 sec.? of 2 sec.? 1 min.? What is its velocity in feet per minute, at the end of 1 min.? Express its acceleration in the following units:

feet per second per second; feet per second per minute;
feet per minute per minute; feet per minute per second.

10. A body is initially at rest at the origin and moves thereafter along the x-axis with a constant acceleration of 8 ft./sec.^{2}. What form do Eqs. (12) and (13) take for this special case? How far does the body move during the first second? What is its velocity at the end of the first second? What is its average velocity during the first second? How far does it move during the first 2 sec.? What is its velocity at the end of 2 sec.? What is its average velocity during the first 2 sec.? How far does it move during the second second? What is its average velocity during the second second?

11. The acceleration of a freely falling body is approximately 32 ft./sec.^{2} or 980 cm./sec.^{2}. An object is dropped from the top of a tall building. The origin may be taken at the starting point and the downward direction as positive. How fast is it falling at the end of 1 sec.? How many feet does it fall during the first second? What is its average velocity during the first second? If the building is 256 ft. high, how long a time is required for the body to reach the ground? What is its velocity when, *i.e.*, just before, it strikes? What was its average velocity for the entire distance? If the building contains 25 stories, each of equal height, at about what floor was the body after 1 sec.? After 2 sec.? How long a time is required for it to fall half the distance? Why is this not half of the total time?

12. A body is thrown vertically downward from the same building with an initial velocity of 8 ft./sec. What is the form taken by Eqs. (12) and (13) for this case? What is the velocity of the body at the end of 1 sec.? How far does it fall during the first second? What is its average velocity during the first second? How long a time is required for it to reach the ground?

13. An automobile traveling at 30 miles/hr. is brought to rest by its brakes in 4 sec. Compute the acceleration (assumed uniform) in miles per hour per second, and in feet per second per second. How many feet does it travel before coming to rest? What distance would be covered in stopping from twice the original speed with the same acceleration?

14. At the instant the lights turn green, a car which has been waiting starts to accelerate at the rate of 4 ft./sec.^{2}, while a second car which just reaches the intersection at this instant continues on at a uniform velocity of 20 miles/hr. How long a time is required for the first car to overtake the second? How fast is it traveling at this instant? What distance has it covered?

15. Which would win a 100-yard dash, a runner who can cover the distance in 10 sec. or an automobile which can accelerate to 60 miles/hr., from rest, in 16 sec.?

16. A ball is thrown up with a velocity of 64 ft./sec. What is its velocity after 1 sec.? After 2 sec.? How high does it rise? How many seconds are required for it to return to earth?

17. A pop fly is caught by the catcher 6 sec. after being struck. How high did it rise? What was its velocity when caught?

18. Starting from the equations

$$x = x_0 + v_0 t + \tfrac{1}{2} a t^2; \qquad v = v_0 + at$$

deduce the equation

$$v^2 = v_0^2 + 2a(x - x_0)$$

19. If two particles moving on the same straight line have positions x_1 and x_2, respectively, at any instant of time, we define the relative position of 2 with respect to 1 as

$$x_{21} = x_2 - x_1$$

  a. Show that the rate of change of x_{21} with respect to t (the relative velocity) is equal to the algebraic difference of velocities between 2 and 1.

  b. Show that the rate of change of relative velocity with respect to time (the relative acceleration) is equal to the acceleration of 2 minus the acceleration of 1.

20. Two bodies A and B move along the same straight line with constant velocities of $+40$ cm./sec. and -80 cm./sec., respectively.

  a. What is the relative velocity of B with respect to A?

  b. What is the relative velocity of A with respect to B?

  c. If at $t = 0$ the relative position x_{BA} is 200 cm., when will they collide (if ever)?

  d. What was the relative position of A with respect to B at $t = -1$ sec.?

21. Two bodies A and B move along a straight line according to the equations

$$\left. \begin{aligned} x_A &= -10t + 5t^2 \text{ cm.} \\ x_B &= 30 + 5t - 10t^2 \text{ cm.} \end{aligned} \right\} t \text{ in seconds}$$

  a. Find the relative velocity of B with respect to A when they meet.

  b. For what value of t do they meet?

  c. What is their relative acceleration at $t = 0$? at $t = 5$ sec.?

  d. Where do they meet with respect to the initial position of A?

  e. When and where is their relative velocity zero? What is their separation at this instant of time?

22. Two particles move along the same straight line according to the equations

$$\left. \begin{aligned} x_1 &= -10t + 2t^2 \text{ ft.} \\ x_2 &= x_0 + 5t - t^2 \text{ ft.} \end{aligned} \right\} t \text{ in seconds}$$

where x_0 is a constant.

  a. Find the velocity and acceleration of each particle at the end of 1 sec.

  b. If the particles collide at the end of 6 sec., find their initial separation.

23. A man standing at the edge of a roof throws a stone vertically upward with an initial velocity of 64 ft./sec. Three seconds later he drops a stone from rest. How far below the edge of the roof do the stones meet?

24. A stone falls from the edge of a cliff from rest and 1 sec. later a second stone is thrown down from the edge of the cliff with an initial speed of 40 ft./sec. If they meet at the bottom, *a.* How high is the cliff?

b. What is their relative velocity at the bottom?

25. The engineer of a train running at a speed of v_1 ft./sec. sights a freight train A ft. ahead of him on the same track moving in the same direction with a speed of v_2 ft./sec. He puts on the brakes giving the train a constant deceleration (negative acceleration) of a ft./sec.[2] Show that, if

$$A > \frac{(v_1 - v_2)^2}{2a}$$

there will be no collision;

$$A < \frac{(v_1 - v_2)^2}{2a}$$

there will be a collision. (Assume $v_1 > v_2$.)

26. A particle moves on a straight line according to the equation

$$x = \sqrt{2kt + x_0^2}$$

Show that the acceleration is

$$a = -\frac{k^2}{x^3}$$

and that at $x = \infty$,

$$v = 0.$$

Find the velocity of the body at $t = 0$.

27. A stone drops from the roof of a building and requires $\frac{1}{8}$ sec. to pass from the top to the bottom of a window 6 ft. high. How high is the roof above the top of the window?

28. A wheel rotates about its axis with a constant angular acceleration of 1 revolution per second per second.

a. Find the angular acceleration in radians per second per second.

b. If its initial angular velocity is 600 r.p.m., find its angular velocity in r.p.m. and in radians per second at the end of 1 min.

c. How many revolutions does the wheel make during this minute? What is the angle through which it turns (in radians)?

29. During a time interval of 2 sec. a wheel rotating with constant angular acceleration turns through 10 revolutions. At the end of this time interval its angular velocity is 360 r.p.m. Find the angular acceleration of the wheel.

30. The angle turned through by the flywheel of an automobile engine in a time interval t is given by

$$\theta = 30t + 0.1t^3 \text{ radians}$$

where t is in seconds and the above equation describes the motion from $t = 0$ to $t = 10$ sec.

a. Find an expression for the angular velocity in terms of the time t.

b. Find an expression for the angular acceleration in terms of t.

c. What is the angular velocity of the wheel for $t = 10$ sec., in radians per second and in r.p.m.?

d. What angle is turned through from $t = 0$ to $t = 10$? How many revolutions does the flywheel make in this time interval?

CHAPTER III

PLANE KINEMATICS OF A MASS POINT

In this chapter we shall continue our discussion of kinematics, now extending the concepts introduced in Chap. II to describe the motion of a particle in a plane. Motion in a plane displays characteristics which are not present in linear motion and which are essential to our study. For example, in linear motion the path of the particle is always a straight line by definition, whereas in a plane there is an infinite variety of curves which the particle may follow in its motion. Furthermore, in linear motion the vectors could possess but two directions, to the right or to the left. In a plane these vectors may now point in any direction and we must learn how to manipulate these quantities when there are two degrees of freedom.

12. Vectors in a Plane.—Displacement, velocity, and acceleration are all vector quantities, as they possess magnitude and direction. A displacement can be represented by a straight line whose length indicates the magnitude and whose direction indicates the direction of the displacement. To make the specification unique, we must indicate by an arrowhead the sense of the vector, *i.e.*, the direction along the straight line in which the displacement occurs. In exactly similar fashion, any vector may be represented by an arrow of given length and direction. As long as we restricted ourselves to linear motion, the direction of our vectors was fixed by the straight line along which the motion occurred, and it was only necessary to specify magnitude and sense. The latter was done by treating vectors as algebraic quantities, and the laws of addition and subtraction of vectors followed algebraic rules. Now these rules of addition and subtraction must be extended to the plane case, where the directions of the vectors may differ from one another. Vectors which lie in the same plane are called *coplanar*.

The position of a point P in a plane, for example on this page, is determined by two independent pieces of information. Let us choose an origin O, say at the lower left-hand corner of the page, and draw a straight line from O to P. Adding an arrowhead at P, we have the vector which represents the displacement from O to P and hence fixes the position of point P. There are two convenient ways of specifying the vector OP and thus the position of P: First, we may specify (*a*) the magnitude (the length) of the vector OP and (*b*) the angle which this line of displacement makes with a horizontal line, such as the bottom edge of the page; and, second, we may give (*a*) the distance to the right of the origin and (*b*) the distance above the origin. In any case, two numbers are necessary corresponding to the two degrees of freedom of a point in a plane. In the second mode of representation the distance of the point P to the right of the origin is clearly the length of the projection of the vector OP along a horizontal line, which we may take as an x-axis. This projection along the x-axis is known as the *x-component* of the vector OP. Similarly, the distance of the point P above O is given by the projection of OP

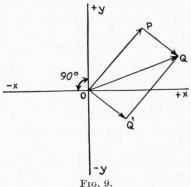

Fig. 9.

along a vertical line which we take as a y-axis. This projection is known as the *y-component* of the vector (see Fig. 9).

In Fig. 9, OP represents a displacement from O to P. Suppose a man walks from O to P and then from P to Q. He has undergone two successive displacements, OP and PQ. Clearly the sum of these two displacements is represented by the vector OQ, and from the figure it is obvious that we cannot add displacements (and hence vectors) algebraically. To obtain the sum of the two vectors OP and PQ we must construct a parallelogram of which OP and PQ are adjacent sides and the diagonal of which is the sum of the two vectors. Since we construct a parallelogram, it is irrelevant if we move PQ parallel to itself to the position OQ' and then form the sum of OP and OQ'. From this law of addition, the law of subtraction follows immediately. Suppose we wish to subtract the vector PQ (or OQ') from the vector OP. This is equivalent to adding the vector $-PQ$ (or $-OQ'$) to the vector OP. Thus we first construct the vector $-PQ$. This is the vector equal in length to PQ but opposite in direction. Then we complete the parallelogram of which *OP* and −*PQ* are adjacent sides. The diagonal of this parallelogram is the difference between *OP* and *PQ*. A little consideration shows that this equals the vector *Q'P* in Fig. 9, *i.e.*, the other diagonal of the parallelogram *OPQQ'*. The important thing to keep in mind is that neither the sum nor the difference of two vectors has in general the same direction as either of the two vectors.

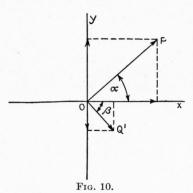

FIG. 10.

In actual calculations of the sum and differences of vectors we may proceed according to the geometrical procedure outlined above, but it is much more convenient to proceed with the help of the components of the vectors. The general idea is to work with the components of the vectors, using the simple algebraic rules for adding the *x*-components and for adding the *y*-components.

Suppose we have to calculate the sum of *OP* and *OQ'* (or *PQ*), and that we know the magnitudes of these vectors and the angles which they make with the *x*- and the *y*-axes (Figs. 9 and 10). We perform the following steps:

1. Resolve each vector into two components, one along the *x*-axis and one along the *y*-axis:

$$x\text{-component of } OP = OP \cos \alpha$$
$$y\text{-component of } OP = OP \sin \alpha$$
$$x\text{-component of } OQ' = OQ' \cos \beta$$
$$y\text{-component of } OQ' = -OQ' \sin \beta$$

The minus sign in the last component shows that this component is negative and points down along the negative *y*-axis.

2. Add all the *x*-components algebraically and all the *y*-components algebraically to obtain the *x*- and *y*-components of the vector which represents the sum or resultant. This is allowed because all the *x*-components lie along the same straight line. Similar considerations hold for the *y*-components. Thus

$$x\text{-component of the resultant} = OP \cos \alpha + OQ' \cos \beta = X$$
$$y\text{-component of the resultant} = OP \sin \alpha - OQ' \sin \beta = Y$$

X and *Y* are used merely as abbreviations.

3. Find the resultant vector whose x-component is X and whose y-component is Y (Fig. 10a). From the right triangle the length of the resultant vector R is given by

$$R = \sqrt{X^2 + Y^2}$$

and the angle θ which this resultant makes with the x-axis is fixed by the relation

$$\tan \theta = \frac{Y}{X}$$

and thus we have the answer.

The advantage of the method of breaking up a vector into components rather than adding by the parallelogram method is that we always deal with right triangles and thus simplify the calculations. These rules of addition hold for all vector quantities, and it is easy to see how we are to add more than two vectors. The rules for subtraction using components follow immediately from the rules above and are left as an exercise for the student. In the study of kinematics, the resolution of vectors into components turns a problem of motion in a plane into two simple problems of

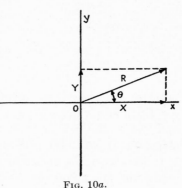

Fig. 10a.

straight-line motion. After solving the problem for each component separately, we then obtain the final result by vector addition.

Thus the magnitude of the resultant displacement s from the origin of a point which has coordinates (x, y) is

$$s = \sqrt{x^2 + y^2} \tag{1}$$

The magnitude of the velocity v is calculated from the values of the components v_x and v_y by

$$v = \sqrt{v_x^2 + v_y^2} \tag{2}$$

and similarly, for the acceleration,

$$a = \sqrt{a_x^2 + a_y^2} \tag{3}$$

The directions of the resultant vectors may then be found immediately.

We shall now illustrate by a simple example. Suppose a man can row a boat at a constant speed of 3 miles/hr. in still water. He rows across a river $\frac{1}{2}$ mile wide and there is a current moving with a speed of 4 miles/hr. The problem is to find his resultant velocity, the distance he moves down stream, and the total distance covered.

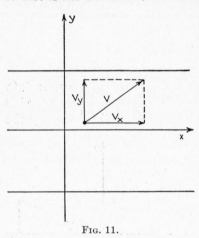

Let us choose our x-axis pointing down stream and our y-axis across the stream (Fig. 11). The boat moves with constant-velocity components

$$v_x = 4 \text{ miles/hr.}$$
$$v_y = 3 \text{ miles/hr.}$$

In t hr., he covers a displacement whose components are

$$x = v_x t = 4t$$
$$y = v_y t = 3t$$

Fig. 11.

Now we know that the distance across the stream (the y-component of the displacement) is $\frac{1}{2}$ mile. Thus we place $y = \frac{1}{2}$ mile and find

$$t = \frac{1}{2} \times \frac{1}{3} = \frac{1}{6} \text{ hr.} = 10 \text{ min.}$$

To find the x-component of the displacement, $i.e.$, the distance he moves down stream, we insert this value of t in the equation for x and find

$$x = 4 \times \frac{1}{6} = \frac{2}{3} \text{ mile}$$

To find the magnitude of the displacement (the total distance covered), we have, according to Eq. (1),

$$s = \sqrt{x^2 + y^2} = \sqrt{(\tfrac{2}{3})^2 + (\tfrac{1}{2})^2} = \sqrt{\tfrac{25}{36}} = \tfrac{5}{6} \text{ mile}$$

The resultant velocity has a magnitude

$$v = \sqrt{v_x^2 + v_y^2} = \sqrt{4^2 + 3^2} = 5 \text{ miles/hr.}$$

and makes an angle θ with the x-axis given by

$$\tan \theta = \frac{v_y}{v_x} = \frac{3}{4}$$

whence

$$\theta = 37° \text{ (approximately)}$$

so that the velocity vector makes an angle of 37° with the down-stream direction. Since the resultant speed is constant, we can also calculate the distance covered directly from it. The speed is 5 miles/hr., and, since it takes 10 min. for the crossing, the distance covered is $5 \times \frac{1}{6} = \frac{5}{6}$ mile, checking the answer we have already found. It must be noted, however, that it is necessary to consider one component of the velocity to calculate the time of crossing.

13. Velocity and Acceleration in a Plane; Circular Motion.—In the last section we have seen how to obtain the resultant velocity and acceleration of a particle moving in a plane from a knowledge of the components of velocity and of acceleration along two mutually perpendicular axes (which we have called the x- and y-axes). Let us now turn to a geometrical investigation of the nature of the resultant velocity and acceleration. Suppose that the curve shown in Fig. 12 represents a portion of the path traversed by a mass point, and that when it is at the point P its vector velocity is v. The magnitude of v is indicated by the length of the arrow labeled v and its direction is that of the tangent to the curve at P. After a very short interval of time which we denote by Δt, the particle will

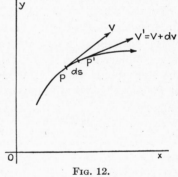

Fig. 12.

move a short distance Δs along the curve to the point P'. If we take Δt very small, Δs will be extremely small and will practically coincide with the displacement from P to P' both in magnitude and direction. Hence we have very nearly

$$\overrightarrow{\Delta s} = \overrightarrow{v}\Delta t \tag{4}$$

or

$$\overrightarrow{v} = \frac{\overrightarrow{\Delta s}}{\Delta t} \tag{4a}$$

and, if we let $\Delta t \to 0$, we get (exactly)

$$\vec{v} = \frac{\vec{ds}}{dt} \tag{5}$$

where we must remember that both $\vec{v}$ and the infinitely small displacement $\vec{ds}$ are vectors. According to Eq. (5), the velocity and the displacement ds along the curve have the same direction. For all practical purposes we may consider ds a little piece of the curve representing the path. As the particle moves along its path, its velocity at any point coincides with the direction of ds at that point. If the path is curved, the pieces ds will have different directions, so that the velocity vector changes its direction (and perhaps its magnitude) as the particle moves along the path. A changing velocity vector means acceleration, so that motion in a curved path is always an accelerated motion, never one of constant velocity since this would mean constant direction (straight-line motion).

Fig. 13.

To see which direction the acceleration vector possesses, we construct a figure (Fig. 13) which represents the velocities of the particle at the two positions P and P'. In this figure we have displaced the vector v' parallel to itself so that it starts from the same point as v. Now the vector v represents the velocity at P, and v' is the velocity of the particle dt sec. later when the particle is at P'. Hence the change in velocity is dv which is shown in Fig. 13 as the vector difference between v' and v. Then, by definition, the acceleration vector is

$$\vec{a} = \frac{\vec{dv}}{dt} \tag{6}$$

and has the direction of dv (not of ds or of v).

A special but important case of plane motion which requires some detailed study is that in which a particle moves in a circular path. This type of motion affords an excellent example of motion in which the direction of the velocity vector changes continually. Let the radius of the circle be R, and let us take the center of the circle as coincident with a set of x-y axes (Fig. 14). The position of the point P on the circle can be specified either by giving its x- and y-coordinates or by giving the magnitude of the radius vector $\vec{R}$ and the angle θ which this vector makes with the positive x-axis. Since the magnitude of the vector R stays constant in circular motion (it is equal to the radius of the circle), we have a motion of only one degree of freedom and can use the single coordinate θ to specify the position of the particle; θ is called an angular coordinate.

If we wish to find the velocity of the particle at the point P, we may proceed as follows: By definition the velocity of the particle is the rate of change with time of its position vector (in our case $\overrightarrow{R}$), and for circular motion this position vector is a rotating vector of constant magnitude. Thus we must find an expression for the time rate of change of a rotating vector. If the particle is at the

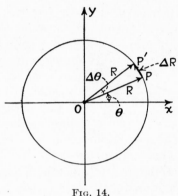

FIG. 14.

position P at time t and at the position P' at a time Δt later, then the average velocity during this time interval is

$$\bar{v} = \frac{\Delta R}{\Delta t} \tag{7}$$

and has the direction of ΔR shown in the figure. During this time interval the angle θ between the radius vector and the x-axis changes by an amount $\Delta\theta$. The velocity of the particle at the point P is then obtained by allowing Δt (and consequently $\Delta\theta$) to approach zero. We note that ΔR equals the chord PP' and remember that, as the angle subtended by the chord of a circle approaches zero, the arc and the chord approach each other in value. Thus in Eq. (7) we replace ΔR by the arc PP' and then let Δt or $\Delta\theta$ approach zero. Since the arc PP' equals $R\Delta\theta$, we have, for the velocity at the point P,

$$v = R \lim \frac{\Delta\theta}{\Delta t} \qquad \text{as} \qquad \Delta t \to 0$$

and if we define ω, the angular velocity of rotation, by the equation

$$\omega = \frac{d\theta}{dt} \tag{8}$$

we have

$$v = R\frac{d\theta}{dt} = R\omega \tag{9}$$

Here v is the magnitude of the velocity vector and R the length of the radius vector. The direction of v is tangent to the circle, at right angles to the radius vector $\overrightarrow{R}$.

We have thus derived the very important result: **The rate of change of a vector of constant magnitude rotating with an angular velocity ω is a vector of magnitude equal to the product of the magnitude of the rotating vector and the angular velocity. The direction of this vector is at right angles to the original rotating vector.**

We now wish to calculate the acceleration of the particle, and we shall first confine ourselves to the case in which the particle moves with constant speed v in the circle. In this case we see from Eq. (9) that the angular velocity ω of the particle is constant. Since the velocity vector $\overrightarrow{v}$ is always perpendicular to the radius vector $\overrightarrow{R}$, it changes its direction exactly the same way as $\overrightarrow{R}$ does

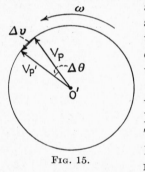

and hence rotates with the same constant angular velocity ω. We can represent this fact on a velocity diagram in which we draw the successive velocity vectors for the particle from a common origin O' (Fig. 15). In the figure, v_P represents the velocity of the particle at the point P of Fig. 14 and $v_{P'}$ the velocity at the point P'. The angle $\Delta\theta$ is the same as shown in Fig. 14. Thus we have a vector of constant magnitude v (for the case of constant speed motion) rotating with a constant angular velocity ω, and we can apply the theorem stated above. Hence we obtain for the acceleration (since the acceleration is the rate of change of the vector velocity) a vector of magnitude

Fig. 15.

$$a = v\omega \qquad (10)$$

and, since ω is the same as in Eq. (9), this can be written

$$a = \frac{v^2}{R} \qquad (11)$$

The direction of this acceleration vector is perpendicular to the vector v. The vector v being tangent to the circle at any point the acceleration vector points along a radius, and a little consideration shows that it is directed toward the center of the circle in which the particle actually moves.

The preceding derivation is a geometrical one, and it is instructive to carry through an equivalent derivation analytically. Referring back to Fig. 14, we have for the x- and y-coordinates of the point P

$$x = R \cos \theta = R \cos \omega t \Big\}$$
$$y = R \sin \theta = R \sin \omega t \Big\} \tag{12}$$

These are the kinetic equations of motion of the mass point. In them ω is constant. We obtain the velocity components by differentiating these equations with respect to t, yielding

$$v_x = -\omega R \sin \omega t \Big\}$$
$$v_y = +\omega R \cos \omega t \Big\} \tag{13}$$

The magnitude of the resultant velocity (the speed) is, according to Eq. (2),

$$v = \sqrt{v_x^2 + v_y^2} = \sqrt{\omega^2 R^2 \sin^2 \omega t + \omega^2 R^2 \cos^2 \omega t} = \omega R$$

which is simply Eq. (9).

Since the direction of v is not constant, there is an acceleration the components of which we find by differentiating Eqs. (13) with respect to t. This yields

$$a_x = -\omega^2 R \cos \omega t \Big\}$$
$$a_y = -\omega^2 R \sin \omega t \Big\} \tag{14}$$

The magnitude of the resultant acceleration is, according to Eq. (3),

$$a = \sqrt{a_x^2 + a_y^2} = \omega^2 R \sqrt{\cos^2 \omega t + \sin^2 \omega t} = \omega^2 R$$

or, using Eq. (9),

$$a = \omega^2 R = \frac{v^2}{R} \tag{15}$$

in exact agreement with the result of Eq. (11).

Now let us find the direction of this acceleration vector. Let α be the angle which this vector makes with the x-axis. Then we have

$$\tan \alpha = \frac{a_y}{a_x}$$

and since

$$\frac{a_y}{a_x} = \frac{-\omega^2 R \sin \omega t}{-\omega^2 R \cos \omega t} = \tan \omega t = \tan \theta$$

we see that

$$\tan \alpha = \tan \theta$$

Hence $\alpha = \theta$, and we find the acceleration vector pointing along the radius as before. We also know that it points toward the center of the circle since the minus signs in Eqs. (14) mean that the x-component of the acceleration points to the left and its y-component points down.

To recapitulate:

Motion in a circle with constant speed is an accelerated motion. The magnitude of this acceleration is v^2/R (v **the speed,** R **the**

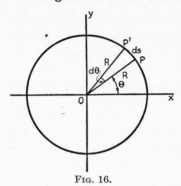

FIG. 16.

radius of the circle), and it is directed at every instant of time toward the center of the circle along the radius R. **This acceleration is due only to a change of direction of the velocity vector.**

14. Circular Motion with Variable Speed.—A more general case is that in which the particle moves in a circular path with variable speed. In this case we have not only an acceleration due to a changing direction of the velocity vector but also an acceleration because of the changing length of this vector. As we have seen in the last section, the component of acceleration due to changing direction of the velocity is at right angles to the velocity itself and the component of acceleration due to the changing length of the velocity vector is in the direction of the velocity. Thus we have two components of acceleration:

1. The central acceleration directed along the radius toward the center.

2. The tangential acceleration directed along the velocity vector, *i.e.*, tangent to the circle and hence perpendicular to the radius of the circle.

Let us consider the second component of the acceleration more closely. If the particle is at the position P at a certain instant of time, after a time interval dt it is at P' at a distance ds along the arc from P (Fig. 16).

From the figure we see that

$$ds = Rd\theta \qquad (16)$$

and the speed at the point P is

$$v = \frac{ds}{dt} = R\frac{d\theta}{dt} = R\omega \tag{17}$$

where $\omega = d\theta/dt$ is the instantaneous angular velocity at P and does not remain constant.

Differentiating with respect to t, we find, for the component of acceleration tangent to the circle,

$$a_t = \frac{dv}{dt} = R\frac{d\omega}{dt} = R\alpha \tag{18}$$

where we call $\alpha = d\omega/dt$ the angular acceleration of the particle. From Eqs. (17) and (18) we see that angular velocity and angular acceleration are proportional to the linear speed and tangential acceleration, respectively, so that we may use them equally well to describe the aspects of the motion due to changes in speed of the particle.

In general it turns out that Eq. (15) is valid for the central acceleration even if the speed does not stay constant, so that we may write for the two components of acceleration:

1. The central part

$$a_r = \frac{v^2}{R} = \omega^2 R$$

2. The tangential part $\tag{19}$

$$a_t = \frac{dv}{dt} = R\alpha$$

Since these are at right angles, the resultant acceleration has a magnitude given by

$$a = \sqrt{a_r^2 + a_t^2} = \sqrt{\left(\frac{dv}{dt}\right)^2 + \frac{v^4}{R^2}} \tag{20}$$

Equation (20) can be derived directly from the kinetic equations of motion, using the method of the last section. We start with the equations

$$\left.\begin{array}{l} x = R\cos\theta \\ y = R\sin\theta \end{array}\right\} \tag{21}$$

differentiate each twice with respect to t, remembering that $\omega = d\theta/dt$ and that $\alpha = d\omega/dt = d^2\theta/dt^2$, thus obtaining expressions for the x- and y-components of the acceleration. The resultant acceleration has a magnitude given by the square root of the sum of the squares of these components. The actual derivation is left as an exercise for the student. Perhaps one word of caution is necessary: In the general case it is not allowable, as it was for constant speed, to place $\theta = \omega t$, since this relation follows from the definition $\omega = d\theta/dt$ only when ω and hence the speed are constant.

A special case of considerable interest is that in which a particle moves in a circle with constant angular acceleration. If this constant acceleration is denoted by α, we easily find the equations

$$\omega = \omega_0 + \alpha t \tag{22}$$

and

$$\theta = \theta_0 + \omega_0 t + \tfrac{1}{2}\alpha t^2 \tag{23}$$

where ω_0 and θ_0 are the initial angular velocity and initial angular position, respectively.

Problems

1. Two vectors have magnitudes of 40 and 60 cm. and make an angle of 40° with each other. Find the magnitude of the sum of these vectors and the angle which this resultant makes with the smaller vector.

2. Two vectors, one of which has twice the magnitude of the other, have a resultant of magnitude 26.5 in. which makes an angle of 40.9° with the smaller vector. Find the magnitude of each vector and the angle between them.

3. The resultant velocity of a particle is made up of three components, as follows: A 10-ft./sec. vector in the direction of the positive x-axis; a 20-ft./sec. vector making an angle of 30° with the positive y-axis in the second quadrant; and a 25-ft./sec. vector making an angle of 45° with the negative x-axis in the third quadrant.

  a. Find the x-component of the resultant velocity.

  b. Find the y-component of the resultant velocity.

  c. Find the magnitude and direction of the resultant.

4. A vector 20 units long makes an angle of 37° with the $+x$-axis in the first quadrant. Find the x- and y-components of this vector. If this vector is added to another vector of length 4 units pointing along the negative x-axis, find the length of the resultant vector and the tangent of the angle it makes with the x-axis.

5. A vector has x- and y-components of $+10$ units and $+5$ units, respectively. Find the magnitude of the vector and the tangent of the angle which it makes with the x-axis. Find the sum of this vector and a vector of length 20 units making an angle of 45° with the negative x-axis in the third quadrant. Give the magnitude of the resultant and the tangent of the angle it makes with the x-axis.

6. A man runs at the rate of 6 miles/hr. (with respect to the deck) from the bow to the stern of a steamboat. The boat attains a speed of 10 miles/hr. in still water and is pointed directly across a river which is flowing south with a speed of 3 miles/hr. Calculate the velocity (magnitude and direction) of the man's motion relative to the bank of the river.

7. A ship heads due north with a speed in this direction of 12 miles/hr. At the end of 2 hr. it is 8 miles east of north. What is the velocity of the current? How far does the ship go in 2 hr.? What angle does the resultant velocity make with the north direction?

8. A raindrop, falling vertically, hits the window of a train moving with a speed of 45 miles/hr. It makes a streak on the pane which makes an angle of 10° with the horizontal. What is the downward speed of the raindrop?

9. Two vectors of lengths A and B make an angle θ with each other. Prove, by taking components along an x- and a y-axis, that the length of the resultant R is

$$R = \sqrt{A^2 + B^2 + 2AB \cos \theta}$$

10. A man can row a boat 4 miles/hr. in still water. If he is crossing a river where the current is 2 miles/hr., in what direction should his boat be headed if he wishes to reach the point directly opposite his starting point? If the river is 4 miles wide, how long will it take him to cross the river?

Find the time it would take him to row 2 miles down the river and then back to the starting point.

Find the time it would take him to row 2 miles upstream and then back to the starting point.

In what direction should he direct the boat if he wishes to cross in the least possible time?

11. The moon rotates in a circle of radius 240,000 miles about the earth once in about 28 days. Find the speed of the moon. Find its angular velocity. What is its acceleration?

12. A stone at the end of a string 1.5 ft. long is rotated in a circle at a constant rate of 90 r.p.m.

a. Find the angular velocity of the stone in radians per second.

b. Find the speed of the stone.

c. What is the acceleration of the stone?

13. A particle moves with a constant speed of 5 cm./sec. in a circle of radius 20 cm. At $t = 0$ the particle is on the positive x-axis.

a. Find the x- and y-components of the acceleration of the particle.

b. Calculate the position of the particle at $t = 4\pi/3$ sec.

c. Calculate the x- and y-components of the velocity of the particle at this instant of time.

d. Calculate the x- and y-components of the acceleration of the particle at this instant.

14. A particle moves in a circle of radius R with constant speed v.

a. Indicate two successive positions of the particle and construct the velocity vectors at these two positions.

b. Draw a separate figure to indicate the change in velocity between these positions.

c. Using similar triangles and the definition of acceleration, derive an expression for the acceleration of the particle.   What is the direction of the acceleration vector?

15. An automobile engine is running at 600 r.p.m.   The accelerator is suddenly depressed, and the engine speeds up to 3,600 r.p.m. in 10 sec.

a. Compute the angular acceleration of the engine during the 10 sec. (Assume it to be uniform.)

b. If the flywheel of the engine is 18 in. in diameter, compute the tangential acceleration of a point on its rim.

c. How many revolutions does the engine make during the 10 sec.?

16. A wheel 25 cm. in diameter accelerates at a constant rate from rest to an angular velocity of 1,200 r.p.m. in 20 sec.

a. Find the angular acceleration of the wheel.

b. How many revolutions are turned through in the 20 sec.?

c. Find the resultant acceleration (magnitude and direction) of a point on the rim at $t = 0$ sec., $t = 1$ sec., and $t = 20$ sec.

17. A wheel starting from rest with constant angular acceleration acquires an angular speed of 1,800 r.p.m. in 30 sec.   The radius of the wheel is 6 in. Calculate the radial and tangential components of the acceleration of a point on the rim $\frac{1}{2}$ sec. after starting.   Draw a diagram indicating the direction of rotation and the direction of each component of the acceleration.

CHAPTER IV

NEWTON'S LAWS; STATICS OF A PARTICLE

Up to this point we have been studying the characteristics and the method of description of various motions, in particular of straight-line motion and of circular motion. We have merely assumed that such motions exist and we have not inquired as to how they are actually produced. In this and succeeding chapters we shall undertake a study of the causes of real motions, comprising the subject of dynamics, and this study lays the foundation for the whole science of mechanics. More precisely, we shall concern ourselves in this chapter with a statement and discussion of the fundamental laws of motion, followed by a study of the statics of a particle to gain familiarity with the composition of forces, and hence we must start by discussing a number of new physical concepts and definitions.

15. The Concept of Inertia.—In order to obtain an understanding of the causes of motion of bodies in nature, we must appeal primarily to our experience, and in particular to those experiences in which we recognize and distinguish among various kinds of motion, *e.g.*, a falling stone or a bullet shot from a rifle. In each of these cases it is noticed that we intuitively associate a definite *cause* of the motion; for the stone, we say that the earth causes the motion, and in the case of the bullet, the expanding gases are the cause of the motion of the bullet. By these statements we mean only that if the bodies which "cause" the motion were to be removed, the motion would lose its original characteristics.

The first question we ask is: How would a material point move if it were free from all external environment, *i.e.*, completely isolated and infinitely distant from all other material bodies in the universe? Of course such a question cannot be answered by an experiment, and, in fact, we may justly wonder how much physical meaning such a question has, since we do not know if huge bodies at enormous distances from our mass point might appreciably modify the motion. On the other hand we can, in certain special motions, keep diminishing the effects of the causes of motion. We cannot remove the earth but can eliminate its influence by placing the material point (*e.g.*, a block) on a rigid, horizontal plane. If we now let the block slide (passing a given point with some definite velocity), we notice that it gradually slows down and stops. This simple experiment seems to indicate that the answer to our question would be that, when freed from external environment, a body remains in a state of rest. Such, indeed, was the attitude of the Greeks toward this matter, and this view persisted up to the time of Galileo. If we repeat our experiment with a smoother block on a smoother surface, we notice that the decrease of velocity ensues more slowly, and that this effect keeps increasing as the block and surface are made smoother and smoother. Therefore, we extrapolate and say that if all roughness and consequent friction could be eliminated, the body would continue indefinitely in a straight line with constant velocity. This constitutes Galileo's answer to our question. Of course, this mode of presentation cannot be looked upon as a proof, since an independent definition of *external influence* is lacking. It is possible, however, to interpret the experiment in the above manner. This principle of Galileo is the interpretation and generalization of, rather than a deduction from, experience. This procedure is the only one which allows science to progress; a fact, or a set of facts, alone can teach nothing new no matter how often it is ascertained, interpretation and generalization thereof alone open the path to progress.

The relation that a body retains a uniform linear motion once started is often described by assigning a property to matter which we call *inertia*. To say that matter possesses inertia is to express the relation of Galileo, and this relation, like every generalization, must appeal to the correctness of the results obtained therefrom for justification.

16. The Concept of Force.—The primitive concept of a *force* is a push or a pull exerted by our own muscles. For the purposes of physics, however, it is necessary to make such a concept more precise, and we must find a method of measuring forces, *i.e.*, comparing different forces. We know that by pushing or pulling on a body, such as the block in our example, we can produce changes in its velocity and the harder the push or pull, the greater the ensuing acceleration. It is very natural to look upon force as the cause of acceleration, *i.e.*, of rate of change of velocity, but our muscular sensations are too vague and uncertain to be used as a measure of force so we must proceed to set up a more exact definition (Sec. 17).

Forces fall into two general classes: first, forces which are exerted on bodies by direct contact with other bodies, or are transmitted through ropes attached to the bodies on which they act; and, second, forces which "act at a distance" and which are due to the mere presence of bodies other than the one on which the force is acting. As an example, a piece of iron held in the neighborhood of a magnet is acted on by a force due to the magnet. To convince ourselves thereof, we remove the magnet and find that the force on the iron changes. All forces acting on a body have their origin in other bodies, and a good test to find out if a body A exerts a force on body B is to remove body A and see if the velocity of B changes. For example, a ladder standing up against a wall is pushed outward by the wall. The fact that the ladder remains at rest must mean that more than one force acts on the ladder and that the resultant of all these forces must be zero. If we imagine the wall to be removed, there is no doubt that the velocity of the ladder would change.

17. The Concept of Mass; Momentum.—It would seem simplest to place the force acting on a body equal to the rate of change of velocity (acceleration) which it produces. Such a procedure is, however, unsatisfactory for two reasons. First, and most important, is the fact that such an assumption is not consistent with experimental facts; the same force produces the same acceleration of the same body in repeated experiments, but, if it acts on different bodies, it produces different accelerations. Second, there is a logical difficulty. Acceleration is a purely kinematical (geometrical) quantity, and force is a dynamical (physical) quantity: Equating the two would hardly be a logical procedure. Instead of considering the velocity of a body (and its changes) alone, we must consider a dynamical quantity which describes the motion of a body, which Newton called the *quantity of motion* and which we now term the *momentum of a body*. We define the momentum of a particle as a quantity proportional to its velocity:

$$\text{Momentum} = mv$$

where the proportionality factor m is called the *inertia mass of the particle*. Qualitatively we think of the mass of a body as a quantity determining the *amount of matter* in a body. Such a concept may be useful but cannot form a satisfactory physical definition. We must lay down some means of measuring mass, *i.e.*, we must define a physical process by which we can compare masses quantitatively. If we then choose a mass to serve as unit mass, our definition becomes complete. We now agree to measure force by placing the force acting on a particle equal to the rate of change of momentum which this force produces. Since we think of mass as a measure of the *quantity of matter* in a body, it seems reasonable to suppose that the mass of a particle does not depend on its motion, provided the particle does not pick up other particles during its motion or lose pieces of itself. Let us make this assumption tentatively, being prepared to reject it if it does not work. Then we may write

Rate of change of momentum =
$$\text{mass times rate of change of velocity}$$

Now let us suppose that we allow the same force (*e.g.*, the force exerted by a spring which is always stretched the same amount) to act on a number n of mass points one after the other. We observe that the velocities of the particles $v_1, v_2, \ldots, v_n$ change at different rates $\dfrac{dv_1}{dt} = a_1,\ \dfrac{dv_2}{dt} = a_2,\ \cdots,\ \dfrac{dv_n}{dt} = a_n$, and we assign a series of factors $m_1, m_2, \ldots, m_n$ to the various particles so that

$$(F) = m_1\frac{dv_1}{dt} = m_2\frac{dv_2}{dt} = \cdots = m_n\frac{dv_n}{dt}$$

Of course we may choose one of the m's, let us say m_1, arbitrarily, and then the remaining m's are fixed by the above equalities. Now we can perform an experiment to see if our assumption about the m's being independent of the motion leads to difficulties. We perform another series of experiments with a different spring (force F') and find that we can satisfy the equations

$$(F') = m_1\frac{dv_1'}{dt} = m_2\frac{dv_2'}{dt} = \cdots = m_n\frac{dv_n'}{dt}$$

with the same m's as before, using the same value of m_1 as in the first case. Hence we conclude that within our experimental error the masses m are constant, so that our assumption is justified. These equations which may be written in the form

$$m_1 a_1 = m_2 a_2 = \cdots = m_n a_n$$

allow us to compare masses and hence to measure them if a unit mass is chosen. This choice is perfectly arbitrary. Suppose our first mass m_1 is chosen as unit mass, then the mass of the third particle, for example, is determined by

$$m_3 = m_1 \frac{a_1}{a_3} = 1 \cdot \frac{a_1}{a_3}$$

and, since a_1 and a_3 can be measured, we may thus measure the number of units of mass in the mass m_3.

In the metric system of units, the unit mass is arbitrarily defined as $\frac{1}{1000}$ of the mass of a piece of platinum kept at Sèvres, near Paris, and this unit mass is called the *gram*. It is very nearly equal to the mass of one cubic centimeter of water at 4°C. and at atmospheric pressure.

In the English system of units, the unit mass is defined as the mass of a certain piece of metal kept at London and is called the *pound mass*.

18. Forces Occur in Pairs.—In Sec. 16, we made the statement that forces acting on a body have their origin in other bodies. It is a matter of experience that whenever a body A exerts a force on a body B, the latter body exerts a force (reaction) on body A. If any one doubts the validity of this statement, let him try kicking a door with his bare foot. The damage done to his toes will convince him of the forces exerted by the door on his foot. It is one of the fundamental postulates of mechanics that the force exerted by B on A is equal in magnitude and opposite in direction to that force which A exerts on B.

19. Newton's Laws of Motion.—The facts, definitions, and postulates discussed in this chapter were first definitely formulated by Sir Isaac Newton in three laws, known as *Newton's laws of motion. These laws form the basis of the science of mechanics.*

LAW I.   Every particle persists in its state of rest or of uniform motion in a straight line, except in so far as it is compelled by impressed force to change that state.

LAW II.   The force acting on a particle is equal to the rate of change of momentum of the particle, and the rate of change of momentum is in the direction of the applied force.

LAW III.   To every action (force exerted *on* body A by body B) there is an equal and opposite reaction (force exerted *by* body A on body B).

In the case where the mass of a body is constant, and we shall restrict our attention to this case, the second law may be symbolically written as

$$F = m\frac{dv}{dt} = ma$$

The second law shows that force is a vector quantity.   It must be assumed in this connection that when a number of forces act on a particle the resultant acceleration calculated from the resultant force is the same as if we calculated the accelerations separately for each force and then combined these accelerations vectorially to find the resultant acceleration.

The importance of Newton's laws cannot be overestimated. They form the starting point of every physical argument in mechanics, and the whole science of mechanics consists of applying these principles to all natural motions.

20. Examples.—The most important task confronting the student in attempting to solve a problem in mechanics is the clear recognition of the forces which act *on* the body whose motion is to be studied.   Let us consider an example.   A billiard ball resting in a groove on a table is set in motion by a collision with another ball.   Due to this collision, the stationary ball will acquire a certain definite velocity, let us say 10 ft./sec. in the direction of the groove.   During the time of collision, the moving ball A exerts a force on the stationary ball B, and the *second* law tells us that the rate of change of velocity of B is proportional to the force exerted on it by A.   The *third* law shows that, during the collision, the ball B pushes back on ball A with a force equal to that which causes its own acceleration.   The force (reaction) may bring ball A to rest, slow it down, or reverse the direction of its motion, depending on the relative masses of A and B.

The ball B now moves along the groove and will slow down and stop.   The *first* law tells us that this could not occur if forces did not act on the ball.   What forces bring the ball to rest?   The air offers a resistance to the motion, pushing against the surface of the ball very much as a man might push.   There is a force (friction) exerted by the table on that part of the surface of the ball resting on it.   Finally, let us suppose that the groove is curved.   If the motion continues for some time around the curve, there must be a force acting, since the first law demands that, in the absence of force, the motion is uniform and recti-linear.   This force is the push of the side of the groove on the ball, and its direction is toward the center of the curve.

To summarize, we have stated that three forces act *on* the ball:

a. The push of the air.

b. The frictional force of the table on the ball.

c. The sidewise push of the groove on the ball toward the center of the curve.

What are the equal and opposite reactions demanded by the third law?

a. The ball pushes back the air and it is this force that really removes the air and carves out a path for the ball.

b. The ball pushes on the table and tries to drag it along in the direction of motion.   This, of course, does not happen, if the table is fastened to the floor.

c. The ball pushes sideways on the groove outward from the center of the curve.   Again, since the table is held fixed, it does not start moving.   Were the table free to move in the direction of this force, it would start to do so, and we shall later learn how to calculate such a motion of table and ball.

In the discussion of *b* and *c* we are referring the motions to a coordinate system fixed on the earth's surface.   Referred to a reference system attached to the fixed stars (an absolute system) the reactions of the ball on the table would be transmitted to the earth, and we must assume a consequent acceleration of the earth which, due to the enormous mass of the earth, would escape experimental detection.

In all problems in mechanics, we must list completely all the forces which act *on* the body whose motion is being studied before any attempt is made to apply Newton's laws to determine the actual motion.

21. The Static Measure of Force.—We now turn to a closer examination of the forces which act on bodies, and our first task is to define a method of measuring force.   The method which we shall first describe depends on the validity of the first and third laws of motion without reference to the second law.   The idea of the method, which we shall term the *static method*, is to make use of the fact that if a body, under the action of several forces, has zero acceleration the vector sum of all the forces acting on the body must be zero. This statement is merely a repetition of the first law of motion. To employ this method of comparing forces, we simplify the procedure as follows: If a single force acts in a given direction on a body, it would produce an acceleration. This acceleration may be made zero (in practice the body is kept at rest) by applying another force opposite in direction to the first, of such magnitude that no acceleration is observed. When this condition is obtained we know that the two forces are equal in magnitude. We must now choose some force as unit force and then we are in a position to measure forces. Historically, the force most familiar to man is the pull of the earth, a pull exerted on every body. We now choose some body as a standard and define a unit force as the earth pull on that body. Such a unit of force is called a *gravitational unit* and there are two such common units. The English gravitational unit of force is the earth pull on (or *weight* of) a pound of matter and this force is termed a *one pound force*. The metric gravitational unit of force is the earth pull on a gram of matter and is called the *gram weight*. For reasons which we shall discuss later, it is further specified that the earth pull is to be taken at 45° N. Lat. and at sea level.

The usual spring balance so often employed to measure forces provides the best example of a device which directly uses the principles just discussed. A pointer is attached to a spring, and a body, *e.g.*, 1 lb. of matter, is hung from the spring. The spring stretches until the pull of the spring on the body is equal in magnitude and opposite in direction to the earth pull on this body. A mark opposite the pointer on a fixed scale may then be labeled 1 lb. and whenever the spring is stretched to this point we know that it exerts a force of 1 lb. Similarly, 2 lb., 3 lb., etc., may be hung from the spring and a complete set of marks may then be made on the scale, and we thus have a calibrated spring balance which may be used to measure forces.

22. Classification of Forces.—As we have already pointed out in Sec. 16, forces fall into two general classes, *contact* forces and *action-at-a-distance* forces. The only force of the latter type which we shall consider is the pull of the earth on a body equal to the weight of the body; a force which is constant in magnitude and direction. This force always acts and must be included in every calculation (except when specifically stated that it may be neglected).

In the former class are the pushes and pulls of bodies in contact with the body under consideration. In particular, we shall often deal with inextensible strings which pull on bodies. By the tension in the string we mean the pull of the string on any body to which it is attached. Another type of force frequently encountered in practical problems is the friction force which always acts in such a direction as to oppose the motion of a body. For the present we need only consider the case of the friction forces appearing when one body slides on another, *e.g.*, a block of metal sliding on a wooden table. When the block is at rest, there are two forces acting *on* it: (1) pull of the earth, W, and (2) the push of the table, N. These are equal in magnitude and opposite in direction. If we pull horizontally on the block, we find that the block does not start to move until we increase the force to a certain value f_m. Since for all horizontally applied forces less than f_m the block has no acceleration, we must conclude that the push of the table on the block is no longer perpendicular to the surface of contact but that it acts in a direction such that its component parallel to the surface of the table is equal and opposite to the applied force. This tangential component is called a *frictional force* and for a body at rest can assume a maximum value equal to f_m. We *define* $\mu_s = f_m/N$ as the *coefficient of static friction* between the two bodies. In this definition N is the normal component of the push of the table top on the block. The actual friction force f acting on a body at rest may thus have any value from zero to f_m and may act in any direction.

After the body is set in motion, we define the *coefficient of sliding friction* μ as the ratio of the friction component to the normal component of the force exerted by the table surface on the block. Thus

$$\mu = \frac{f}{N}$$

In general $\mu < \mu_s$, and for moderate velocities and reasonably smooth surfaces of contact μ may be considered constant. The above relation is also valid for inclined or curved surfaces.

23. Equilibrium of a Particle.—A particle is said to be in equilibrium if its acceleration is zero. If the particle is at rest, we speak of static equilibrium, and if it moves with constant velocity, we speak of kinetic equilibrium. According to the first law of motion the vector sum of all the forces acting on the particle must vanish. We shall now formulate this condition analytically, referring back to the discussion in Sec. 12. Suppose the vector forces in a plane acting on a particle in equilibrium are denoted by $F_1, F_2, \ldots, F_n$. We form the sum of the vector forces in the same manner as in Sec. 12 and must add the x- and y-components of the forces to find the x- and y-components of the resultant force F. If a vector is zero, each of its components must be zero. The proof of this statement is left to the student. Thus the conditions for equilibrium are

$$\left.\begin{array}{l} F_x = F_{1x} + F_{2x} + \cdots F_{nx} = 0 \\ F_y = F_{1y} + F_{2y} + \cdots F_{ny} = 0 \end{array}\right\} \tag{1}$$

As an example of the application of the above laws let us

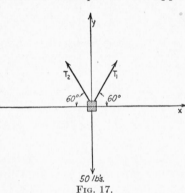

50 lbs.
Fig. 17.

consider the problem of a 50-lb. body supported by two strings which make an angle of 60° with the horizontal. We desire the tension in each string. The first step is to draw a figure (Fig. 17) and indicate all the forces acting on the 50-lb. body. We choose the x-axis horizontal and the y-axis vertical and the origin at the 50-lb. body.

The sum of the x-components

is

$$+T_1 \cos 60° - T_2 \cos 60° + 50 \cos 90° = 0$$

and for the y-components

$$+T_1 \sin 60° + T_2 \sin 60° - 50 \cos 0° = 0$$

The first equation gives

$$T_1 = T_2$$

Inserting this value of T_2 in the second equation, we find

$$T_1 \sin 60° + T_1 \sin 60° = 50$$

whence

$$T_1 = T_2 = \frac{50}{2 \sin 60°} = \frac{50}{1.73} = 29 \text{ lb.}$$

The tension in each string is found.

As a second example let us consider a block being pulled up an inclined plane by a string which passes over a light pulley at the top of the plane and from which a weight is suspended. The body on the plane weighs 12 lb., the hanging body weighs 8 lb., and the plane is inclined at an angle of 30° with the horizontal. It is observed that the hanging weight descends with constant velocity, and it is desired to find the coefficient of friction and the tension in the string (Fig. 18).

We choose x- and y-axes with an origin at O, the x-axis parallel to the plane and the y-axis perpendicular to the plane. We

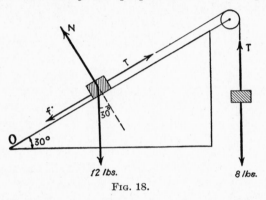

12 lbs.   *8 lbs.*

Fɪɢ. 18.

have indicated all the forces acting on the two bodies. On the hanging weight we have the pull of the earth and the pull of the string T. On the 12-lb. body there is (1) the pull of the earth, (2) the pull of the string, and (3) the force exerted by the plane which we have represented by its x- and y-components $-f$ and N, respectively. Since both bodies move with constant velocity, the sum of the forces acting on each separately must be zero. First we consider the 8-lb. body. The forces acting on it yield as their sum

$$8 - T = 0$$

whence

$$T = 8 \text{ lb.}$$

as the tension in the string. Now consider the 12-lb. body. The x-components of the various forces acting on it are as follows:

$$
\begin{aligned}
x\text{-component of } T &= +T \\
x\text{-component of } f &= -f \\
x\text{-component of } N &= 0 \\
x\text{-component of weight} &= -12 \sin 30° = -6 \text{ lb.}
\end{aligned}
$$

Thus, for equilibrium,
$$+T - f - 6 = 0$$
whence
$$f = T - 6 = 8 - 6 = 2 \text{ lb.}$$

so that the friction force is 2 lb. The y-components of these same forces are:

y-component of T $\quad = 0$
y-component of f $\quad = 0$
y-component of N $\quad = +N$
y-component of weight $= -12 \cos 30° = -10.4$ lb.

so that, for equilibrium,
$$+N - 10.4 = 0$$
$$N = 10.4 \text{ lb.}$$

The coefficient of friction μ is defined by
$$\mu = \frac{f}{N}$$
so that in our case
$$\mu = \frac{2}{10.4} = 0.19$$

which completes the solution.

There are several points worthy of special mention in the above solution. First, we note that the tension in the string numerically equals the weight of the hanging body. It is clear that this is true only because there is no acceleration of this body. Were this body to descend with an accelerated motion, the above mentioned equality could never exist and the tension in the string would be less than the weight of the body. Second, we note that the tension in the string is T (and not $2T$). The body on the plane exerts a force T on the hanging body, and this force is transmitted by the string. Now according to the third law the hanging body exerts an equal and opposite pull back on the body on the plane. This pull is also transmitted by the string. It is the magnitude of this force transmitted by the string from one body to another body which is called the *tension* in the string.

Problems

1. Draw a neat diagram, and construct a force diagram with approximately correct scales of *all* the forces acting *on* the block. State in words the "reactions" as given by Newton's third law to the forces you have drawn. State on what bodies these "reactions" act and "by" what bodies they are exerted.

a. A block is pushed by a horizontal force along a rough (with friction!) horizontal surface at constant speed.

b. A block is pulled along a rough horizontal surface at constant speed by a rope making an angle of 30° above the horizontal.

c. A block is pushed along a rough horizontal surface at constant speed by a downward force making an angle of 30° with the horizontal.

d. A block slides down a smooth inclined plane. (No friction.)

e. A block rests on a rough inclined plane.

f. A block is pulled up a rough inclined plane at constant speed by a rope parallel to the incline.

g. A block is allowed to slide down a rough inclined plane at constant speed by pulling up on a rope parallel to the incline.

h. A block is pushed up a rough inclined plane at constant speed by a *horizontal* force.

i. A block rests on a horizontal rough surface.

j. A block on a horizontal rough surface is pulled horizontally with a force of 8 lb. but remains at rest.

k. (1) A block slides along a smooth horizontal table with constant speed.
    (2) The same block has left the table and is falling freely. Neglect air resistance.

2. A 1-kg. weight is supported by two ropes, one inclined at an angle of 40° and the other at angle of 50° with the vertical. Find the pull of each rope on the weight.

3. A 10-lb. body is hung from a ceiling by two strings, one of which is 5 ft. long. The body is 4 ft. below the ceiling, and the tension in the 5-ft. string is half of the tension in the other string. Calculate the length of the latter string and the tension in each string.

4. A 100-lb. body hangs on a rope 10 ft. long. If the body is displaced horizontally a distance of 3 ft. and held there by a horizontal force, find

a. The magnitude of the horizontal force.

b. The tension in the rope.

5. An 8-lb. block is held at rest on a frictionless inclined plane by a horizontal force of magnitude 13.8 lb. What angle does the inclined plane make with the horizontal?

6. A 200-lb. weight is supported by two ropes, *A* and *B*. The rope *A* makes an angle of 37° with the horizontal and the rope *B* makes an angle of 60° with the horizontal. Find the tension in each rope.

7. A 20-lb. block is held at rest on a frictionless inclined plane making an angle of 37° with the horizontal by a force acting downward at an angle of 60° with the surface of the plane. Calculate the magnitude of this force and the resultant push of the plane on the block (magnitude and direction).

8. A 15-lb. block is placed on an inclined plane of base 16 ft. and altitude 12 ft. A string attached to this block runs over a light frictionless pulley at the top of the plane. When a 10-lb. weight is hung on the free end of the string, the block on the plane ascends with constant velocity.

What weight must be hung on the string so that the 15-lb. block descends along the plane with constant velocity?

9. A 10-lb. block slides down an inclined plane with constant speed. The incline is 20 ft. long and the top of the plane is 12 ft. above the bottom.

a. Calculate the coefficient of friction between the block and the plane.

b. How big a push parallel to the plane would be necessary to cause the block to move up the plane with constant speed?

10. A weight W is supported by two strings A and B. String A makes an angle of 60° with the horizontal and is fastened to the ceiling. String B makes an angle of 30° with the horizontal and runs over a fixed frictionless pulley. A 10-lb. weight hangs from the free end of string B. Find the weight W and the tension in string A.

11. A 10-lb. metal block rests on a horizontal table and the coefficient of static friction between block and table is 0.6. What horizontal force will just start the block in motion? If an upward force is applied at an angle of 60° with the horizontal, how large can it be without starting the block? If the force acts downward at an angle of 60° with the horizontal, what is the maximum value of the force possible without motion of the block?

12. A weight is supported by two ropes, each of length 50 cm., which are fastened to two rings. The rings are free to move on a horizontal rod, and the coefficient of static friction between rings and rod is 0.75. Find the maximum separation possible for the rings without slipping.

13. A 10-lb. block rests on a 60° inclined plane. The coefficient of static friction between block and plane is 0.8. What is the least force acting parallel to the plane on the block which will prevent motion? What is the maximum force possible without motion?

14. Solve Prob. 13 if the external force on the block is horizontal.

15. A metal block slides down a 37° inclined plane with constant velocity. What is the coefficient of sliding friction between block and plane?

16. A 4-lb. block stands at rest on a 30° inclined plane. What is the force of friction exerted on the block by the plane? If a 4.8-lb. force pushing up parallel to the plane causes the block to ascend with constant velocity, how large a force must be applied downward parallel to the plane to cause the block to slide down the plane with constant velocity?

17. A 4-lb. body is connected to a 12-lb. body of the same material by a string and both rest on a 37° inclined plane, the 4-lb. body occupying the lower position. Another string attached to the 12-lb. body passes over a small pulley at the top of the plane. When an 18-lb. body is hung from the free end of the string, the latter is observed to descend with constant velocity.

a. Calculate the coefficient of friction between the 4-lb. and 12-lb. bodies and the plane.

b. Calculate the tension in each string.

c. If the positions of the 4-lb. and the 12-lb. bodies are reversed, calculate the weight which must be hung on the free end of the string such that it descends with constant velocity.

d. What hanging weight would allow the bodies on the plane to descend with constant velocity?

CHAPTER V

LINEAR AND PLANE DYNAMICS

In the last chapter we have formulated Newton's laws of motion and have discussed applications of the first law. We are now ready to proceed to complete our program by applying the second law of motion. This law, which states that the resultant force acting on a particle is equal to the mass of the particle times the rate of change of its velocity, now allows us to combine the considerations of the last chapter concerning forces with the kinematical results which we obtained in Chaps. II and III. In static problems we had merely to add forces, and consequently the units which we used for forces were arbitrary and did not necessarily have any connection with the units of any other physical quantities. In applications of the second law, however, there is an intimate interconnection and we must start our study with a closer analysis of this interconnection between various systems of units.

24. Dynamical Measure of Force; Units.—The second law of motion suggests a method for measuring forces, known as the *dynamical method,* quite different from the method encountered in the last chapter. If we arbitrarily choose a unit mass, such as the gram mass or the pound mass, then we are not at liberty to choose the unit force in such a system of units arbitrarily. Indeed the second law $F = ma$ provides an equation which fixes the size of the unit force, once the unit mass is chosen, as the unit acceleration is determined by our previously chosen units of length and time. The force which imparts unit acceleration to a unit mass is the unit force. Were this not so, we would have a conflict with Newton's second law of motion. Thus we measure a force by applying it to a body of known mass and measuring the acceleration produced. This procedure leads to the so-called *absolute* system of units. As we have already stated, the units of length, time, and mass are taken as the fundamental units, defined arbitrarily as we have seen, and all other mechanical quantities are defined in terms of these three quantities.

If we measure mass in grams, length in centimeters, and time in seconds (the so-called *c.g.s. system* of units), the unit of force in this system becomes $\left(\text{from the law } F = m\dfrac{dv}{dt}\right)$ equal to one gram-centimeter per (second)^2. We give the name *one dyne* to the unit one gram-centimeter per (second)^2, but this does not make it an arbitrary fundamental unit. A mass of one gram acted on by a force of one dyne acquires an acceleration of one centimeter per (second)^2. This absolute system of units is universally employed in scientific work, and we shall make much use of it.

Now we must consider the situation when we wish to employ the *gravitational* units of force which we arbitrarily introduced in our study of statics. If we wish to use the second law employing these units of force, it is clear that we may not choose an arbitrary unit of mass in this gravitational system of units. For example, if we wish to determine the unit of mass to be used with the pound force, we apply the second law and find it equal to one pound-(second)^2 per foot. We give this mass unit the name *one slug*, but again the slug is not a fundamental unit.

To recapitulate:

(*a*) **In the absolute system of units length, mass, and time are defined arbitrarily. Force is a derived quantity.** (*b*) **In the gravitational system of units length, force, and time are defined arbitrarily. Mass is a derived quantity.**

25. Freely Falling Bodies.—If we now wish to answer the question as to the relation between the mass and force units in the absolute and gravitational systems we must turn to experiment and determine the accelerations produced by the pull of the earth on a body. It turns out that all bodies which are allowed to fall freely in a vacuum at the earth's surface fall with very nearly the same constant acceleration. We denote this acceleration by the letter g and its numerical value is 32 ft./sec.^{2} = 980 cm./sec.^{2}. According to the second law, there must be a pull of the earth on the body which falls, and it is this pull which was used in defining a unit of force in a gravitational system of units. For example, a mass of 1 gram is pulled downwards by the earth with a constant force

$$F = mg = 1 \text{ gram} \times 980 \text{ cm./sec.}^2$$
$$= 980 \text{ gram-cm./sec.}^2 = 980 \text{ dynes}$$

Thus, we say that a mass of 1 gram "weighs" 980 dynes. A gram weight of force equals 980 dynes. Careful measurements show that g varies slightly from point to point on the earth's surface, and hence the earth pull on the pound mass, which is the force causing this acceleration, must vary slightly from point to point on the earth's surface. We therefore must fix a point on the earth's surface to be used in connection with the definition of the pound force. As we have stated, the earth pull on a pound mass at sea level and 45°N. Lat. is the unit of force in the English gravitational system. What is the unit of mass to be used in applying Newton's second law corresponding to the pound force? Since a unit force must cause unit acceleration of this unit mass, obviously the pound mass *cannot* be used in connection with the pound force, as it acquires an acceleration of 32 ft./sec.^{2} (*i.e.*, of 32 units) under the action of such a force. The unit of mass in the English gravitational system (the slug) must be 32 times as large as the pound mass. One slug acquires an acceleration of 1 ft./sec.^{2} when acted on by a force of 1 lb.

The metric gravitational system is built up quite similarly to the English system. The unit of force is the earth pull (at sea level and 45° N. Lat.) on a gram mass and is called *one gram weight*. What unit of mass belongs to the gram-weight unit of force? Obviously not the gram mass, as it acquires an acceleration of 980 cm./sec.^{2} under the action of such a force, and our unit must have an acceleration of 1 cm./sec.^{2} under such conditions. Hence the unit of mass in the metric gravitational system must be 980 times as big as the 1-gram mass.

In the application of Newton's laws, we shall make use principally of two systems of units:

 a. Metric absolute: *cm. gm. sec.* fundamental units.

 b. English gravitational: *ft. lb. sec.* fundamental units.

In *a* the force unit is derived and is called the *dyne*.

In *b* the mass unit is derived and is called the *slug*.

One system of units must be used in the solution of any problem. A mixture of units leads to nonsensical results.

26. Application of Newton's Laws to Rectilinear Motion.—A large number of mechanical problems which one has to solve are of the following type; to determine the motion of a body which is subjected to the action of certain forces. The first step toward the solution of such a problem is the determination of all the forces which act *on* the body. The mass of the body must be determined, and this is usually done by weighing. With the help of Newton's second law the acceleration of the body can be found from the above data. From the acceleration we arrive at the kinetic equation of motion by reversing the process of differentiation, *i.e.*, by integration.

Applied to the case of the motion of a mass point along a straight line, we proceed as follows: If a number of forces F_1, F_2, . . . , F_n all acting in the direction of the straight line are impressed on the body, we find the resultant force F as the algebraic (vector) sum of the individual forces

$$F = F_1 + F_2 + F_3 + \cdots + F_n \tag{1}$$

If the earth pull on the mass point is W, we find the mass m from

$$W = mg \tag{2}$$

g is the acceleration of a falling body.

Applying the second law, we find

$$F = m\frac{dv}{dt}$$

or

$$\frac{dv}{dt} = \frac{F}{m} \tag{3}$$

and this acceleration may depend on the time t, on the position x, on the velocity v, or on all three quantities. For the present we restrict ourselves to the case where the acceleration is *constant*. This means that the forces acting are constant. We then write

$$\frac{F}{m} = a \tag{4}$$

where a denotes the constant acceleration (it may be zero!).

Putting Eq. (4) in Eq. (3) we find

$$\frac{dv}{dt} = a \tag{5}$$

and, integrating with respect to t, we obtain

$$v = a\int dt + c = at + c \tag{6}$$

where c is an arbitrary constant. The correctness of Eq. (6) may be checked by differentiation. It is, furthermore, clear that from a purely mathematical standpoint the constant c may have any value whatsoever. Physically, we fix the value of c by noticing that when $t = 0$, in Eq. (6),

$$v_0 = c \tag{7}$$

so that the value of c is the velocity at $t = 0$.

We can now write Eq. (6) as

$$v = \frac{dx}{dt} = at + v_0 \tag{8}$$

and, integrating again,

$$\left. \begin{array}{l} x = a \int t\, dt + v_0 \int dt + c_1 \\ x = \dfrac{at^2}{2} + v_0 t + c_1 \end{array} \right\} \tag{9}$$

The value of the arbitrary constant c_1 is again determined by placing $t = 0$ in Eq. (9) and we find

$$x_0 = c_1 \tag{10}$$

where x_0 is the position of the mass point at $t = 0$, so that our final answer for this case is

$$x = \frac{1}{2}at^2 + v_0 t + x_0 \tag{11}$$

Equations (8) and (11) have already been encountered in Chap. II, where they were obtained from purely kinematical considerations concerning linear motion with constant acceleration.

From this example we learn the following important fact: The acceleration of a body alone is *not* sufficient to completely determine its motion. *We must also know its position and velocity at some instant of time which we may call* $t = 0$. In other words, the acceleration *and* the initial conditions completely determine the motion. This last statement is true even if the acceleration is not constant but varies in any way whatsoever. If we know x and v for any instant other than $t = 0$, we can find x_0 and v_0 from Eqs. (8) and (11).

27. Example.—A 16-lb. body is pushed along a floor by a constant force of 10.0 lb. for 3.00 sec. During its motion it is also acted on by a force of friction equal to one-tenth of its weight. If the body starts from rest, find *a.* How far it moves in 3.00 sec.

b. How fast is it going at the end of this time.

c. How far and how long it moves before coming to rest.

During the first 3 sec., the body is acted on by two forces:

(1) $F_1 = + 10.0$ lb.   (to the right, let us say).

(2) $F_2 = -\frac{16}{10} = -1.6$ lb.

The minus sign states that the friction acts to the left (opposite to the direction of motion which we have taken to the right) and tends to stop the body.   The resultant force is

$$F = F_1 + F_2 = 10.0 + (-1.6) = 8.4 \text{ lb.}$$

To say that we have a 16-lb. body is perfectly definite since a 16-lb. body undergoes an earth pull (*i.e.*, has a weight) of 16 lb., according to the definition of the pound force.

The mass of the body is

$$m = \frac{W}{g} = \frac{16}{32} = 0.5 \text{ slug}$$

The acceleration during the first 3 sec. is

$$a = \frac{F}{m} = \frac{8.4}{0.5} = 16.8 \text{ ft./sec.}^2$$

As the body starts from rest, $v_0 = 0$.   What shall we do to fix x_0? Remember that we must choose an origin, and we can place it anywhere along the line of motion.   If we measure displacements from the position of the body at $t = 0$, we have $x_0 = 0$, and this is a convenient, but not necessary procedure.   Hence

$$v = 16.8t + 0$$

and

$$x = 8.4t^2 + 0 \cdot t + 0$$

For $t = 3$ sec.

$$v = 16.8 \times 3 = 50.4 \text{ ft./sec.}$$
$$x = 8.4 \times 9 = 75.6 \text{ ft.}$$

which are the answers to *a* and *b*. x is the distance measured from the starting position.   After reaching this position, the body is acted on by another force, so we must consider the subsequent motion of the body as a separate problem.   In this second problem we shall understand by t' the number of seconds after the 10-lb. push stops acting.

The force acting is

$$F_2 = -1.6 \text{ lb.}$$

The mass is

$$m = 0.5 \text{ slug}$$

and the acceleration

$$a = -\frac{1.6}{0.5} = -3.2 \text{ ft./sec.}^2$$

For this problem we have from the answers to a and b:

$$x_0 = 75.6 \text{ ft.}$$
$$v_0 = 50.4 \text{ ft./sec.}$$

so that we have

and

$$\left. \begin{array}{l} v = -3.2t' + 50.4 \\ \\ x = -1.6t'^2 + 50.4t' + 75.6 \end{array} \right\} \qquad (a)$$

When the body comes to rest,

$$v = 0$$

and we find, from the first of the Eqs. (a),

$$3.2t' = 50.4$$
$$t' = 15.8 \text{ sec.}$$

so the *total* time elapsed until the body comes to rest is

$$T = 3.0 + 15.8 = 18.8 \text{ sec.}$$

To find the position when the body stops, we place the value $t' = 15.8$ sec. in the second equation and find

$$x = -1.6(15.8)^2 + 50.4(15.8) + 75.6$$
$$= -398 + 794 + 76 = 472 \text{ ft.}$$

which is the *total distance* covered by the body.

In cases where the acceleration, *i.e.*, the forces, are not constant, problems are solved in exactly the same manner, the only difference occurring in the actual evaluation of the integrations. Many times it is not possible to perform the integrations by elementary methods.

28. Newton's Laws for Plane Motion.—The fundamental fact which always must be kept in mind when we attack a mechanical problem concerning the motion of a particle in a plane is that force (and acceleration) is a vector. To find the resultant force acting on a particle it is necessary to perform a vector addition of all the forces acting on this particle. As we have seen, it is simplest to work with the x- and y-components of the vectors. Thus if we have n forces F_1, F_2, $\ldots$, F_n, we first find the x- and y-components of each force and add the x-components and the y-components of these forces separately. This yields the x- and y-components of the resultant force, respectively, and we have

$$\left. \begin{aligned} F_x &= F_{1x} + F_{2x} + \cdots + F_{nx} \\ F_y &= F_{1y} + F_{2y} + \cdots + F_{ny} \end{aligned} \right\} \tag{12}$$

Now we proceed to find the x- and y-components of the acceleration of the particle, using the second law of motion. In component form the second law of motion is

$$\left. \begin{aligned} F_x &= m\frac{dv_x}{dt} \\ F_y &= m\frac{dv_y}{dt} \end{aligned} \right\} \tag{13}$$

so that we have found the x- and y-components of the acceleration, from which the magnitude and direction of the resultant acceleration of the particle may be immediately found. The simplest procedure to follow to find the motion of the particle is to use Eqs. (13) as they stand, integrating each of them separately to find how the x- and y-coordinates vary with time. Let us suppose that we have done this. The actual motion of the body is then the composition of two straight-line motions at right angles to each other.

Thus we have reduced the problem of determining the plane motion of a particle to the much simpler problem of determining the motion of a body on a straight line. To be sure we must do the latter problem twice, once for the x-motion and once for the y-motion, and then combine the results vectorially. For each of the rectilinear motions we must know two initial conditions, in addition to the acceleration for a complete solution, so that we must know not only the two components of acceleration of the body but also the two components of its initial displacement from the origin (its initial position) and the two components of its initial velocity. Thus a motion is completely specified when dv_x/dt, dv_y/dt, v_{x0}, v_{y0}, x_0, and y_0 are determined. There is, however, a new aspect of motion in a plane which was lacking in the discussion of motion in a straight line. In the latter case the orbit or path is fixed and is the straight line along which the body moves. In the former, the path may be any curve in the plane of the motion, and it may be determined by the following method: Let us suppose we have solved Eqs. (13) and have obtained the two kinetic equations of motion of the type

$$\left.\begin{array}{l} x = f_1(t) \\ y = f_2(t) \end{array}\right\} \tag{14}$$

These equations tell us how the x- and y-coordinates of the particle vary with time; from them we may determine the position of the particle for any and every instant of time. If we plot the points so obtained for a number of values of t, we shall obtain a graph of the path. In many cases one can obtain the mathematical equation of the path. Let us suppose we solve the first of Eqs. (14) for t in terms of x and insert this value of t in the second equation. We then obtain a relation of the type

$$y = \phi(x) \tag{15}$$

which is the equation of the orbit.

As an illustration of the application of the above methods, we consider the motion of a projectile, *i.e.*, the motion of a particle under the action of the earth pull alone. Suppose a body is projected from a point on the earth's surface with an initial speed v_0 in a direction making an angle θ with the horizontal. The motion takes place in a plane defined by the vertical and the direction of v_0 and is motion with constant acceleration. We choose an origin at the initial position of the body, the x-axis horizontal and the y-axis vertical and positive upward. Since the pull of the earth is vertical, the horizontal motion ensues with constant velocity. The vertical motion is one of constant downward acceleration, and the composition of these two motions yields the resultant motion of the projectile.

If v_{0x} and v_{0y} denote the initial values of the horizontal and vertical components of velocity, the kinetic equations of motion corresponding to Eqs. (14) are

$$x = v_{0x}t; \qquad y = v_{0y}t - \tfrac{1}{2}gt^2 \tag{16}$$

and the velocity-time equations are

$$v_x = v_{0x}; \qquad v_y = v_{0y} - gt \tag{17}$$

v_{0x} and v_{0y} are related to v_0 and θ by the equations

$$v_{0x} = v_0 \cos \theta; \qquad v_{0y} = v_0 \sin \theta \tag{18}$$

The maximum height attained by the projectile occurs when $v_y = 0$, hence when

$$v_{0y} - gt = 0$$
$$t = \frac{v_{0y}}{g}$$

and the maximum height is, inserting this value of t in the second of Eqs. (16),

$$y_{\text{max}} = \frac{v_{0y}^2}{g} - \frac{v_{0y}^2}{2g} = \frac{v_{0y}^2}{2g} = \frac{v_0^2 \sin^2 \theta}{2g} \tag{19}$$

The last equality is obtained with the help of the second of Eqs. (18).

The range of a projectile is defined as the horizontal distance covered before the particle returns to its initial height, *i.e.*, to $y = 0$. From the second of Eqs. (16), $y = 0$ when

$$v_{0y}t - \tfrac{1}{2}gt^2 = 0$$

from which we obtain

$$t = 0 \qquad \text{or} \qquad t = \frac{2v_{0y}}{g}$$

The value $t = 0$ is the instant of starting, and the other value is the time of flight, which we note is twice the time required to reach the maximum height. Inserting this second value of t in the first of Eqs. (16), we find for the range

$$x_{\text{max}} = \frac{2v_{0x} \cdot v_{0y}}{g} = \frac{v_0^2}{g}(2 \cos \theta \sin \theta) = \frac{v_0^2 \sin 2\theta}{g} \tag{20}$$

For a given initial speed v_0 the maximum range occurs for $\sin 2\theta = 1$, since this is the maximum value the sine of an angle may have. Hence for maximum range $2\theta = 90°$, or $\theta = 45°$.

The path or trajectory is found, as we have outlined, by solving the first of Eqs. (16) for t and inserting this value in the second of these equations. The result yields the equation of a parabola and is shown in Fig. 19.

29. Constrained Motion.—We shall often encounter problems in which the path or orbit of a body is given, and this type of

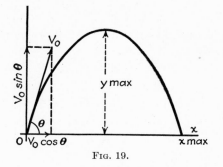

Fig. 19.

problem is of sufficient importance to warrant a special discussion. In such cases we speak of the motion as constrained, since the body is constrained to move in a specific path. Motion of a body on an inclined plane or in a circle are examples of this type of motion. In such problems there always appear certain unknown forces which serve to keep the body in its prescribed path, and the determination of these forces constitutes part of the problem. In the case of motion on an inclined plane, the push of the plane on the body is such a force; in the case of a body whirled in a circle at the end of a string, the tension in the string is unknown at the start and must be determined with the help of Newton's laws of motion.

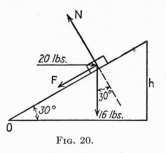

Fig. 20.

As an example of the method to be employed in handling such problems let us consider the motion of a body on an inclined plane. If we choose the x-axis parallel to and along the plane and the y-axis perpendicular to this direction, we avoid difficulties with the equation of the path. The x-axis is the path of the body, and the problem becomes simpler than if we attempted to use horizontal and vertical axes.

Suppose the body weighs 16 lb. and that it is pushed up a plane making an angle of 30° with the horizontal by a *horizontal* force of 20 lb. The coefficient of sliding friction is 0.096 and the body starts at the bottom of the plane from rest. If the plane is 10 ft. long, let us calculate the acceleration of the body up the plane, the time necessary to move the body 10 ft. up the plane, and the velocity of the body at the top of the plane (Fig. 20).

We choose x- and y-axes with the origin at O, the x-axis parallel to the plane and the y-axis perpendicular to the plane. Since the body stays on the plane, $a_y = 0$ and the sum of the y-components of all the forces acting *on* the body must be zero.

y-component of the 20-lb. force $= -20 \sin 30° = -10$ lb.
y-component of the weight $= -16 \cos 30° = -14$ lb.
y-component of the push of the plane on the body $= +N$ lb.

Hence

$$N - 10 - 14 = 0$$

or

$$N = 24 \text{ lb.}$$

The sum of the forces in the x-direction is obtained as follows:

x-component of the push of the plane
$$= -F = -\mu N = -2.3 \text{ lb.}$$
x-component of the 20-lb. force $= +20 \cos 30° = +17.3$ lb.
x-component of the weight $= -16 \sin 30° = -8.0$ lb.

Hence the resultant force acting up the plane is

$$F_x = 17.3 - 8.0 - 2.3 = 7.0 \text{ lb.}$$

From the second law of motion, we find the acceleration

$$\frac{dv_x}{dt} = a = \frac{F_x}{M} = \frac{7.0}{0.5} = 14 \text{ ft./sec.}^2$$

Since the body starts from rest, the distance

$$s = \tfrac{1}{2}at^2 = \tfrac{14}{2}t^2 = 7t^2$$

The time necessary to reach the top is

$$t = \sqrt{\tfrac{10}{7}} = 1.2 \text{ sec.}$$

The velocity at the top of the plane is obtained from

$$v = at$$

so that

$$v = 14 \times 1.2 = 17 \text{ ft./sec.}$$

The method which we have employed for handling motions in a plane depends on the fact that a vector may be represented by its x- and y-components, and, while it is the simplest method in most of the cases which we shall investigate, it is not always so. We have already seen that a vector is determined by a specification of its magnitude and of its direction (the angle made with the x-axis). Thus we might resolve the resultant vector force into two components, one along the radius from the origin to the particle and the other at right angles to this direction. The complication in this method over our previous method is that the component of force, and hence of acceleration, along the radius keeps changing direction as the particle moves. Yet in the case of circular motion this method is of advantage, and we shall investigate this case more closely.

To fix our ideas, let us suppose we have a stone of mass m attached to one end of a string of length R and the stone is whirled in a circle in a horizontal plane. The reason for choosing a horizontal plane is that we may not be concerned with the earth pull on the body which is irrelevant to our particular problem. We have already seen that for circular motion the acceleration vector may be resolved into two components, the central acceleration along the radius and the tangential acceleration perpendicular to the radius. These have the values

$$\left.\begin{aligned} a_r &= -\frac{v^2}{R} = -\omega^2 R \\ a_t &= R\alpha \end{aligned}\right\} \tag{21}$$

where v is the speed of the particle, ω its angular velocity, and α its angular acceleration. Thus the resultant force acting on the particle has the components

$$\left.\begin{aligned} F_r &= ma_r = -m\frac{v^2}{R} = -m\omega^2 R \\ F_t &= ma_t = mR\alpha \end{aligned}\right\} \tag{22}$$

In our case of the stone on the string, if there are no forces acting on the stone other than the pull of the string, the tangential component of force is zero, *i.e.*,

$$F_t = mR\alpha = 0$$

and the stone must move with constant speed.   The tension in the string then is the force causing the central acceleration. This force is just the force necessary to keep pulling the stone out of a rectilinear path (in which it would move under the action of no forces according to the first law of motion) into the circular path in which it actually moves.

A numerical example may help clarify the situation.   Suppose a block of metal is at rest on a horizontal turntable at a distance of 2.4 ft. from the center of the turntable.   If the turntable is now rotated slowly, the block will rotate with the table and stay at rest with respect to the table.   As the angular velocity is increased, the block will eventually start to slip on the turntable. If the coefficient of static friction between block and table is 0.3, what is the highest angular velocity with which the turn-table may rotate without having the block slip?   We recall that the friction exerted by the table on the block may take on any value from zero to a maximum value given by $f = \mu N$, where N is the normal component of the push of the table on the block.   Since there is no vertical acceleration, we have

$$N = mg$$

and hence the maximum friction force is

$$f = \mu N = \mu mg$$

If now the turntable is rotated with an angular velocity ω small enough so that the block does not slip, the force of friction pulls the block toward the center with a force

$$F = m\omega^2 R$$

where R is the distance from the center of the turntable to the block. Obviously the maximum angular velocity possible without slipping of the block occurs when the friction force reaches its maximum value.   Thus

$$\mu mg = m\omega_{max}^2 R$$

whence

$$\omega_{max}^2 = \frac{\mu g}{R} = \frac{0.3 \times 32}{2.4} = 4$$

and

$$\omega_{max} = 2 \text{ radians/sec.}$$

Thus, at any angular velocity less than $1/\pi$ r.p.s., the block remains at rest with respect to the turntable. At any higher angular velocity, the block slips on the table and no longer performs circular motion. The situation is analogous to the case of the stone on the string. As the stone is whirled faster and faster, the tension rises according to Eq. (22). Eventually the breaking strength of the string is reached, the string breaks, and the stone flies off at a tangent to the circle.

These two examples show us how to proceed in the general case. We resolve the forces acting into components in the direction of motion (tangential components) and perpendicular to this direction (normal components). Then we write Newton's second law in the form

$$\left.\begin{aligned} F_t &= ma_t \\ F_n &= ma_n = m\frac{v^2}{R} \end{aligned}\right\} \tag{23}$$

Here F_t is the sum of the tangential components of all the forces acting on the body, and F_n is the corresponding sum of the normal components. The normal component of acceleration $a_n = v^2/R$, where R is the radius of curvature of the path (the radius of the circle for circular motion and infinitely great for straight-line motion). The tangential component a_t is the rate of change of speed of the particle in its motion.

Simultaneous solution of the two equations then yields complete information concerning both the motion and the unknown forces.

30. Conservation of Momentum for Rectilinear Motion.—Up to this point, we have been considering one body and the forces acting on it. If we now consider the interactions of two bodies, we must make use of the third law as well as of the second law. Consider two bodies, free to move on a straight line, which exert forces on each other (*e.g.*, they may be connected by a spring) but are subjected to *no* other forces. This system of bodies is called *isolated* if this condition is fulfilled. If we denote by F_1 the force acting *on* body 1 and by F_2 the force acting *on* body 2, the third law states that

$$F_1 = -F_2 \tag{24}$$

but, by the second law,

$$F_1 = \frac{d}{dt}(m_1 v_1)$$

if m_1 is the mass of the first body and v_1 its velocity.

Similarly,

$$F_2 = \frac{d}{dt}(m_2 v_2)$$

so that using Eq. (24),

$$\frac{d}{dt}(m_1 v_1) = -\frac{d}{dt}(m_2 v_2)$$

or

$$\frac{d}{dt}(m_1 v_1) + \frac{d}{dt}(m_2 v_2) = 0$$

This can be written

$$\frac{d}{dt}(m_1 v_1 + m_2 v_2) = 0$$

and says that the rate of change of the *total* momentum of the system (momentum of body 1 plus the momentum of body 2) is zero. Hence the *total* momentum is constant, and we write

$$m_1 v_1 + m_2 v_2 = \text{constant} \tag{25}$$

In words: The *total* momentum of an isolated system is constant.

This law is called the *conservation of momentum* and is valid no matter what the nature of the interaction forces is. It is essential that the system be subjected to the action of *no* external forces.

Example.—Two bodies of masses m_1 and m_2, respectively, attract each other with forces which vary with the distance between them. If they both start from rest, find the velocity of m_2 when the velocity of m_1 is v_1.

Since both bodies start from rest and since the only forces acting are the interactions between the bodies, we know that the sum of the momenta (*i.e.*, the total momentum) is zero for $t = 0$ and does not change with time. Hence

$$(m_1 v_1 + m_2 v_2)_t = (m_1 v_1 + m_2 v_2)_{t=0} = 0$$

so that

$$v_2 = -\frac{m_1}{m_2} v_1$$

This result is correct even if a collision takes place and holds both before and after the collision.

31. Conservation of Momentum for Plane Motion.—Since momentum is a vector quantity we should expect that the law of conservation of momentum for plane motion would be equivalent to two independent relations. This is indeed the case, as we see from the following. Let us again consider bodies 1 and 2 which exert forces on each other but are not subjected to the action of any outside forces.

By the third law

$$F_1 = -F_2 \tag{26}$$

where F_1 is the force acting *on* body 1 and F_2 is the force acting *on* body 2. Equation (26) in component form is

$$\left.\begin{array}{l} F_{1x} = -F_{2x} \\ F_{1y} = -F_{2y} \end{array}\right\} \tag{27}$$

Applying the second law to each of these equations, we find easily that

$$\left.\begin{array}{l} \dfrac{d}{dt}(m_1 v_{1x} + m_2 v_{2x}) = 0 \\[2ex] \dfrac{d}{dt}(m_1 v_{1y} + m_2 v_{2y}) = 0 \end{array}\right\} \tag{28}$$

so that

$$\left.\begin{array}{l} m_1 v_{1x} + m_2 v_{2x} = C_1 \\ m_1 v_{1y} + m_2 v_{2y} = C_2 \end{array}\right\} \tag{29}$$

where C_1 and C_2 are two arbitrary constants. The following example illustrates the application of the above law.

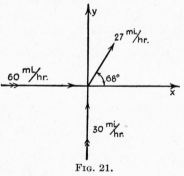

Fig. 21.

Example.—An automobile weighing 2.0 tons moving with a speed of 60 miles/hr. collides at an intersection with a truck of weight 10 tons which is moving with a speed of 30 miles/hr. on a street perpendicular to the street on which the automobile moves. If the two cars lock together, find the velocity (speed and direction) of the two after collision. Let us choose x- and y-axes as indicated in Fig. 21. We have for the components of momentum before collision:

$$2.0 \times 60 + 10 \times \ 0 = 120 \text{ ton-miles/hr.} = C_1$$
$$2.0 \times \ 0 + 10 \times 30 = 300 \text{ ton-miles/hr.} = C_2$$

Note that the units which we use may be anything *provided* we use the same units throughout. After collision the total mass is $M = 2 + 10 = 12$ tons, so that

$$MV_x = 120 \text{ ton-miles/hr.}$$
$$MV_y = 300 \text{ ton-miles/hr.}$$

and hence

$$V_x = \tfrac{120}{12} = 10 \text{ miles/hr.}$$
$$V_y = \tfrac{300}{12} = 25 \text{ miles/hr.}$$

which are the velocity components after collision.

The speed of both after collision is

$$V = \sqrt{(10)^2 + (25)^2} = 27 \text{ miles/hr.}$$

and the angle made with the x-axis is determined by

$$\tan \theta = \frac{V_y}{V_x} = \frac{25}{10} = 2.5$$

whence

$$\theta = 68°, \text{ approximately (Fig. 21).}$$

32. Impulse-momentum Theorem.—There is a general consequence of Newton's second law which is easily derived.   We write this law as

$$F = \frac{d}{dt}(mv)$$

i.e., the rate of change of momentum of the body is equal to the applied force.   If we integrate this equation with respect to t, we get

$$\int_0^t F dt = \int_{v_0}^v d(mv) \tag{30}$$

where v_0 is the velocity of the body at $t = 0$ and v its velocity at time t.   The right-hand side may immediately be integrated, yielding

$$mv - mv_0$$

so that

$$\int_0^t F\, dt = mv - mv_0 \tag{31}$$

The quantity on the left-hand side of this equation is called the *impulse of the force F* in the time interval 0 to t.   The right-hand side of the equation is the change in momentum of the body (final momentum minus initial momentum).

Thus we have derived the theorem:

The impulse of a force is equal to the change of momentum of the body acted on by this force.

33. Application of the Impulse-momentum Theorem to Plane Motion.—For motion in a plane the theorem that the impulse of a force is equal to the change of momentum of the body on which it acts is equivalent to two independent relations. They are

$$\left.\begin{aligned}\int_0^t F_x \, dt &= mv_x - mv_{x_0}\\[6pt]\int_0^t F_y \, dt &= mv_y - mv_{y_0}\end{aligned}\right\} \tag{32}$$

The proof of these relations is left as an exercise for the student.

As an application of this law, let us suppose that the automobile and truck of the previous example crash into a pole and are brought to rest. What is the impulse of the force which brings them to rest?

If we wish to express the force in pounds, we must change the mass to slugs and the velocity to feet per second. We then have a mass of

$$\frac{12 \times 2,000}{32} = 750 \text{ slugs}$$

moving with velocity components

$$V_x = 10 \text{ miles/hr.} = 15 \text{ ft./sec.}$$
$$V_y = 25 \text{ miles/hr.} = 37 \text{ ft./sec.}$$

brought to rest.

Hence the x-component of the impulse is

$$\int_0^t F_x \, dt = 750 \times 0 - 750 \times 15 = -11,000 \text{ lb.-sec.}$$

and for the y-component we have

$$\int_0^t F_y \, dt = 750 \times 0 - 750 \times 37 = -28,000 \text{ lb.-sec.}$$

The resultant impulse is

$$\text{Impulse} = \sqrt{(11,000)^2 + (28,000)^2} = 30,000 \text{ lb.-sec.}$$

in a direction opposite to the resultant velocity V.

We can reach the same result somewhat more simply by considering the motion after the collision along a new axis which we shall call x'. For this straight-line motion, we have (40 ft./sec. = 27 miles/hr.)

$$\int_0^t F_x \, dt = 750 \times 0 - 750 \times 40 = -30,000 \text{ lb.-sec.}$$

as before.   It should be noted that 1 lb.-sec. = 1 slug-ft./sec., if the pound means pound force as it does here.

Problems

1. What is the earth pull on a 1-gram body?   What acceleration of this body does this force produce?   How large a force would produce an acceleration of this body of 1 cm./sec.^{2}?

What is the earth pull on a 1-lb. body?   What acceleration of this body does this force produce?   On what mass would this force act to produce an acceleration of 1 ft./sec.^{2}?

2. A 50-gram body is acted on by a constant force of −1,000 dynes (acting to the left).   If the velocity of the body is +100 cm./sec., how long does it take for the force to produce the same speed in the opposite direction? How far does the body move in this time?   What is the change of momentum during this time?

3. A 10-lb. body hangs on a spring scale which is fastened to the roof of an elevator.

a. If the elevator ascends with a constant velocity of 10 ft./sec., what does the scale read?

b. If the elevator has an upward acceleration of 2 ft./sec.^{2}, what does the scale read?

c. What must be the acceleration to cause the scale to read 5 lb.?

d. If the elevator cable breaks and the elevator falls freely, what does the scale read?

4. A 16-lb. body *A* and a 40-lb. body *B* lie at rest on a perfectly smooth table touching each other.   If a 9-lb. force pushes parallel to the table top on *A* toward *B* calculate the acceleration of both bodies.   What force does *B* exert on *A*?   What force does *A* exert on *B*?

5. Two 8-lb. bodies standing on a smooth table are connected by a string *A*.   One of the bodies is connected by a string *B* which runs over a small frictionless pulley to a third body which hangs from string *B*.   This third body falls 5.3 ft. in 1 sec. from rest.

a. What is the acceleration of each body?

b. What does the third body weigh?

c. What is the tension in the strings *A* and *B*?

6. A bullet of mass 1 gram is shot from a gun with a speed of 300 meters/ sec.   It pierces a wooden board 2 cm. thick and emerges with half its initial speed.   What is the change in momentum?   If the average force exerted by the board on the bullet is 1.69×10^8 dynes, how long does it take for the bullet to pierce the board?

7. A 300-gram block is started sliding on a horizontal table top with a velocity of 200 cm./sec.   The coefficient of friction between block and table is 0.2.   Find

a. The distance moved in coming to rest.

b. The position of the block when its initial momentum is halved.

8. A 16-lb. body is pushed along a horizontal table by a downward force of 12 lb., making an angle of 30° with the horizontal.   If the coefficient of friction is 0.1, find

a. The acceleration of the body.

b. Its momentum at the end of 2 sec., if it starts from rest.

9. A 1-kg. block initially at rest on a table is pushed horizontally by a constant force of 100,000 dynes for 1 sec., and this force ceases to act at this instant of time. If the coefficient of sliding friction between the block and table is 0.02, how far does the block slide before it comes to rest?

10. A stone weighing 2 lb. falls from the edge of a roof 36 ft. high and penetrates 6 in. into the muddy ground. Assuming that the force which brings it to rest is constant, find the magnitude of this force.

11. A 200-gram body is pulled along a smooth table by a string which runs over a small frictionless pulley and on which hangs a 500-gram body.

If the system starts from rest and the 500-gram body is initially 70 cm. above the floor, find the speed of each body when the 500-gram body hits the floor.

12. An 800-gram block rests on a horizontal table and is connected by a string passing over a small frictionless pulley at the end of the table to a 400-gram body which initially is 150 cm. above the floor. The system starts from rest, and the coefficient of friction between the block and table is 0.4.

a. What is the velocity of the 800-gram block when the 400-gram body hits the floor?

b. If the 800-gram block remains on the table after the other one hits the floor, how much farther will it move before coming to rest?

13. A block that weighs 450 grams rests on a horizontal surface, and from it a cord runs horizontally over a frictionless pulley to a weight of 300 grams which hangs freely from the cord. Find the acceleration of the block if the coefficient of friction between block and surface is 0.6.

14. The total weight of an elevator and its load is 1,600 lb. What is the tension in the supporting cable when ascending at a uniform speed of 20 ft./sec.? When descending at a rate of 10 ft./sec.? What is the tension in the cable when the elevator is dropping with an acceleration of 32 ft./sec.²? What is the tension when there is an upward acceleration of 8 ft./sec.²? What is the tension when the elevator is moving downward but the speed is decreasing at the rate of 6 ft./sec.²?

15. Masses of 600 grams and 200 grams are fastened to the ends of a cord which passes over a frictionless pulley. Find the acceleration of the 200-gram weight and the tension in the cord.

16. A body is pulled along a table by a rope exerting a constant horizontal force of 20.8 lb. with an acceleration of 2 ft./sec.². If there is a friction force equal to one-tenth the weight of the body, what does the body weigh? If at the end of the third second from rest the body breaks into two equal pieces, how far does the part to which the rope is attached move in the next second? How far does the other piece move in coming to rest?

17. A 10-gram body initially moving to the left is acted on by a force of 100 dynes to the right. It returns to its initial position 10 sec. after the force starts to act.

a. Find its initial velocity.

b. Where and when does it reverse the direction of its motion?

18. A particle is constrained to move on a vertical circular ring (radius 40 cm.) which is rotating about a vertical axis through its center with a uniform angular velocity of 7 radians/sec. At what height above the lowest point of the ring will the particle take its position, neglecting friction?

19. A cyclist weighing 256 lb. (with his bicycle) rides on the inside of a vertical circle of radius 15 ft. When at the top point of the circle, he has a speed of 20 miles/hr. How hard does the track push on the cycle? How slow can the rider move at this point and not leave the track?

20. A 10-lb. block is dragged up an inclined plane making an angle of 60° with the horizontal at constant speed by a 9-lb. force directed up the plane.

a. What is the coefficient of friction between block and plane?

b. Starting from rest, how far down the plane would the block move in 2 sec. if the upward force did not act?

21. Calculate the acceleration of a block sliding down a plane inclined 30° with the horizontal if the coefficient of friction is 0.30.

22. An 8-lb. body on an inclined plane making an angle of 37° with the horizontal is connected by a string passing over a light pulley at the top of the plane to an 8-lb. weight which hangs vertically. The coefficient of friction is 0.2.

a. Find the tension in the string.

b. Find the acceleration of each mass.

c. If at the end of 1 sec. the string is severed, how long after it starts does the body on the plane take to return to its initial position, assuming that it starts from rest?

23. A 10-lb. block is projected up a 37° inclined plane with an initial velocity of 22.4 ft./sec. at the bottom of the plane. The coefficient of friction between the block and the plane is $\frac{1}{8}$.

a. How far up the plane will the block move?

b. How fast is it moving at the bottom of the plane on its way down?

24. Two blocks, A and B, each weighing 8 lb., are placed in contact at the top of an inclined plane 25 ft. long and 15 ft. high, A being above B. The coefficient of friction between A and the plane is 0.1, and the coefficient of friction between B and the plane is 0.15. The system starts from rest.

a. How long does it take for the blocks to reach the bottom of the plane?

b. What is the force exerted on B by A?

c. What would happen if the position of the blocks were reversed?

25. Two masses m_1 and m_2 $(m_1 > m_2)$ are hung on the ends of string which runs over a smooth, very light pulley (Atwood's machine). If the string is cut t sec. after the bodies start to move from rest, show that the mass m_2 will continue to rise a farther distance of

$$h = \frac{gt^2}{2}\left(\frac{m_1 - m_2}{m_1 + m_2}\right)^2$$

26. Two bodies of mass m_1 and m_2 are placed on two inclined planes of angles α and β placed back to back and are connected by a string running over a smooth block at the top of the planes. The coefficients of friction are μ_1 and μ_2, respectively.

a. Show that if m_1 moves down the plane its acceleration is

$$a_1 = g\left[\frac{m_1\,(\sin\alpha - \mu_1\cos\alpha) - m_2\,(\sin\beta + \mu_2\cos\beta)}{m_1 + m_2}\right]$$

b. Show that if m_2 moves down the plane its acceleration is

$$a_2 = g\left[\frac{m_2\,(\sin\beta - \mu_2\cos\beta) - m_1\,(\sin\alpha + \mu_1\cos\alpha)}{m_1 + m_2}\right]$$

c. From *a* and *b* derive the conditions under which there will be no motion if the system is originally at rest. Apply these conditions to the case where $\mu_1 = \tan \alpha$ and $\mu_2 = \tan \beta$.

27. A 50-gram body moving along the x-axis with a constant speed of 20 cm./sec. is acted on by a force of $100/\sqrt{3}$ dynes making an angle of 30° with the negative x-axis in the second quadrant. If at $t = 0$ it is at the origin and has a velocity of 20 cm./sec. along the positive x-axis:

a. Find the x-component, the y-component, and the resultant acceleration.

b. Find the position and vector velocity of the body at the end of 1 min.

c. What is the maximum value of the x-coordinate of the body? When is this reached? Where is the body at this instant of time?

d. Make a plot of the path of the body.

28. A body of mass m is acted on by a constant force whose components are F_{x0} and F_{y0}. If at time $t = 0$ it has a velocity v_0 in the positive x-direction, find the equation of the orbit. Make a graph of this result.

29. A body moves in a plane according to the equations of motion

$$x = A \sin \omega t$$
$$y = B \cos \omega t$$

a. Find the equation of the path of the body. What sort of a curve is it?

b. Solve *a*, if $A = B$.

c. Find an expression for the magnitude of the resultant velocity in terms of x and y.

30. An electron of charge e moves in a horizontal plane with a constant velocity v. If a constant vertical magnetic field is applied, there is a force acting on the electron given by $F = eHv$, where H is a measure of the magnetic field strength, which acts at right angles to the direction of motion. Hence the motion is motion in a circle with constant speed. Show that the radius of the circle is

$$R = \frac{mv}{eH}$$

What does this mean when $H = 0$, *i.e.*, no magnetic field?

31. An automobile weighing 2,400 lb. is being towed up a 5° inclined plane. What is the tension in the tow rope if the automobile is moving at a constant speed of 20 miles/hr.? What is the tension if there is an acceleration of 3 miles/hr. per second up the hill? (Neglect friction.)

32. A block weighing 24 lb. is pulled up a 30° inclined plane by a rope parallel to the plane which passes over a pulley and has a weight of 40 lb. hanging freely at the other end. Find the acceleration of the 40-lb. weight if the coefficient of sliding friction between the 24-lb. weight and the plane is 0.4.

33. A piece of ice slides down a roof 15 ft. long which is inclined 30° with the horizontal. The edge of the roof is 40 ft. above the ground and 2 ft. from the side of the building. If the ice starts from rest at the top of the roof and the coefficient of friction with the roof is 0.1, how far from the side of the building is the point where the ice strikes the ground?

34. If the distance from center field to home plate is 100 yards, assuming that the ball is thrown at an inclination of 45° with the horizontal, with what velocity must the ball leave the fielder's hand if it is to reach home plate?

35. When a baseball leaves the pitcher's hand at an elevation of 5.5 ft. above the ground, it is moving horizontally with a speed of 120 ft./sec. If the distance to the plate is 60 ft., how high is the ball above the ground when it passes over the plate?

36. A ball is projected directly upward with a velocity of 160 ft./sec. At what time is its vertical velocity equal to zero? How high will it rise? Find the velocity at 2 sec. and 8 sec. after leaving the ground.

37. A shell is fired horizontally from the top of a cliff 400 ft. high with a speed of 1,000 ft./sec.

a. How far from the bottom of the cliff does it land?

b. How long is it in flight?

c. What is its speed when it hits?

38. A bullet is shot from a gun on the ground at an angle of 45° with the horizontal and hits a cliff 100 ft. above the ground. The cliff is 1,000 yards from the gun.

a. What is the muzzle velocity of the gun?

b. How long is the bullet in flight?

c. Has it reached the highest point of its path before hitting the cliff?

39. A brick slides down a roof inclined 37° to the horizontal. The edge of the roof is 35 ft. above the ground. If the coefficient of friction is 0.1, and the body starts from rest at a point 30 ft. from the edge of the roof:

a. Find the velocity of the body when it leaves the roof; when it hits the ground.

b. How far along the ground from a point directly under the edge of the roof will it hit?

40. A projectile is fired with a velocity v_0 at an angle θ with a horizontal plane at the bottom of an inclined plane of angle α. Show that it will hit the plane at a distance along the plane given by

$$r = \frac{2v_0^2}{g} \frac{\cos \theta \sin (\theta - \alpha)}{\cos^2 \alpha}$$

From this show that, if θ alone is varied, a maximum range is obtained when

$$\theta = \frac{\alpha}{2} + \frac{\pi}{4}$$

Hint: $\sin (2\theta - \alpha) = 2 \cos \theta \sin (\theta - \alpha) + \sin \alpha$.

41. A bombing plane, diving at 256 miles/hr. at an angle of 37° with the vertical, drops a bomb. If the altitude of the plane was 2,500 ft. find (neglect air resistance):

a. The time it takes the bomb to hit the ground.

b. The distance from the point where it strikes to the point directly beneath the place where it was released.

c. Its speed when it strikes.

42. A golf ball is driven with an initial velocity of 128 ft./sec. at an angle of 30° above the horizontal. (Neglect air resistance.)

a. Find the maximum height reached.

b. Find the time needed to reach this point.

c. Find the radius of curvature of the trajectory at this point.

43. A metal block is projected up along a 37° inclined plane with an initial velocity of 40 ft./sec. at the bottom of the plane. The incline is 20 ft. long, and the coefficient of friction between the plane and block is $\frac{1}{4}$.

a. What is the velocity of the block as it leaves the top of the plane?

b. How long does it take for the block to reach the top of the plane?

c. If after leaving the plane the body falls freely, what is its speed when it hits the ground?

44. The long-range guns which bombarded Paris during the war weighed 320,000 lb., had a barrel 120 ft. long, and fired a projectile weighing 256 lb. with a muzzle velocity of 5,000 ft./sec. at an elevation of 53° above the horizontal.

a. Compute the initial recoil velocity, assuming the gun completely free to recoil.

b. Compute the horizontal range in the absence of air resistance. What percentage of this value is the actual range of 130,000 yards?

c. Compute the maximum height (in miles) reached by the projectile, neglecting air resistance. (1 mile = 5,280 ft.)

d. Assuming uniform acceleration in the bore of the gun, compute the time required for the projectile to travel the length of the barrel.

e. Compute the time of flight in minutes, neglecting air resistance.

45. A body of mass 300 grams initially at rest is pushed along a smooth table by a constant force of 600 dynes. The force ceases to act at the end of 2 sec., and 3 sec. after the body starts it collides with another of twice its mass and sticks to it.

a. Find the velocity of the two bodies after the collision if the larger one is at rest before the collision.

b. How far does the first body move before it hits the second?

46. Two freight cars are rolling toward one another on a level track. The first weighs 40 tons and is traveling 5 ft./sec., the second weighs 125 tons and is traveling 4 ft./sec. The two cars couple together after colliding. Find their final speed, and the direction in which they move. Neglect rolling friction between cars and track.

47. A $\frac{1}{2}$-oz. bullet strikes and remains embedded in a 5-lb. bird in the air. The bullet has a horizontal velocity of 800 ft./sec., and the bird is flying horizontally in the same direction 64 ft. above the ground with a velocity of 20 ft./sec. just before the impact. Assuming that the bird begins to fall when it is struck, what will be the distance of the point where the bird strikes the ground from the point on the ground directly below the bird's position when it was hit?

48. A 6-lb. block rests on a horizontal frictionless table, the top of which is 4 ft. above the ground. A bullet weighing 0.06 lb. is fired horizontally into the block where it remains embedded, and it is observed that the block acquires a speed of 16 ft./sec.

a. What was the speed of the rifle bullet?

b. How far from the edge of the table does the block hit the floor?

c. How fast is the block moving as it hits the floor?

49. A rifle weighing 10 lb. fires a bullet weighing $\frac{1}{8}$ lb. The initial recoil velocity of the rifle is 12.5 ft./sec. The rifle is brought to rest by the gunner in 0.02 sec.

a. Compute the muzzle velocity of the bullet.

b. Compute the impulse of the force against the gunner's shoulder, by the impulse-momentum theorem.

c. If this force is constant, find its value from the definition of impulse.

50. An automobile moving with a velocity of 60 miles/hr. hits another of 1.5 times its weight, at rest, and sticks to it.   Find the velocity of both after collision.

51. Two masses of mass 4 and 8 lb., respectively, attract each other with a constant force of 2 lb.   If they are 32 ft. apart at $t = 0$ and the 4-lb. body is at rest at $t = 0$ and they collide at the end of 2 sec. find their relative velocity at $t = 0$.   How far has each moved in these 2 sec.?   Calculate the total momentum of the system at $t = 0$ sec., $t = 1$ sec., and $t = 1.5$ sec. Discuss the last answer.

52. A block of mass M resting on a table is hit horizontally by a hammer and the impulse of the force is G.   If there is a friction force equal to fW where W is the weight of the body and f is a proper fraction, show that the body comes to rest in time

$$t = \frac{G}{fMg} = \frac{G}{fW}$$

and moves a distance

$$s = \frac{1}{2}\frac{G^2}{fgM^2} = \frac{1}{2}\frac{G^2}{fWM}$$

53. Two bodies each of mass 2 grams attract each other with a force proportional to their separation.   When their separation is 10 cm. the force is 10^4 dynes.   If they are at rest initially and are separated at $t = 0$ by a distance of 20 cm., find their relative velocity when they collide.

HINT:
$$a_x = \frac{dv_x}{dt} = \frac{dv_x}{dx}\frac{dx}{dt} = v_x\frac{dv_x}{dx}.$$

54. A 2-lb. body free to move along the x-axis is acted on by two forces:
1. A constant force, to the right, of 6 lb.; $F_1 = +6$ lb.
2. A force to the left, $F_2 = -2t$ lb.
If the body starts from rest,

a. Find the expression for its velocity at any time t.

b. Find the expression for its position at any time t.

c. Where does it reverse the direction of its motion?   When?

d. How long does it take to return to its initial position?   How fast is it then moving?

55. A 24-lb. shell lying on a flat smooth surface explodes into three equal pieces.   Two of them shoot out at right angles to each other with speeds of 40 miles/hr. and 60 miles/hr., respectively.   Find the momentum (magnitude and direction) of the third piece.   If the explosion takes place in 10^{-3} sec., find the average force (magnitude and direction) pushing on each piece during the explosion.

56. A 500-lb. shell is fired from a 10-ton armored railway car at rest on a track running north and south.   The shell is shot in a horizontal plane with a velocity of 1,000 ft./sec. in a direction making an angle of 60° with the track.

a. What is the recoil velocity of the car?

b. If the shell is in the gun for 0.01 sec., what is the average lateral force exerted by the rails on the wheels of the car?

CHAPTER VI

WORK AND ENERGY; POTENTIAL ENERGY

We have now reached a point in our discussion where it pays to summarize our results and from this summary to plan in which direction we must next proceed. We have developed a method of solving the problem of motion of a particle under the action of given forces in which we apply the second law of motion directly, calculating the acceleration of the particle and then proceeding to the kinetic equations of motion by integration. However, it is clear that the equation $dv/dt = F/m$ can be integrated directly for v only if the force is constant or depends on t, and our next problem is to investigate the solution of problems for other types of forces. A most important type of force (perhaps the most common in physical problems) is that in which the force depends on the position of the body. Thus our equation for the acceleration becomes (if we consider straight-line motion for simplicity) $dv/dt = f(x)$ where $f(x)$ is some function of x given by the forces acting. This equation cannot be directly integrated as it stands, since this would yield $v = \int f(x)dt$, an integral whose value may be found only if it is known how x varies with t. This latter information, however, constitutes the solution of our problem, so that we are obliged to look for a different scheme of solution. The method employed is so fruitful that a number of new concepts and definitions have been introduced, especially useful for this kind of problem, and the study of these and the method of solution form the subject matter of this chapter.

34. Fundamental Definitions; Motion in a Straight Line.— When a particle is acted on by a force or by a number of forces, it will, in general, be accelerated and perform some sort of motion. The simplest possible case occurs when a single constant force acts on the body and the body moves in a straight line in the direction of the force. For this case we define the *work* done by the force on the body as the latter moves a certain distance as the product of the magnitude of the force and the magnitude of the displacement undergone by the body.

If the straight-line motion takes place under the action of several constant forces, *e.g.*, a block sliding down an inclined plane, then some or all the constant forces may not act in the direction of motion of the body. If we consider one of these forces which makes an angle ϕ with the line of motion, then only the component of this force along the line of motion contributes anything to the acceleration of the body. This component is $F \cos \phi$ (Fig. 22), and if the body moves from a position x_1 to a position x_2, we define the work done by F on the body when the body is displaced from x_1 to x_2 as

$$W = F \cos\phi(x_2 - x_1) \tag{1}$$

The work done by a force may be either positive or negative, according to whether the component $F \cos \phi$ acts in the direction of motion or opposite to it. Thus, for example, the work done by a friction force *on* a body will always be a negative quantity. It is common in such a case to talk of the work done *against* friction, this being the negative of the work done *by* friction on the body. If we calculate the work done on the particle by one of the forces acting on it according to Eq. (1) and repeat this process for all the forces acting on the body, *the algebraic sum of the works done by the individual forces equals the work done by the resultant of all these forces.* The proof of this statement is left as an exercise for the student.

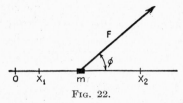

FIG. 22.

In the general case of motion along a straight line, the force (or forces) will not be constant. In this case we must generalize our definition of work. Suppose the force F in Fig. 22 is a variable force. We imagine the line along which the body moves to be divided into a huge number of small intervals, each interval of length dx. If the length of these intervals is sufficiently small, we may treat the force acting on the body as it moves one interval dx as constant and write for the work done by the force in this motion

$$dW = F \cos\phi \, dx \tag{2}$$

where F is now the magnitude of the force at the position where dx is located and ϕ the angle which F makes with the line at that point. The total work done by F on the body as the latter moves from x_1 to x_2 is the sum of all the dW's over all the intervals between x_1 and x_2, or in calculus notation,

$$W = \int_{x_1}^{x_2} F \cos\phi \, dx \tag{3}$$

where the limits x_1 and x_2 indicate that we take the value of the integral for $x = x_2$ and subtract from this its value for $x = x_1$.

The unit of work in the c.g.s. system is one dyne-centimeter, and is called one *erg*. In the English gravitational system of units the unit of work is the foot-pound.

Definition.—*The product of one-half the mass of a particle and the square of its speed is called the kinetic energy of the particle.* In symbols, we write

$$K.E. = \tfrac{1}{2}mv^2 \tag{4}$$

We shall now derive the following fundamental theorem:

The work done by the resultant force acting on a particle during any part of its motion is equal to the gain of kinetic energy of the particle during that part of its motion.

For the case of straight-line motion we note that the resultant force must act along the line of motion. Were this not so, the particle would move in a curved path. During a displacement dx of the particle, the force F does an amount of work

$$dW = Fdx = m\frac{dv}{dt} \cdot dx \tag{5}$$

since the second law requires that $F = m(dv/dt)$.

The right-hand side of Eq. (5) may be written as

$$m\frac{dx}{dt} \cdot dv = mv \, dv$$

since by definition $v = dx/dt$. Thus Eq. (5) becomes

$$dW = Fdx = mv \, dv \tag{6}$$

where dv is the change v occurring in the interval dx.

If we now integrate Eq. (6), *i.e.*, sum up the work done in all the intervals dx lying between x_1 and x_2, we have

$$W = \int_{x_1}^{x_2} Fdx = \int_{v_1}^{v_2} mv \, dv \tag{7}$$

where v_1 is the speed of the particle when it is at x_1 and v_2 its speed when at x_2. The right-hand member of Eq. (7) may be evaluated immediately and one obtains

$$W = \int_{x_1}^{x_2} F dx = \frac{mv_2^2}{2} - \frac{mv_1^2}{2} \tag{8}$$

which, remembering the definition given by Eq. (4), is the required result.

35. Work-energy Theorem for Plane Motion.—In the general case of motion in a plane, *i.e.*, in the case of variable forces and of motion in a curved path, it is possible to apply the foregoing argument with but little modification. We reduce the problem here to the one previously handled by considering the path not as a whole but by dividing it up into a large number of small sections, each of length ds and small enough so that we may consider it a straight line and that the force acting during the corresponding time interval is constant. We then apply our definition (2) to each small portion and add up the results to get the total work done. For each little length ds, the work done is

$$F \cos \phi \, ds$$

and the sum becomes, as each ds is taken smaller and smaller,

$$W = \int F \cos \phi \, ds \tag{9}$$

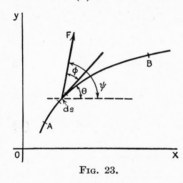

Fig. 23.

where the integral is to be taken over the portion of the path under consideration (Fig. 23) from A to B.

We must now find an expression for W in terms of the components of F along the x- and y-axes (F_x and F_y). From Fig. 23 we see that $\phi = \psi - \theta$, where ψ is the angle which F makes with the x-axis, and θ is the angle made by ds (tangent to the curve) and the x-axis. We make use of a theorem in trigonometry.

$$\cos \phi = \cos (\psi - \theta) = \cos \psi \cos \theta + \sin \psi \sin \theta \tag{10}$$

Inserting this expression for $\cos \phi$ into Eq. (9), we find

$$W = \int F \cos \psi \, ds \cos \theta + \int F \sin \psi \, ds \sin \theta \tag{11}$$

But

$$F \cos \psi = F_x; \qquad F \sin \psi = F_y$$
$$ds \cos \theta = dx; \qquad ds \sin \theta = dy$$

so that Eq. (11) becomes

$$W = \int F \cos \phi \, ds = \int F_x \, dx + \int F_y \, dy \qquad (12)$$

or, in words, the work done on the body is equal to the sum of the work done by the x-component of the resultant force acting on the body and the work done by the y-component of this force.

We now can easily find the kinetic energy-work theorem for any motion in a plane. We have already shown that

and

$$\left. \begin{aligned} \int F_x \, dx &= \frac{m}{2}v_x^2 - \frac{m}{2}v_{x0}^2 \\[2mm] \int F_y \, dy &= \frac{m}{2}v_y^2 - \frac{m}{2}v_{y0}^2 \end{aligned} \right\} \qquad (13)$$

since each of these equations represents the case of motion along a straight line. If we now add these two equations, the left-hand side represents the total work done on the body by Eq. (12). Thus

$$W = \frac{m}{2}(v_x^2 + v_y^2) - \frac{m}{2}(v_{x0}^2 + v_y^2) = \frac{m}{2}v^2 - \frac{m}{2}v_0^2 \qquad (14)$$

where v represents the magnitude of the final resultant velocity (the speed) and v_0 the initial speed. Thus we find again that the work done on a body by a force is equal to the change of kinetic energy of the body caused by this force.

36. Potential Energy; Straight-line Motion.—The theorems developed in the preceding sections suggest strongly that one might classify forces advantageously according to a scheme dependent on the idea of the work done by these forces. This turns out to be an important and useful procedure, and forces thus classified fall into three classes.

First, there are the forces which do no work on a body during its motion and hence which do not affect the changes of speed that occur. These forces necessarily act in a direction normal to the direction of motion of body. As examples we call attention to constraint forces such as the pull of a string on a body when the latter is twirled in a circle or the normal component of the push of a plane on a body which slides on its surface.

To classify the forces which do work on a body, it is best to start with a simple example. Suppose a body moves on a straight line under the action of a single force pushing or pulling it in a direction opposite to its direction of motion.   Such a force will decrease the speed and hence the kinetic energy of the body and bring it to rest.   The body may then stay at rest or may return in the opposite direction to its initial motion.   Suppose the latter is the case and that when the body reaches a given position its kinetic energy is just equal to the kinetic energy it previously possessed at that point when moving in the original direction. In this case the body has lost kinetic energy during part of its motion but regains all of it as it returns to its former positions. Forces which produce this effect are called *conservative* forces, and we think of the decreasing kinetic energy of the body being stored up in what we may call energy of position or "potential" energy. This potential energy is regained as kinetic energy when the body returns.

If, on the other hand, the body comes to rest and stays there or returns to its initial positions with decreased kinetic energy, we say the force is *dissipative*, as the original kinetic energy has been totally or partially lost during the motion.   In such a case we clearly cannot think of the kinetic energy being stored up and hence cannot introduce the notion of energy of position.   As an example consider a ball thrown vertically upward.   As it moves upward it loses speed, comes to rest, and returns to its initial position.   An elementary calculation shows that it returns to its initial position with the same speed (and hence kinetic energy) as when it started up.   The only difference between the initial and final velocities is one of direction, not of magnitude.   Thus we think of the body losing kinetic energy as it proceeds upward, gaining potential energy, and on the way down its kinetic energy increases and its potential energy decreases.   A similar situation exists in the case of a block moving on a frictionless table and being stopped by a spring.   As the block slows down, the spring is compressed, and the original kinetic energy is regained as the spring pushes the block back to its starting point.   Thus, as examples of conservative forces, we have the pull of the earth and the force exerted by a spring on a body in contact with it. On the other hand consider a block sliding along a table with friction.   The friction force brings the block to rest, and it remains at rest.   All the original kinetic energy has been lost, and the block of itself will not return to its initial position.   Thus a friction force is a *dissipative* force, and its action always results in a loss of mechanical energy.

We must now formulate the preceding qualitative ideas in quantitative precise form. In the examples of conservative forces which we have given, the negative work done by the force in stopping the body must just be equal to (and opposite in sign to) the positive work done by the same force as the body returns to its initial position. *The total work done by this force in a round trip is zero,* and, in general, if this is so, the force doing the work is a conservative force. When a conservative force acts on a body we define the potential energy of the body as follows: We first arbitrarily choose some position of the body for which we say its potential energy is zero. Let this point be denoted by x_0. Then the potential energy of the body in any other position is equal to the negative of the work done by the conservative force when the body moves or is moved from x_0 to its new position. We denote the potential energy by the letter V, and since this depends on the position of the body, we shall write $V(x)$. In symbols the above definition becomes

$$V(x) = -\int_{x_0}^{x} F_x \, dx \tag{15}$$

where F_x denotes the conservative force. It should be noted that Eq. (15) is entirely equivalent to the relation

$$F_x = -\frac{dV}{dx} \tag{16}$$

It follows from the defining equation [Eq. (15)] that if a body moves from a position x_1 to a position x_2 under the action of a conservative force the gain in potential energy is equal to

$$V_2 - V_1 = -\int_{x_1}^{x_2} F_x \, dx \tag{17}$$

or, in words, to the negative of the work done by the force during this motion. Since the potential energy of a body depends *only* on its position, it follows that the work done by a conservative force on a body depends only on the initial and end points of the motion and cannot depend on the intermediate details of the motion or on the intermediate positions. Thus a conservative force is one which may vary only with the position x and not, for example, with the velocity of the body.

Combining the theorem of Eq. (8) with Eq. (17), we obtain for a motion under the action of a conservative force

$$V_2 - V_1 = \frac{mv_1^2}{2} - \frac{mv_2^2}{2}$$

or rewritten

$$\frac{mv_1^2}{2} + V_1 = \frac{mv_2^2}{2} + V_2 \qquad (18)$$

In words, the sum of the kinetic and potential energies of the body is the same at the point x_1 as at the point x_2 and is therefore constant. We call the sum of the kinetic and potential energies the *total mechanical energy* and denote it by the letter E. We may then write Eq. (18) in the form

$$\frac{mv^2}{2} + V = E \qquad (18a)$$

In the case of a body acted on by several forces, some conservative and some dissipative, we can still speak of the potential energy associated with the conservative forces and hence of the total mechanical energy of the body, although it does not stay constant. In fact, the decrease of total mechanical energy during any motion must just be equal to the work done against the dissipative forces. If we consider again a ball thrown into the air but take air resistance into account, we see that the ball will not rise so high as when air resistance is lacking since at the top of its path its total energy is all potential and this is less than its initial energy by an amount equal to the work done against friction.

One more word may be added concerning a convenient choice of origin for potential energy. For the case of constant forces there is no particular advantage in any single position over any other, and the particular problem usually dictates a convenient origin for potential energy. When the force varies with position, however, it is usually most convenient to set the potential energy equal to zero at a position where the force vanishes. Thus, if a force varies inversely as a power of the distance from a fixed point, we place the potential energy equal to zero when the body is at infinity, whereas, if the force varies directly as a power of the distance from a fixed point, we set the potential energy zero at the fixed point.

37. Potential Energy; General Case for Plane Motion.—For the general case of motion in a plane, we say that a potential energy is associated with a force if

The work done by the force on the body as it moves from a point *B* to a point *C* is equal and opposite in sign to the work done

by this force on the body as it moves from C to B along *any* path whatsoever.

Several consequences of this statement are at once evident. The work done by a conservative force on a body moving from B to C along any path is independent of the path. Also, the total work done by a conservative force as a body moves around any closed path is zero.

If we consider only conservative forces, since the work done by these forces on the body does not depend on the path followed by the body, it can depend only on the end points (the initial and final points). As before, the work done on the body is equal to the loss of potential energy and is equal to the increase of kinetic energy of the body. We then have the relation

$$\left(\frac{mv^2}{2} + V\right)_B = \left(\frac{mv^2}{2} + V\right)_C \tag{19}$$

i.e., the sum of the potential and kinetic energies of the body at any point is equal to the same sum at any other point and hence is constant. *This is the principle of the conservation of mechanical energy for conservative motions.*

The important point to remember is that the proof of this theorem depends on the condition that the work does not depend on the path followed and that only for this case is mechanical energy conserved. In all other cases we find other forms of energy appearing at the expense of the lost mechanical energy, such as heat in the case of frictional forces.

38. Example: Equipotential Surfaces.—To illustrate the statements of the preceding section, let us consider the case of a body moving under the action of the pull of the earth, *i.e.*, its weight. This is the case of the motion of a body under the action of a constant force and the direction of the force is vertically downward. When the body is at the surface of the earth, we shall call its potential energy zero, thus fixing an origin for potential energy. If the body is moved along the earth's surface, *i.e.*, horizontally, the work done on it by its weight is zero since the angle between the direction of motion and the force is 90°. The same is true in every horizontal plane at a given height h above the earth's surface. Thus the potential energy of the body does not change as it moves in any horizontal plane, and we call these planes surfaces of constant potential energy, or for brevity, *equipotential surfaces.* In general, when a body moves under the action of a conservative force, there will exist a family of surfaces on which the potential energy is constant, and the normals to these equipotential surfaces will everywhere coincide with the direction of the conservative force.

Let us now apply the test as stated in Sec. 37 to see if a constant force such as the weight of a body is conservative. We

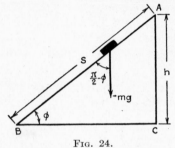

shall calculate the work done by the pull of the earth as the body moves from a point A to the point C a distance h below A (Fig. 24) and see if this work depends on the path between A and C.

First, suppose the body moves from A to C in the vertical line connecting these points. The work done by the weight is

Fig. 24.

$-mg\ (0 - h)$, if we take the upward direction (y-axis) as positive and let the y-coordinate of C be zero and that of A be h. Thus the work done is

$$W_{AC} = +mgh.$$

Now suppose the body moves down an inclined plane of angle ϕ (Fig. 24). The work done by the weight of the body as the latter moves from A to B is

$$W_{AB} = -mg \cos (90° - \phi)(-s) = mg \sin \phi \cdot s$$

where s is the length of the inclined plane and we use $-s$ for the distance, since we are measuring positive displacement upward and in our case the body undergoes a negative displacement. From the figure we see that $s \cdot \sin \phi = h$ and hence

$$W_{AB} = +mgh$$

Since the path from B to C is horizontal, the work done in moving the body horizontally from B to C is zero; $W_{BC} = 0$. Thus we have

$$W_{AC} = W_{AB} + W_{BC} = +mgh$$

which is the same result as in the case where the body moves directly from A to C.

For a general proof that the work W_{AC} does not depend on the path between A and C, we proceed as follows: Let the coordinates of point A be x_1 and y_1; those of C be x_2 and y_2. Now from Eq. (12) we have, for the work done by a force with components F_x and F_y,

$$W = \int F_x \, dx + \int F_y \, dy$$

In our case we have

$$F_x = 0; \qquad F_y = -mg$$

so that

$$W_{AC} = 0 + \int_{y_1}^{y_2} (-mg) dy = -mg(y_2 - y_1) = +mg(y_1 - y_2)$$

and since $y_1 - y_2$ is equal to h, we have in general

$$W_{AC} = +mgh$$

and this does not depend on the path between A and C but rather only on the difference between the y-coordinates of these points, *i.e.*, on the difference in height, which is the distance between the equipotential planes at y_1 and y_2. Thus we find that the force of gravity is a conservative force, and that for falling bodies the principle of the conservation of mechanical energy is valid. This is of course no longer true when there are friction effects. If we call the potential energy zero for $h = 0$, then the potential energy of a body at a height h is mgh. The velocity with which a body starting at the height h from rest hits the ground is obtained as follows: The decrease of potential energy is mgh and this is equal to the increase of kinetic energy and, as the body starts from rest, this is $mv^2/2$. We then have

$$mgh = \frac{mv^2}{2}$$

or

$$v = \sqrt{2gh}$$

which we also obtain from kinematical considerations.

39. Power.—In the preceding sections we have been discussing the work done on a body by forces. The length of time necessary to perform the work is completely arbitrary. In order to include the time, we define power as the rate of doing work. Thus, if an amount of work ΔW is done by a force in time Δt, the average power developed by the force is

$$\text{Average power} = \frac{\Delta W}{\Delta t}$$

and, if we let $\Delta t \to 0$, we get

$$\text{Power} = \frac{dW}{dt} \tag{20}$$

For the case of straight-line motion

$$\Delta W = F\Delta s$$

so that

$$\text{Average power} = F\frac{\Delta s}{\Delta t}$$

and, if we let $\Delta t \to 0$,

$$\text{Power} = F\frac{ds}{dt} = Fv \tag{21}$$

so that the instantaneous power is the product of the force and the velocity of the body.

In the case of plane motion, we have for ΔW from Eq. (12)

$$\Delta W = F_x\Delta x + F_y\Delta y = F \cos\phi\Delta s$$

so that

$$\text{Average power} = F_x\frac{\Delta x}{\Delta t} + F_y\frac{\Delta y}{\Delta t} = F \cos\phi\frac{\Delta s}{\Delta t}$$

and, if $\Delta t \to 0$,

$$\text{Power} = F_x \cdot v_x + F_y \cdot v_y = F \cos\phi \, v \tag{22}$$

The unit of power in the c. g. s. system is 1 erg/sec. As this is such a small unit, 10,000,000 ergs/sec. are used as a unit called one *watt*.

$$1 \text{ watt} = 10^7 \text{ ergs/sec.} = 10^7 \text{ dyne-cm./sec.}$$

In the English gravitational system the unit is 1 ft.-lb./sec., where the pound force is meant. Again this unit is too small to be convenient in practice so that ratings of machines are usually given in horse power, where

$$1 \text{ hp.} = 33,000 \text{ ft.-lb./min.} = 550 \text{ ft.-lb./sec.}$$

Problems

1. A 100-gram body is projected vertically with a speed of 98 meters/sec.
a. How much work has been done on the body by the pull of the earth, when the body is at the highest point of its path?

b. What is its potential energy (referred to its potential energy at $t = 0$), when at the top of its path?

c. Show that this is a conservative motion. Set up the law of conservation of energy for this motion.

d. Solve for the velocity of the body when it is 300 meters high. When it is 1,000 meters high. Discuss your answers.

2. An 8-lb. iron block falls vertically through a height of 4 ft. and strikes the top of a nail which is partly driven into a wooden block, driving it in 1 in. farther.

a. Calculate the loss in potential energy of the block while falling.

b. Find from (*a*) the kinetic energy of the block at the instant it strikes the nail.

c. Find the work done in driving the nail.

d. Find the force which would be required to press the nail into the wooden block.

e. Compute the deceleration of the iron block while it is being stopped by the nail.

3. A freight car weighing 12 tons is at rest with brakes released on a level track. A second car weighing 4 tons and moving 8 ft./sec. strikes the first, and the two couple together and move as one. The cars then come to a grade, rising vertically 1 ft. in 200 (measured along the track). How far along the incline will they move before coming to rest? Neglect friction. How does their potential energy in this position compare with the original kinetic energy of the 4-ton car?

4. The force necessary to compress a helical spring a distance x is proportional to x. A force of 4 lb. is found to compress the spring 6 in. A 4-lb. block resting on a table is pressed against the spring, compressing it 12 in. (Neglect friction between block and table.)

a. What force F is necessary to hold it in this position?

b. How much work in foot-pounds was done in compressing the spring?

c. If the force F is suddenly removed how much kinetic energy will the 4-lb. block acquire?

d. What will be the velocity of the block at the instant it leaves the spring?

5. A 200-gram body moves on a straight line under the action of a force

$$F = -10^4 x - 200 x^3 \text{ dynes}$$

The body is initially at rest at a point 10 cm. from its equilibrium position $x = 0$.

a. How much work is done on the body as it moves from its initial position to $x = 0$?

b. What is the speed of the body at $x = 0$?

c. How far does the body move before reversing its direction of motion?

6. A 10-ton freight car moving with a velocity of 40 ft./sec. hits a spring bumper and is brought to rest, compressing the bumper 18 in. If the force necessary to compress the bumper a distance x is given by

$$F = kx$$

a. Find the kinetic energy of the freight car before collision.

  b. Find the value of k in the expression for F.   (Units.)
  c. What force will compress the spring 6 in.?

  7. A mass point of mass 8 grams is acted on by a force in dynes given by

$$F = 10 - 2x$$

where x is in centimeters.   When the body is at $x = 0$, it is at rest.
  a. How much work is done by F, when the body moves from $x = 0$ cm. to $x = 5$ cm.; from $x = 0$ cm. to $x = 10$ cm.?
  b. What is the velocity of the body at $x = 5$ cm.? at $x = 10$ cm.?
  c. Draw a graph of work vs. displacement.

  8. A 2-gram body, free to move along the x-axis, is attracted to a point O by a force of magnitude

$$F = \frac{2,700}{x^3} \text{ dynes}$$

where x is in centimeters.
  a. How much work is done on the body when it moves from $x = 2$ cm. to $x = 4$ cm.?
  b. How much work is done by the body when it moves from $x = -10$ cm. to $x = -3$ cm.?
  c. Find the potential energy and total energy at $x = 5$ cm. and $x = 3$ cm., if the body is at rest at $x = 10$ cm., if the potential energy is zero when $x = \infty$.
  d. Find a general expression for the potential energy of a body of mass m acted on by this force.

  9. A body weighing 40 lb. is pushed up a frictionless 30° inclined plane 10 ft. long by a constant force F.   If the velocity at the bottom of the plane is 4 ft./sec. and the velocity at the top 12 ft./sec., how much work is done by the force F?

  10. A block is projected up a 37° inclined plane.   At the bottom of the plane it has a velocity of 16 ft./sec.   The coefficient of sliding friction between block and plane is $\frac{1}{8}$.
  a. How far up the plane does it slide?
  b. How long does it require to slide back to the bottom?
  c. What is its velocity at the bottom on its way down?

  11. A body starting from rest slides down a plane of length l which is inclined at an angle θ with the horizontal.   If the coefficient of friction is μ, find an expression for the velocity at the bottom by using Newton's laws directly and also by using the work-energy principle.

  12. A sled starts from a height of 30 ft. above an ice pond and slides down a slope 50 ft. long, across the ice a distance of 120 ft., and up a slope inclined at an angle of 30° with the horizontal.   If the coefficient of friction is 0.10 for all portions of the path, how far along the second slope will the sled go before coming to rest?

  13. A 25-lb. block is pushed 100 ft. up the sloping surface of a plane inclined at an angle of 37° to the horizontal, by a constant force F of 32.5 lb. acting parallel to the plane.   The coefficient of friction between the block and plane is 0.25.
  a. How much work is done by the force F?

b. Compute the increase in kinetic energy of the block.

c. Compute the increase in potential energy of the block.

d. Compute the work done against friction.

14. A 10-lb. body is pulled up an inclined plane 12 ft. high and 20 ft. along the slope by a force of 10 lb. acting parallel to the plane. The body starts from rest at the bottom of the plane and the coefficient of friction is 0.25. Calculate:

a. The work done by the 10-lb. force as the body moves to the top of the plane.

b. The work done against friction in the above motion.

c. The work done against gravity in the above motion.

d. The speed of the body at the top of the plane.

15. An 8-lb. block on a table is pulled toward a point O by a spring with a force $F = -4x$, where F is in pounds and x is in feet. The coefficient of friction between block and table is 0.5. The block starts from rest at a point 2 ft. from O.

a. Compute the work done by the spring when the block has moved 1 ft. toward O.

b. How much work has been converted into heat during this motion?

c. What is the speed of the body after moving 1 ft. from its original position?

16. A particle weighing 1 lb. slides without friction on the inside of a vertical circular track of radius $\frac{2}{3}$ ft. The speed of the particle is 9 ft./sec. when it is at the top point of the circle.

a. Calculate the speed of the particle when it is at the bottom of the circle.

b. Calculate the speed of the particle when it is at the lower end of a diameter making an angle of 60° with the vertical.

c. What is the push of the track on the particle when the latter is in the position described in (*b*)?

17. A roller-coaster car starts from rest at the top of an incline and coasts without friction. The bottom of the incline is a section of a vertical circle of radius 40 ft. If the starting point is 16 ft. higher than the bottom, what is the upward force on a 160-lb. passenger when the car is at the lowest point of the curve?

18. A small body of mass 10 grams hangs from a light inextensible cord 1 meter long. It is pulled aside until the cord makes an angle of 60° with the vertical, and then released.

a. Find its velocity as it passes through its lowest point.

b. Find the tension in the cord, in dynes, at this point.

19. Prove that, if a stone is whirled in a vertical circle at the end of a string, the tension in the string when the stone is at the bottom point of the circle is greater than the tension when the stone is at the top point by six times the weight of the stone. What physical principles are involved in the solution of this problem?

20. A particle of mass 100 grams is constrained to slide without friction on a vertical circle of radius 25 cm. If the particle is released at the end of a horizontal diameter, what will be the force exerted on the particle by the supporting frame when the particle is at the lowest point of the circle?

21. A body slides on the inside of a frictionless vertical circular track $7\frac{1}{2}$ in. in diameter. It passes the lowest point of the circle with a speed v_0. Find the smallest value of v_0 such that the body does not leave the track at the highest point of the circle.

22. An 80-lb. body is attracted to a point O by a force in pounds,

$$F = -10x$$

where x is measured in feet from O. There is also a friction force of 10 lb. acting on it while it is in motion.

  a. If the body reaches a point 9.0 ft. to the left of O and then turns back, where was it at $t = 0$ if it started from rest?

  b. How much work was done by the friction force during the motion?

  c. What is the loss of potential energy during the motion?

  d. Find the total energy of the body when $x = 1$ ft., if its potential energy is zero at $x = 0$.

23. Two bodies of mass 20 and 60 grams, respectively, initially at rest with respect to one another, attract each other with a force proportional to the distance between them. At $t = 0$, this force is 1,500 dynes. How far apart must they be initially, if they are to collide with a relative velocity of 100 cm./sec.?

24. A body of mass m is attracted by a fixed mass point at O by a force given by

$$F = -\frac{km}{r^2}$$

where k is a constant and r is the distance from O to the mass point m. If $k = 10^{-3}$ cm.^{3}/sec.^{2}, and m is 10 grams, calculate:

  a. The work done by F in moving m from a point P ($r = 10$ cm.) along the line connecting O to P to a distance $r = 100$ cm. (point Q).

  b. The work done by F as m moves along the arc of a circle of radius 100 cm., center at O, from Q to a point R on the opposite side of O.

  c. The work done by F as m moves along the line OR from $r = 100$ cm. to $r = 10$ cm. (point S).

  d. The work done by F as m moves from S back to P along the arc of the circle of radius 10 cm. (center at O).

  e. Find the sum of a, b, c, and d. What conclusions can you draw from this answer?

25. A mass point of mass m is acted on by a force

$$F = -\frac{1}{x^2} + \frac{2}{x^3}$$

  a. Make a plot of F vs. x.

  b. Make a plot of the potential energy of m vs. x. Where on this curve is the point corresponding to $F = 0$? What does this mean?

26. A cannon weighing 2 tons fires a projectile weighing 20 lb. If the muzzle velocity is 800 ft./sec. at an angle of 41.4° with the horizontal, what is the initial velocity of recoil of the cannon if it is free to move in a horizontal direction? What is the kinetic energy of the projectile? of the cannon? What becomes of the vertical component of the momentum imparted to the cannon?

27. A horse pulls a horse car with a force of 300 lb. at an angle of 30° with the track. The car moves with a speed of 5 miles/hr.

   a. How much work is done by the horse in 10 min.?

   b. What is the power exerted by the horse?

28. An automobile truck can run up a grade of 1 in 60 with a speed of 8 miles/hr. If there is a friction force equal to $\frac{1}{40}$ the weight of the car, how fast does it run down the same hill, the horse power of the motor being the same?

29. An automobile weighing 2,400 lb. *rolls* down a 4° grade (inclination with horizontal = 4°) at a constant speed of 30 miles/hr. What is the power output of the engine when it is *climbing* the same hill at the same speed?

30. The force required to tow a barge at constant velocity is proportional to the velocity. If it takes 10 hp. to tow a certain barge at a speed of 2 miles/hr., how many horse power would it take to tow it at a speed of 6 miles/hr.?

31. The forces acting on a body can be classified into two types: conservative and dissipative. For the case of a body moving in a straight line, prove that the power of the dissipative forces is equal to the rate of decrease of total mechanical energy of the body. (Only the conservative forces give rise to a potential energy.)

CHAPTER VII

SPECIAL DYNAMICS OF A MASS POINT

In this chapter we shall apply the principles and methods of point dynamics as we have developed them to certain problems of special interest. We shall learn how to make use of the various principles, sometimes utilizing more than one in a given problem. Many times it is possible to solve a given problem by several methods. In general, one method is simpler than the others and it is important that the student learn how to analyze a problem and to determine the method most appropriate for its solution.

40. The Ballistic Pendulum.—Consider a mass M, such as a block of wood, suspended by a string of length L to form a pendulum. If the linear dimensions of M are small compared to the length L, we have a simple pendulum (*cf.* Sec. 45). If this mass M is subjected to a horizontal blow (impulsive force), it will swing in the arc of a vertical circle, rising to a maximum height h above its equilibrium position and the string will sweep out an angle θ. Either h or θ may be used as a measure of the impulsive force. When a pendulum is employed in this manner, it is known as a *ballistic pendulum*.

The case which we shall discuss is that in which the impulsive force is caused by shooting a bullet of mass m into the block of wood, and the problem before us is to derive a relation from which we may calculate the speed of the bullet before impact. Let us call the velocity of the bullet v (Fig. 25). We shall make the following assumptions:

1. We have a simple pendulum, so that M may be treated as a mass point.

2. The bullet is brought to rest inside the block of wood.

3. The bullet is brought to rest in such a short time that the block M does not move appreciably during this time.

4. The mass of the bullet is very small compared to the mass M.

These conditions may be easily obtained in an actual experiment. By virtue of assumption 3, we may divide our problem into two parts:

a. The stopping of the bullet by the block, during which the only forces acting in a horizontal plane are the push of the bullet on the block and the push of the block on the bullet. During this process we have conservation of momentum for the system bullet and block.

b. The subsequent swinging of the block to the position *P*. This is a conservative motion, so that we may apply the principle of conservation of energy to this part of the motion.

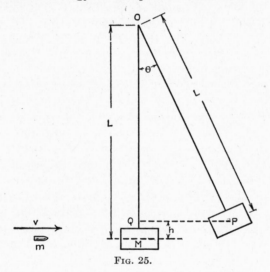

Fig. 25.

Since the block has no momentum before the impact, the total momentum of block and bullet before impact is

$$mv$$

If the block and bullet acquire a velocity V due to the impact, the total momentum after impact is

$$(M + m)V$$

and, since these are equal, we have

$$mv = (M + m)V \tag{1}$$

Now, since $m << M$, we may write instead of Eq. (1)

$$v = \frac{M}{m}V \tag{1a}$$

In the second part of the motion we have the block and bullet with an initial velocity V brought to rest at a height h above their initial position. The loss of kinetic energy must equal the gain of potential energy, so that

$$\tfrac{1}{2}(M + m)V^2 = (M + m)gh \tag{2}$$

where g is the acceleration of a freely falling body. Inserting the value of V from Eq. (2) into Eq. (1a), we find that

$$v = \frac{M}{m}\sqrt{2gh} \tag{3}$$

Since h is usually very small compared to L, it is inadvisable to try to measure it directly; much more accurate results can be obtained by measuring the angle θ. From Fig. 25 we see that

$$OM = L$$
$$OQ = L \cos \theta$$

so that

$$QM = h = L(1 - \cos \theta) = 2L \sin^2 \frac{\theta}{2}$$

Substituting this value of h into Eq. (4), there follows that

$$v = \frac{2M}{m} \sin \frac{\theta}{2}\sqrt{gL} \tag{3a}$$

as our final result. All the quantities of the right-hand side of the equation are easily measurable, so that our problem is solved. If the angle θ is small enough so that $\theta/2 << 1$, we may replace the $\sin \theta/2$ by $\theta/2$ in radians and Eq. (3a) simplifies to

$$v = \frac{M\theta}{m}\sqrt{gL} \tag{3b}$$

41. Collisions : Coefficient of Restitution.—Let us first examine the problem of a body initially moving perpendicular to a fixed surface and then colliding with it. During the collision the moving body is brought to rest relative to the surface by a force whose impulse equals the change of momentum of the body, *i.e.*, equal to the initial momentum of the body. Due to the compression of the fixed surface, it exerts this force even after the body has come to rest and thus accelerates the body in the direction opposite to its original motion. The impulse of this force, called the *impulse of restitution*, is equal to the momentum gained by the body and thus equals its momentum as it leaves the surface. The ratio of the impulse of restitution to the impulse of the stopping force depends, as is found experimentally, only on the nature of the materials of which the colliding body and surface are composed and not on the momenta before and after collision. This constant ratio is measured by the coefficient of restitution which is defined by

$$-\frac{v_n}{u_n} = e \tag{4}$$

where u_n is the velocity of the body just before collision and v_n its velocity after collision. This ratio is of course equal to the ratio of final to initial momentum and also to the ratio of the impulse of restitution to impulse of the stopping force. The negative sign is introduced since u_n and v_n are always of opposite signs and thus e is a positive number. The subscripts n are introduced to indicate that the velocities are normal to the surface. In this form the above definition of e is valid for collision at an angle with the surface, if u_n and v_n denote normal components of velocity.

The coefficient of restitution e may have any value between 0 and unity. In symbols $0 \lessgtr e \lessgtr 1$. The limiting case $e = 1$ is called an *elastic collision* and in this case the speed of the colliding body is unaffected by the collision. Hence the kinetic energy of the body is unchanged by an elastic collision. The other limiting case $e = 0$ is called a *perfectly inelastic collision* and in this case the body loses all its kinetic energy, since v_n is zero.

Let us consider the case of a body initially at rest dropped from a height h above a fixed horizontal surface. If the coefficient of restitution is e, the loss of kinetic energy upon collision is

$$\frac{m}{2}(u_n^2 - v_n^2) = \frac{mu_n^2}{2}(1 - e^2)$$

If the body rebounds to a height h', then the loss of potential energy in one bounce is $mg(h - h')$. Since this must be equal to the loss of kinetic energy during impact, we have

$$h - h' = \frac{u_n^2}{2g}(1 - e^2)$$

and, since the velocity just before collision is given by $u_n^2 = 2gh$, we have

$$h - h' = h(1 - e^2)$$

or

$$h' = e^2 h \qquad (5)$$

For a perfectly elastic impact, $h = h'$; and for a perfectly inelastic impact, $h' = 0$; *i.e.*, the body does not rebound at all.

Now let us consider the case where the impinging body strikes the surface at an angle θ with the normal to the surface and rebounds at an angle ϕ with this normal. We suppose further that the surface is perfectly smooth, *i.e.*, $\mu = 0$.

Since there is no friction, there is no component of force acting parallel to the surface, and hence the momentum parallel to the surface is unchanged by the collision. Thus,

$$mu \sin \theta = mv \sin \phi$$

The normal component of u is $u_n = u \cos \theta$ and the magnitude of the normal component of v is $v_n = v \cos \phi = eu_n = eu \cos \theta$, if the coefficient of restitution is e. Thus we have

$$u \sin \theta = v \sin \phi$$
$$eu \cos \theta = v \cos \phi$$

If we now divide one equation by the other, we find

$$\tan \theta = e \tan \phi \qquad (6)$$

In words: If $e = 1$ (elastic impact), the angle of incidence θ equals the angle of reflection ϕ, just as in the case of optics. If $e = 0$, $\tan \phi = \infty$ and $\phi = 90°$, so that upon completely inelastic impact the body just slides along the surface after collision. For other values of e, we see that $\phi > \theta$, *i.e.*, the rebound always makes a larger angle with the normal than the impact.

We shall now examine the laws of collision between two bodies initially moving with constant velocities along the same straight line, as, for example, two billiard balls moving in the same straight groove. The impact takes place normal to the surface of each ball. Let u_1 and u_2 be the velocities of the balls before impact and v_1 and v_2 their velocities after impact. Relative to ball 2, ball 1 has the (relative) velocity $u_1 - u_2$ before collision and $v_1 - v_2$ after collision, so that the coefficient of restitution is now defined by

$$e = -\frac{v_1 - v_2}{u_1 - u_2} \qquad (7)$$

If ball 2 were to be held fixed, we see that this agrees with our former definition. Since no forces act upon the bodies except during the time of collision we must have conservation of momentum, *i.e.*,

$$m_1 u_1 + m_2 u_2 = m_1 v_1 + m_2 v_2 \qquad (8)$$

As a special case, we consider the impact of two balls of equal mass. We thus have the two equations

and

$$\left. \begin{aligned} u_1 + u_2 &= v_1 + v_2 \\ eu_1 - eu_2 &= -v_1 + v_2 \end{aligned} \right\} \qquad (9)$$

If we add the two equations and then subtract one from the other, we find for v_1 and v_2:

$$\left. \begin{aligned} v_1 &= \frac{u_1}{2}(1 - e) + \frac{u_2}{2}(1 + e) = \frac{1}{2}(u_1 + u_2) - \frac{e}{2}(u_1 - u_2) \\ v_2 &= \frac{u_1}{2}(1 + e) + \frac{u_2}{2}(1 - e) = \frac{1}{2}(u_1 + u_2) + \frac{e}{2}(u_1 - u_2) \end{aligned} \right\} \qquad (10)$$

In the case of an elastic collision, $e = 1$, and Eqs. (10) become

$$v_1 = u_2; \qquad v_2 = u_1 \qquad (11)$$

so that the bodies exchange velocities.

We now proceed to calculate the change of kinetic energy during impact. Before the collision, we have

$$(K.E.)_1 = \frac{m}{2}(u_1^2 + u_2^2) = \frac{m}{2}\left[\frac{(u_1 + u_2)^2}{2} + \frac{(u_1 - u_2)^2}{2}\right]$$

and, after the collision,

$$(K.E.)_2 = \frac{m}{2}(v_1^2 + v_2^2) = \frac{m}{2}\left[\frac{(u_1 + u_2)^2}{2} + \frac{e^2}{2}(u_1 - u_2)^2\right]$$

If we now form the difference, it follows that

$$(K.E.)_1 - (K.E.)_2 = \frac{m}{4}(1 - e^2)(u_1 - u_2)^2 \qquad (12)$$

which is always positive, since $e^2 < 1$. In the limiting case of an elastic collision $(K.E.)_1 = (K.E.)_2$, so that energy is conserved in this special case. In all other cases there is a loss of kinetic energy during the collision, and this loss is greatest for perfectly inelastic collisions ($e = 0$), in which case

$$(K.E.)_1 - (K.E.)_2 = \frac{m}{4}(u_1 - u_2)^2 \tag{13}$$

42. Periodic Motion; Kinematics of Simple Harmonic Motion.

By periodic motion of a particle is meant a motion in which all aspects of the motion, *viz.*, position, velocity, and acceleration are repeated at equal intervals of time. The interval of time between successive recurrences of the same position and velocity of the body is called the *period* of the motion. Periodic motions are always confined to restricted regions of space. If the body moves back and forth on a portion of a straight line or of a curve, one calls the motion *vibratory*. As examples of vibratory motion we have the motion of tuning forks, musical instruments, or vibration of springs or of bodies in general. If the body moves in a closed curve we talk of *rotatory* motions, such as the motion of the earth about its axis, its motion around the sun, or the motion of the planets.

In this section we shall examine in detail the kinematics of a special, important type of straight-line periodic motion known as *simple harmonic motion*. If we wish to describe a straight-line periodic motion analytically, we must write an equation giving the coordinate of the particle as a function of the time. Functions which describe periodic motion are known as periodic functions. One of the simplest and by far the most important of these functions is the sine or cosine of an angle. If we imagine the angle starting with the value zero and increasing continuously, both the sine and cosine change until the angle becomes equal to 2π radians or 360°, and then they return to their initial values. Further increase in the angle repeats the values already obtained. Thus we can say that a sine or cosine function of an angle is periodic with an angular period of 2π radians.

Simple harmonic motion is defined as motion of a particle in which the position of the particle is proportional to the sine or cosine of an angle and the angle increases uniformly with the time. If we call x the coordinate of the particle, we should write an expression such as $x = A \cos \theta$ and $\theta = \omega(t - t_0)$, where A and ω are proportionality constants and t_0 is the initial value of the time t. Combining these two expressions, we have

$$x = A \cos [\omega(t - t_0)] \tag{14}$$

Equation (14) may be looked upon as the kinematical definition of simple harmonic motion. Let us examine the details of such a motion. Since the maximum value of the cosine of an angle is $+1$ and its minimum value -1, the largest and smallest values of x attained in this motion are $+A$ and $-A$, respectively. Thus the motion is confined to the portions of the x-axis which lie between these limits. A is called the *amplitude* of the motion, and the angle $\omega(t - t_0)$ is called the *phase* of the motion. This angle is, of course, to be expressed in radian measure. As t increases, the phase increases, and the cosine of the angle reaches the value $+1$, then decreases to the value -1, then again increases to the value $+1$, and repeats this behavior indefinitely. Thus the particle oscillates back and forth along the straight line, reaching a maximum displacement from the origin ($x = 0$) equal to A.

From the definition of the period of a periodic motion, it is the time required for the particle to move from $x = +A$ to $x = -A$ and then back again to $+A$, *i.e.*, the time for one complete vibration. During this time T, the phase of the motion increases by 2π radians. Expressing this as an equation, we have

$$\omega(t - t_0) + 2\pi = \omega(t + T - t_0)$$

so that

$$\omega = \frac{2\pi}{T} \tag{15}$$

The number of complete vibrations per unit time is called the *frequency* of the motion. Denoting this by n, we have from the definitions of period and frequency

$$n = \frac{1}{T} \tag{16}$$

Inserting this into Eq. (15), we find

$$\omega = 2\pi n \tag{17}$$

Thus the constant ω is 2π times the frequency and is often called the *angular frequency*.

With the help of Eqs. (15), (16), and (17) we may rewrite Eq. (14) in the equivalent forms

$$x = A \cos \left[2\pi n(t - t_0)\right] = A \cos \left[\frac{2\pi}{T}(t - t_0)\right] \tag{18}$$

Figure 26 is a graph of Eq. (14) or (18) with t_0 set equal to zero. The curve shown is typical of those obtained for any arbitrary value of t_0. Thus, for example, if we chose $t_0 = T/4 = 1/4n$, we can write Eq. (18) in the form

$$x = A \cos\left(2\pi nt - \frac{\pi}{2}\right) = A \sin 2\pi nt$$

The graph of this equation is identical with that of Fig. 26, if we place the origin of t at O' instead of at O. Similarly, different values of t_0 correspond to different origins but to identical curves. Furthermore, the example above shows the complete

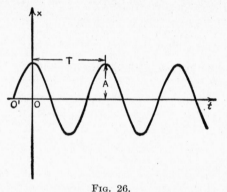

FIG. 26.

equivalence of cosine and sine functions in describing simple harmonic motion.

From Eq. (14) we obtain an equation for the velocity of the particle by differentiating with respect to the time

$$v = \frac{dx}{dt} = -\omega A \sin[\omega(t - t_0)] \tag{19}$$

and differentiating again we obtain for the acceleration

$$a = \frac{dv}{dt} = -\omega^2 A \cos[\omega(t - t_0)] = -\omega^2 x = -4\pi^2 n^2 x \tag{20}$$

Equation (19) shows that the velocity has a phase different from that of the displacement by $\pi/2$ radians or $90°$. Thus, when the particle is at the end points of its path ($x = \pm A$), the velocity is zero, and the velocity is biggest when $x = 0$. The acceleration of the particle is proportional to its displacement and opposite in direction, *i.e.*, out of phase by π radians or $180°$.

42a. Initial Conditions for Simple Harmonic Motion.—The general equation for simple harmonic motion contains two arbitrary constants, the amplitude A and the initial time t_0. According to our general theory these are to be determined from initial conditions, *i.e.*, from the values of x and v at $t = 0$. To simplify the notation, we rewrite Eq. (14) in the form

$$x = A \cos (\omega t - \delta)$$

where $\delta = 2\pi n t_0$. $-\delta$ is called the initial phase of the motion. In this notation the velocity at any time is given by [see Eq. (19)]

$$v = -\omega A \sin (\omega t - \delta)$$

In the first of these equations we place $x = x_0$ and $t = 0$, and in the second we place $v = v_0$ and $t = 0$. In this manner we obtain

$$x_0 = A \cos \delta \tag{21}$$
$$v_0 = \omega A \sin \delta \tag{22}$$

where we have made use of the fact that $\cos (-\delta) = \cos \delta$ and $\sin (-\delta) = -\sin \delta$.

Solving these equations for A and δ, we find easily

and
$$\left. \begin{aligned} A &= \sqrt{x_0^2 + \frac{v_0^2}{\omega^2}} \\ \tan \delta &= \frac{v_0}{\omega x_0} \end{aligned} \right\} \tag{23}$$

from which A and δ may be readily found if x_0 and v_0 are known.

To illustrate the use of these equations, let us suppose we have a body initially displaced a distance x_0 from the origin and at rest. We have the initial conditions $x_0 \neq 0$, $v_0 = 0$. Inserting $v_0 = 0$ into Eqs. (23), there follow:

$$A = x_0$$
$$\tan \delta = 0; \qquad \delta = 0$$

Thus the equation of motion becomes

$$x = A \cos 2\pi n t = x_0 \cos 2\pi n t$$

for these initial conditions.

If, on the other hand, we choose $t = 0$ at the instant of time when the body passes through the origin, we have at $t = 0$, $v_0 \neq 0$, $x_0 = 0$. Inserting the latter value of x_0 in Eqs. (23), we find

$$A = \frac{v_0}{\omega}$$

$$\tan \delta = \infty; \qquad \delta = \frac{\pi}{2}$$

so that for these initial conditions the equation of motion becomes

$$x = \frac{v_0}{\omega} \cos \left(\omega t - \frac{\pi}{2} \right) = \frac{v_0}{2\pi n} \sin 2\pi n t$$

43. Dynamics of Simple Harmonic Motion; Hooke's Law.—
We now turn to the question of the nature of the force which
must act on a particle to produce simple harmonic motion.   From
Eq. (20) we have seen that the acceleration of a particle moving in
simple harmonic motion is proportional to its displacement and
directed opposite to it, *i.e.*, toward the origin $x = 0$.   Thus from
Newton's second law we conclude that a particle will perform
simple harmonic motion along a straight line if acted on by a
force which pulls it toward a fixed point on the line (the origin)
and which has a magnitude proportional to the displacement of
the particle from the origin.

Analytically this force is represented by

$$F = -kx \tag{24}$$

and is called a *linear restoring force;* linear because it varies with
the first power of x and restoring because it always tends to
restore the particle to the position $x = 0$, which is an equilibrium
position.   The negative sign insures the latter behavior since,
when the particle is to the right of the origin, x is positive and the
force is negative, indicating that it acts to the left.   Similarly,
when the particle is to the left of the origin, x is negative and
the force positive, *i.e.*, acting to the right. k is a positive
constant which depends on the nature of the body exerting this
force.

If a helical spring is stretched or compressed from its normal
length, it is found experimentally that the force F' necessary
to hold a stretched or compressed spring in equilibrium is proportional to the increased or decreased length of the spring.
Thus,

$$F' = kx$$

where x is the change in length of the spring from its normal
length, and the proportionality factor k is called the *stiffness
coefficient* of the spring.   From the third law of motion it follows
that the spring exerts an equal and opposite force $-kx$ on the
agent which holds the spring in equilibrium, and this is just the
linear restoring force defined in Eq. (24).   If a body of mass m is
hung on such a spring, it will assume a certain equilibrium
position.   We shall call the length of the spring its normal length
when this equilibrium condition is maintained.   Now, if the
spring is further stretched or compressed, and suddenly released,

the mass m will be acted on by a resultant force given by Eq. (24) and will perform simple harmonic motion under the action of this force.

Equation (24) is known as *Hooke's law* for one-dimensional motion. It is true in general that if any body or system of bodies is displaced slightly from a position of stable equilibrium, the restoring force very nearly follows Hooke's law and the smaller the displacement the more nearly this law is obeyed. We shall meet this law again when we discuss the mechanics of deformable bodies.

If we write Newton's second law of motion for a body acted on by a linear restoring force $-kx$ and utilize Eq. (20) for the acceleration of the body as it performs simple harmonic motion, there follows:

$$F = -kx = ma = -m\omega^2 x$$

and hence

$$\omega = 2\pi n = \sqrt{\frac{k}{m}} \qquad (25)$$

The frequency n is given by

$$n = \frac{1}{2\pi}\sqrt{\frac{k}{m}} \qquad (25a)$$

and the period T by

$$T = 2\pi\sqrt{\frac{m}{k}} \qquad (25b)$$

so that the frequency and period of the motion depend only on the stiffness coefficient k and the mass m of the vibrating body and not on the amplitude of the motion.

Using Eq. (25) we can now rewrite the purely kinematical equations (14) and (18) in the form

$$x = A \cos\left[\sqrt{\frac{k}{m}}(t - t_0)\right] \qquad (26)$$

and thus have a complete solution of the dynamical problem. To summarize, if a particle of mass m is acted on by a linear restoring force of stiffness coefficient k, it will perform simple harmonic motion with a frequency determined by the values of k and m. The amplitude and initial phase of the motion are determined by the initial conditions (x_0 and v_0).

Let us apply the energy considerations of Chap. VI to the above motion. We have shown there that a linear restoring force is conservative, and hence we have a potential energy of the particle

$$V = -\int_0^x F_x\,dx = \int_0^x kx\,dx = \frac{kx^2}{2} \tag{27}$$

if we call the potential energy zero when $x = 0$.

The law of conservation of mechanical energy requires that the total energy be constant, *i.e.*,

$$\frac{mv^2}{2} + \frac{kx^2}{2} = E \tag{28}$$

where E is the total energy of the motion. Let us see if this checks. Using Eqs. (19) and (14) for v and x, respectively, we have

$$\frac{mv^2}{2} = \frac{m\omega^2}{2}A^2 \sin^2\left[\omega(t - t_0)\right]$$

and

$$\frac{kx^2}{2} = \frac{k}{2}A^2 \cos^2\left[\omega(t - t_0)\right]$$

From Eq. (25) we can express ω in terms of k and m and find readily that $\omega^2 = k/m$. Using this relation, the law of conservation of energy becomes

$$\frac{kA^2}{2}\left(\sin^2\left[\omega(t - t_0)\right] + \cos^2\left[\omega(t - t_0)\right]\right) = \frac{kA^2}{2} = E$$

and this is constant as predicted. The maximum value of the potential energy is $kA^2/2$, and since this occurs when the velocity and hence the kinetic energy vanish (the turning points of the motion), it equals the total energy.

Equation (28) may thus be written in the form

$$\frac{mv^2}{2} + \frac{kx^2}{2} = \frac{kA^2}{2} \tag{29}$$

or solving for v

$$v = \pm\sqrt{\frac{k}{m}} \cdot \sqrt{A^2 - x^2} \tag{29a}$$

which is a convenient form for many applications.

44. Forced Harmonic Motion; Resonance.—The simple harmonic motion discussed in the preceding sections constitutes a motion with constant total energy which would continue indefinitely in the absence of forces other than the linear restoring force acting on the body. Thus, if a mass hanging in equilibrium on a coiled spring is displaced from its equilibrium position and suddenly released, it will oscillate forever with an energy just equal to the work done on it in displacing it from equilibrium.   In all practical cases, however, there will be friction forces acting (they may be made exceedingly small), so that the motion will gradually become of smaller and smaller amplitude and eventually the body will come to rest.   The initial energy of the vibrating body will disappear from the system and reappear as heat. The vibrations of a body when acted on *only* by restoring forces (and friction) are called the *free vibrations* of the body.

It is possible to produce and maintain simple harmonic motion by applying an additional external force to the particle, provided this force varies sinusoidally with the time.   Such a motion is called a *forced* vibration.   The actual motion of the body will consist of a superposition of two motions: (1) a free vibration entirely similar to the motion performed in the absence of an external force.   If even a small amount of friction is present, this motion will eventually die out and hence is called a *transient* motion.   (2) There will be a motion of the body with a frequency equal to that of the external force, and this motion will persist as long as the external force acts.   This second type of motion is called the *steady-state* motion of the particle.

Let us investigate this second type of motion in more detail, and for simplicity we shall neglect the effects of friction.   We then have a particle acted on by two forces, a linear restoring force $-kx$ and an external force $F_0 \cos \omega t$ where ω is the angular frequency of this force.   Newton's second law applied to this problem yields

$$F = -kx + F_0 \cos \omega t = m\frac{dv}{dt}$$

This can be rewritten in the more convenient form (using $v = dx/dt$)

$$m\frac{d^2x}{dt^2} + kx = F_0 \cos \omega t \tag{30}$$

Since we are interested only in the steady-state forced motion which occurs with the same frequency as that of the external force, let us try to find a solution of this equation of the form

$$x = C \cos \omega t \tag{31}$$

and to determine C from Eq. (30).   This is to be looked upon as a trial, and we must be prepared to reject it if it does not work, *i.e.*, if C does not turn out to be a constant, independent of t. Differentiating Eq. (31), we find $dx/dt = -\omega C \sin \omega t$, and, differentiating again, we have

$$\frac{d^2x}{dt^2} = -\omega^2 C \cos \omega t$$

Now substituting back in Eq. (30), there follows

$$-m\omega^2 C \cos \omega t + kC \cos \omega t = F_0 \cos \omega t$$

and since the factor $\cos \omega t$ cancels out of the equation, our scheme works.   Solving for C, we have

$$C = \frac{F_0/m}{\dfrac{k}{m} - \omega^2} = \frac{F_0/m}{\omega_0^2 - \omega^2}$$

if we set $k/m = \omega_0^2$, ω_0 being 2π times the natural frequency of the body in the absence of an external force.   We now obtain the final result by substituting this value of C in Eq. (31) and have

$$x = \frac{F_0}{m(\omega_0^2 - \omega^2)} \cos \omega t \tag{32}$$

This is the equation of forced simple harmonic motion in the absence of friction.   The amplitude of the motion is proportional to the amplitude of the driving force and depends in a remarkable way on the frequency of the driving force.   We note that if the frequency ω of the driving force becomes nearly equal to the natural frequency ω_0, the amplitude becomes very large since the denominator becomes very small.   Indeed if $\omega = \omega_0$, our equation predicts an infinite amplitude.   This cannot occur in practice, and, just for this case, friction (which we have entirely neglected) becomes important no matter how small the friction forces are.   At any rate, the amplitude becomes very large when ω is almost equal to ω_0, and the abnormally large motion which occurs under these conditions is known as the phenomenon of *resonance*.

There are many familiar examples of resonance.   When driving an automobile one often notices that at a certain speed parts of the body may be set into vibration but that this does not occur appreciably at other speeds.   In this case the motor supplies the driving force which has a frequency proportional to its speed.   In acoustics, one tuning fork will set another into so-called "sympathetic" vibration if the latter has the same frequency (pitch) as the first but not otherwise. In electrical circuits one has a common example of resonance in the fact that the circuits can be tuned to a definite frequency and respond appreciably only to waves of this frequency.

To get a better picture of resonance, Fig. 27 shows a plot of the magnitude of the amplitude $F_0/[m(\omega_0^2 - \omega^2)]$ against the

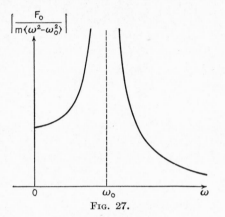

FIG. 27.

angular frequency ω of the applied force. This shows how the amplitude of the motion changes as ω changes and that in the neighborhood of ω_0 it becomes so large that we can say that the body responds appreciably to an external force only if the frequency of the external force is equal to the natural frequency of the body.

Equation (32) shows us that, if $\omega < \omega_0$, the motion is in phase with the exciting force and that, if $\omega > \omega_0$, it is 180° out of phase. In both cases the power delivered to the vibrating body is zero *on the average* and one can readily show that for half a period the external force does work on the body and that for the other half the body does an equal amount of work on the source of the force. This is no longer true when friction is present, as the external force must *on the average* do an amount of work per unit time just equal to the rate of dissipation of mechanical energy by friction.

45. The Simple Pendulum.—A simple pendulum is a mass point suspended by a string (or by any body whose mass can be neglected compared to the mass of the mass point) from a fixed point and free to swing in a vertical plane. If the pendulum swings through an angle so small that the motion of the mass point takes place almost in a straight line, it performs simple harmonic motion.   Even if the angle is large, we have periodic

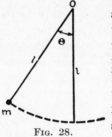

FIG. 28.

(not simple harmonic) motion and can obtain an insight into the question of the value of the period by considering the various quantities on which the period can depend.   The period T may depend on the mass m of the body, on the pull of the earth, *i.e.*, on g, on the length of the string l, and on the maximum angle Θ through which the pendulum swings (Fig. 28).

The equation expressing T as a function of these quantities must, like every physical equation, have the same dimensions on each side of the equation.

The dimensions of T are those of time.   Thus

$$[T] = t$$
$$[l] = l$$
$$[g] = lt^{-2}$$
$$[m] = m$$

and the angle Θ is dimensionless as it is measured by the ratio of two lengths.

We immediately see that the period cannot depend on the mass of the body and must depend on the other quantities in the form

$$\left[\frac{l}{lt^{-2}}\right]^{\frac{1}{2}} = [t]$$

Therefore we can write

$$T = f(\Theta)\sqrt{\frac{l}{g}} \tag{33}$$

and thus the only question remaining is to find $f(\Theta)$ which may or may not depend on Θ.

For the case of small angles θ we proceed as follows: The forces acting on the mass are the pull of

FIG. 29.

the earth mg and the tension in the rope T (Fig. 29).   Since there is no motion in the direction of the string, we need only consider the components of the forces perpendicular to it.   Perpendicular to the string, the force is

$$F = -mg \sin \theta = ma$$

so that

$$a = -g \sin \theta$$

Now, for small angles θ, we can take the direction perpendicular to the string as horizontal and write *approximately*

$$a = a_x = -g \sin \theta$$

but

$$\sin \theta = \frac{x}{l}$$

so that

$$a_x = -\frac{g}{l}x$$

If we replace g/l in this equation by k/m it becomes the equation for simple harmonic motion. Thus it follows from Eq. (25) that

$$n = \frac{1}{2\pi}\sqrt{\frac{g}{l}}$$

whence

$$T = \frac{1}{n} = 2\pi\sqrt{\frac{l}{g}} \tag{34}$$

which is the same as Eq. (33), with $f(\Theta) = 2\pi$ and hence independent of Θ. For larger amplitudes, $f(\Theta)$ does depend on Θ.

46. Lissajous Figures.—When a particle moves in a plane under the action of two mutually perpendicular linear restoring forces, the paths described are known as *Lissajous figures*. Both the x- and y-coordinates of the particle perform simple harmonic motion. Without loss of generality we may take $\delta = 0$ for the x-component of the motion. This choice merely fixes the instant of time which we call $t = 0$. For the y-component of the motion, however, we must retain the term δ, since the y-component of the displacement of the particle is arbitrary at the time which we have chosen as $t = 0$. We thus write as the equations of motion

$$\left. \begin{array}{l} x = A \cos 2\pi n_1 t \\ y = B \cos (2\pi n_2 t - \delta) \end{array} \right\} \tag{35}$$

We shall restrict ourselves to an analysis of several special cases of these equations.

Example 1.—Let us consider more closely the case of equal frequencies $n_1 = n_2 = n$. The simplest case occurs when $\delta = 0$.

(a) $\delta = 0$:

$$x = A \cos 2\pi nt \Big\}$$
$$y = B \cos 2\pi nt \Big\} \qquad (35a)$$

so that the orbit is obtained by simply dividing the second equation by the first. This yields

$$y = \frac{B}{A}x$$

which is the equation of a straight line making an angle $\tan^{-1} B/A$ with the positive x-axis and passing through the origin.

(b) $\delta = \pm\frac{\pi}{2}$:

$$x = A \cos 2\pi nt$$
$$y = B \cos \left(2\pi nt \mp \frac{\pi}{2}\right) = \mp B \sin 2\pi nt$$

We can rewrite these equations as

$$\frac{x}{A} = \cos 2\pi nt$$

$$\mp \frac{y}{B} = \sin 2\pi nt$$

Squaring and adding, we obtain the equation

$$\frac{x^2}{A^2} + \frac{y^2}{B^2} = 1$$

which represents an *ellipse* with semimajor and semiminor axes A and B directed along the x- and y-axes. In the particular case of equal amplitudes $A = B$, we get

$$x^2 + y^2 = A^2$$

which represents a circle of radius A.

In general for $n_1 = n_2$, the path is an ellipse but the major axis does not coincide with the x- or y-axes except for $\delta = \pm\pi/2$. This ellipse is always contained within a rectangle of width $2A$ and height $2B$ as we see easily from Eq. (35). The limits $\pm A$ and $\pm B$ are known as the *libration* limits of the motion.

Example 2.—Here we consider $n_2 = 2n_1$; $\delta = \mp\pi/2$; $A = B$. The equations of motion are

$$x = A \cos 2\pi n_1 t$$
$$y = \pm A \sin 4\pi n_1 t = \pm 2A \cos 2\pi n_1 t \sin 2\pi n_1 t$$

whence

$$y = \pm 2x \sin 2\pi n_1 t$$

but

$$\sin 2\pi n_1 t = \frac{\sqrt{A^2 - x^2}}{A} \text{ (see Fig. 30)}$$

so that

$$y^2 = \frac{4x^2}{A^2}(A^2 - x^2)$$

For $y = 0$, x has the values

$$x = 0, \qquad x = \pm A$$

For $y = \pm A$, x has the values

$$x = \pm \frac{A}{\sqrt{2}} = \pm 0.707A$$

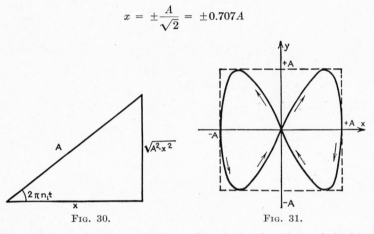

FIG. 30.   FIG. 31.

Other points on the curve may be easily calculated. The path is shown in Fig. 31.

Thus we see that the path is split into two parts but closes on itself. In general, if the ratio of n_2 to n_1 can be expressed as the ratio of two whole numbers, the path is closed. If not, it never closes on itself. The larger the two numbers whose ratio represents n_2/n_1, the larger the number of points where the path crosses itself.

47. Effect of the Earth's Rotation on the Value of g.—We have tacitly assumed that we have referred all motions to a system of reference which is at rest, an *absolute* system of coordinates. In practice, we refer our motions in most cases to a system of reference attached to the earth. The earth possesses a rotation about its axis, and hence a system of coordinates attached to the earth is an accelerated system of coordinates. We must inquire how Newton's laws (which refer to an absolute system fixed in space) are modified when one refers motions to accelerated systems. First let us consider a frame of reference moving with a constant velocity v_0 in the x-direction with respect to the absolute fixed system. If v represents the velocity of a particle with respect to the absolute system and v' the velocity of the particle with respect to the moving reference system, we then have

$$v = v' + v_0$$

and for the accelerations ($v_0 = $ constant),

$$\frac{dv}{dt} = \frac{dv'}{dt}$$

so that the acceleration has the same value in both systems and *the systems are dynamically equivalent.*

Suppose the second system has an acceleration a_0 in the direction of the x-axis with respect to the fixed system. Let a_x be the acceleration of a body with respect to the fixed system and a'_x that referred to the accelerated system. By the second law

$$F_x = ma_x$$

where F_x is the component of force acting in the x-direction on m. The acceleration a_x may be thought of as compounded of the acceleration of the system a_0 and the acceleration of the particle referred to the moving system, a'_x. Since these accelerations are all in the same direction,

$$a_x = a'_x + a_0$$

so that

$$F_x = ma'_x + ma_0$$

which may be written

$$F_x - ma_0 = ma'_x \tag{36}$$

which shows that *the motion is the same as if the system of reference were at rest, providing we imagine the force F_x diminished by an amount ma_0.*

We now apply this result to motions referred to axes fixed to the earth's surface and which consequently partake of the earth's rotation and conse-

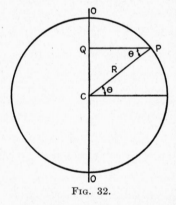

Fig. 32.

quent acceleration. In Fig. 32, let OO be the earth's axis, C the center, and P any point on the earth's surface at a latitude θ. The point P describes a circle of radius $PQ = R \cos \theta$ and has an acceleration towards Q equal to

$$\frac{v^2}{R \cos \theta} = \omega^2 R \cos \theta$$

if ω is the constant angular velocity of the earth on its axis. *The motion of a point referred to P may be now calculated if in applying Newton's second law we subtract from the component of force along PQ an amount $m\omega^2 R \cos \theta$.*

Combining this last force with the actual earth pull at P, we get the *apparent* (to us) pull of gravity, which we mean when we speak of the weight of a body. To find the apparent weight of a body at P, we must add the pull of the earth mg_0 to the force $-m\omega^2 R \cos \theta$ vectorially. mg_0 acts along PC, which we call the x-axis, the y-axis being perpendicular thereto.

$$x\text{-component of } -m\omega^2 R \cos \theta = -m\omega^2 R \cos^2 \theta$$
$$y\text{-component of } -m\omega^2 R \cos \theta = -m\omega^2 R \cos \theta \sin \theta$$
$$x\text{-component of } mg_0 = +mg_0$$

Thus the components of the resultant are

$$F_x = m(g_0 - \omega^2 R \cos^2 \theta)$$
$$F_y = -m\omega^2 R \sin \theta \cos \theta$$

Squaring and adding, and denoting the resultant by mg as always,

$$m^2g^2 = m^2(g_0^2 - 2\omega^2 Rg_0 \cos^2\theta + \omega^4 R^2 \cos^2\theta)$$

or

$$g^2 = g_0^2\left(1 - \frac{2\omega^2 R}{g_0}\cos^2\theta + \frac{\omega^4 R^2}{g_0^2}\cos^2\theta\right)$$

so that

$$g = g_0\left(1 - \frac{2\omega^2 R}{g_0}\cos^2\theta + \frac{\omega^4 R^2}{g_0^2}\cos^2\theta\right)^{\frac{1}{2}}$$

Taking the diameter of the earth as $D = 7{,}930$ miles, and g_0 as 32.3 ft./sec.^{2} (the acceleration at the north pole), we find that

$$\frac{\omega^2 R}{g_0} = \frac{1}{290}, \text{ very nearly}$$

so that the last term in the parentheses may be neglected, and we have finally

$$g = g_0\left(1 - \frac{\omega^2 R}{g_0}\cos^2\theta\right)$$

Thus the apparent weight of a body at a latitude of $45°$ is less than the true weight by $\frac{1}{290}(\frac{1}{2}\sqrt{2})^2 = \frac{1}{580}$ of the weight.

The resultant force does *not* act along the line PC. It acts at angle Ψ with this line given by

$$\tan\Psi = \frac{\omega^2 R \cos\theta \sin\theta}{g_0 - \omega^2 R \cos^2\theta} \cong \frac{\omega^2 R \cos\theta \sin\theta}{g_0} = \frac{1}{290}\sin\theta\cos\theta$$

giving the deviation of the plumb line from the earth's radius at the point P. The foregoing calculations are based on the assumption of a perfectly spherical earth. The actual shape of the earth is not a true sphere so that our formulas must be modified. Actually the dependence on θ (latitude) is correct. The factor $\frac{1}{290}$ must be replaced by $\frac{1}{190}$.

In the future we shall, as before, neglect the effects due to the rotation of the earth, since the error is small and we can now correct for it if necessary.

Problems

1. A 4-kg. block hangs from a string 2 meters long. If a bullet of mass 2.0 grams moving horizontally with a velocity of 400 meters/sec. strikes and remains imbedded in this block, find:

a. The velocity of the block after collision.

b. The kinetic energy gained by the block during the collision.

c. The loss of kinetic energy during collision.

d. The height the block rises above its initial position.

e. The angle through which the string swings.

2. Prove that, if a ballistic pendulum struck by a bullet moves through a horizontal distance d (the angle $\theta < <1$), the velocity of the bullet is given very nearly by

$$v = \frac{M}{m}d\sqrt{\frac{g}{L}}$$

where the symbols have the same meaning as in the text.

3. A bullet weighing 0.01 lb. is shot through a 2-lb. wooden block suspended on a string 5 ft. long. The pendulum is observed to swing through an angle of 5°. Find the speed of the bullet as it emerges from the block, if its initial speed is 1,000 ft./sec.

4. A bullet weighing $\frac{1}{2}$ oz. and moving at a speed of 800 ft./sec. strikes and remains imbedded in a block weighing 50 lb. which was initially at rest. What is the velocity of the block directly after the impact?

5. A bullet weighing 0.1 lb. and moving with a speed of 840 ft./sec. strikes and remains imbedded in a block weighing 2 lb. which was initially at rest on a plane inclined at an angle of 6° with the horizontal. If the coefficient of friction between block and plane is 0.4 how far up the plane will the block slide before coming to rest?

6. A 10-gram bullet moving with a velocity of 100 meters/sec. strikes a block of wood resting on a horizontal surface and penetrates 10 cm. (Assume the force acting on the bullet while it is being brought to rest is constant.) The block of wood weighs 10 kg. and the coefficient of sliding friction between the block and the horizontal surface on which it rests is 0.80. What is the maximum velocity of the wooden block?

7. A ball weighing W lb. is hung at the end of a rope and pulled aside until the rope makes an angle ϕ with the vertical and then released. Find an expression for the tension in the rope when it makes an angle θ with the vertical. For what value of θ will T be a maximum? for what value a minimum?

8. A 500-gram block rests on a horizontal table, the coefficient of friction between block and table being $\frac{1}{4}$. A 2-gram bullet traveling horizontally with a velocity of 300 meters/sec. hits the block and goes through it. The block is observed to move 10 cm. before coming to rest. Calculate the velocity of the bullet as it emerges from the block.

9. A 4-lb. block hangs on the end of a string 4 ft. long. It is hit a horizontal blow which imparts a velocity of 14 ft./sec. to the block.

a. What is the impulse of the blow?

b. What is the maximum height to which the block rises?

c. What is the tension in the string when it makes an angle of 60° with the vertical?

10. A 600-gram block of wood rests on a smooth horizontal table. A bullet of mass 2 grams moving horizontally with a speed of 300 meters/sec. strikes and remains embedded in the block. After moving a distance of 1 meter, the block is brought to rest by a horizontal spring bumper of stiffness coefficient 10^6 dynes/cm.

a. Calculate the maximum velocity attained by the block.

b. What fraction of the original kinetic energy of the bullet remains as kinetic energy after the bullet comes to rest in the block?

c. How far is the spring compressed in bringing the block to rest?

11. A 10-gram ball is dropped from a height of 25 cm. on a fixed horizontal surface and rebounds to a height of 9 cm.

a. What is the coefficient of restitution?

b. What is the change of momentum of the ball during the collision?

c. What is the change of kinetic energy upon collision?

12. A body impinges with a velocity u at an angle θ on a perfectly smooth surface. Prove that it loses an amount of kinetic energy equal to

$$\tfrac{1}{2}mu^2(1 - e^2) \cos^2 \theta$$

where e is the coefficient of restitution.

13. A body strikes a smooth horizontal surface at an angle of 30° with the normal and rebounds at an angle of 60° with the normal. On the rebound it rises to a maximum height of 1 ft.

a. Find the coefficient of restitution.

b. Find the velocity with which the body hit.

c. How far from the original point of contact does the body hit the second time?

14. In Prob. 13 find how high the body rises on its second rebound.

15. A body impinges with a velocity u on a surface of coefficient of friction μ at an angle θ and rebounds with a velocity v at an angle ϕ. (Both angles measured with respect to the normal.) Prove that

$$e \tan \phi = \tan \theta - (1 + e)\mu$$

where e is the coefficient of restitution.

16. A ball weighing 100 grams and moving with a speed of 40 cm./sec. impinges directly on another weighing 50 grams and moving in the opposite direction with a speed of 20 cm./sec. If the coefficient of restitution is 0.5, what are the velocities after impact?

17. A 3-lb. block rests at the foot of an inclined plane 30 ft. long and 18 ft. high. The coefficient of sliding friction between block and plane is 0.50 and the coefficient of static friction is 0.80. A rope 32 ft. long passes from the 3-lb. weight up the plane and over a small pulley and a 5-lb. weight hangs freely at the end of the rope. The system starts from rest. When the 5-lb. weight reaches the horizontal, it is suddenly brought to rest. Where does the 3-lb. weight come to rest? Will it remain there?

18. A particle moves in simple harmonic motion with an amplitude of 10 cm. and a frequency of 4 per second.

a. Make plots of displacement, velocity, and acceleration vs. time. Plot these one over the other.

b. What is the maximum velocity of the particle? Where does it occur?

c. Where is the force pulling the particle greatest? What is the acceleration at this point?

d. What are the velocity and acceleration when the displacement is +5 cm.?

19. A 5-kg. body hung on a spring displaces it 20 cm. It is removed and then 100 grams is hung on the same spring; the spring stretched and released.

a. Find the stiffness coefficient of the spring.

b. Find the period of the motion.

20. A mass of 2 kg. hangs from a spiral spring. A 200-gram body hung below the mass stretches the spring 2 cm. farther. The 200-gram body is then removed and the mass set into oscillation. Find the period.

21. A block rests on a horizontal surface which is executing simple harmonic motion in a horizontal plane at a rate of two oscillations per second. If the coefficient of static friction between the block and the plane is 0.50, how large can the amplitude be without the block slipping with respect to the surface?

22. The tip of one of the prongs of a tuning fork performs simple harmonic motion with a frequency of 256 vibrations per second and an amplitude of 0.1 cm.

a. What is the maximum speed attained by the tip of the prong?

b. What is the maximum acceleration attained by the tip of the prong?

c. What is the acceleration when the displacement is 0.05 cm.?

23. A particle of mass 1 gram oscillates in simple harmonic motion with a frequency of 10 vibrations per second and an amplitude of 10 cm.

a. Calculate its speed when it is 6 cm. from its equilibrium position.

b. What is the force in dynes acting on it at this point?

24. The piston of an automobile moves with simple harmonic motion of amplitude 2 in. and makes 3,600 complete vibrations in 1 min. At what part of the stroke is the acceleration a maximum? How great is the acceleration at this point? If the piston weighs 1 lb., what is the force acting on it at the same point?

25. A spiral spring hangs from a hook. If a mass of 500 grams is hung upon it, it stretches 20 cm. If the 500-gram mass is pulled 10 cm. farther down and released, find:

a. The period.

b. The force which the spring exerts on the mass when it is at the lowest and highest points of its motion.

c. The maximum velocity the mass has in its motion.

26. The length of a certain spring from which a mass of 1 kg. is suspended is found to be 20.02 cm. The addition of 800 grams increases the length to 21.00 cm. A total mass of 5 kg. is now hung on the spring and the whole set into oscillation. What will the frequency be? If the amplitude of the oscillation is 2 cm. what is the maximum kinetic energy of the body?

27. A body of mass 100 grams hangs from a long spiral spring. When pulled down 10 cm. below its equilibrium position and released, it vibrates with a period of 2 sec.

a. What is its velocity as it passes through the equilibrium position?

b. What is its acceleration when it is 5 cm. above the equilibrium position?

c. When it is moving upward, how long a time is required for it to move from a point 5 cm. below its equilibrium position to a point 5 cm. above it?

d. How much will the spring shorten if the body is removed?

28. *a.* A vertically arranged helical spring is compressed 5 cm. by a force of 30,000 dynes. A 1.0-gram body is placed on the spring; the spring is compressed 25 cm. and suddenly released. How high will the 1.0-gram body rise? How long will it be in the air?

b. If a 10-gram body is hung from the same spring and allowed to oscillate, what would be the period?

29. A helical spring of stiffness coefficient 19,600 dynes/cm. hangs vertically with a hook on its free end. A 100-gram body is placed on the hook and suddenly released. How far below this initial position does the body descend? What are the amplitude and period of the resulting simple harmonic motion? (Assume that the spring exerts no force on the 100-gram body before it is released.)

30. A body is hung on a spring and performs simple harmonic motion with a frequency of 4 vibrations per second. The same spring is then set up as a horizontal spring bumper, and the same body, resting on a horizontal table, is pressed against the spring, compressing it 4 in. The body is suddenly released. How far along the table top does the body move if the coefficient of friction between the body and the table is $\frac{1}{3}$?

31. A platform moves up and down with simple harmonic motion having an amplitude of 0.096 in. What is the maximum frequency which the motion can have so that a block on the top of the platform will remain in contact with it continuously?

32. A 4-lb. body, hung on a spring, is observed to make 40 vibrations in 31.4 sec. The system is now brought to rest, and an additional 2-lb. body is hung on the spring. Find the amount by which the spring is stretched. How long would a simple pendulum have to be to oscillate with the above frequency?

33. A simple pendulum 8 ft. long swings with an amplitude of 1 ft.

a. What is the period of the pendulum?

b. What is the velocity of the bob at its lowest point?

34. A simple pendulum consists of a small 10-gram mass at the end of a cord 1 meter long. It is pulled aside 10 cm. from its equilibrium position and released. Find its position and velocity after one-eighth of a period.

35. A particle of mass 1 gram has a natural frequency of 47.8 vibrations per second. It is subjected to the action of an external sinusoidal force

$$F = 25 \times 10^4 \cos (400t) \text{ dynes}$$

where t is in seconds.

a. Calculate the amplitude of the forced steady-state motion of the particle.

b. What other frequency might the external force have and still produce the same amplitude? What difference, if any, would there be in the motion of the particle?

36. A body is pulled toward a point O by a force proportional to its distance from O and hence performs simple harmonic motion. Prove that the average kinetic energy of the body equals its average potential energy. (Average over the time of one vibration.)

37. Assuming that the pull of the earth on a body below its surface varies proportionally to the distance from the earth's center, find by how many per cent the period of a simple pendulum changes if it is taken down a mine shaft 5 miles deep. Radius of the earth = 4,000 miles.

38. A particle is acted on by two linear restoring forces at right angles and performs motion according to the equations

$$x = A \cos 2\pi n_1 t$$
$$y = B \sin 6\pi n_1 t$$

Make a plot of the path of the particle. Make this plot for the case where $y = B \cos 6\pi n_1 t$.

39. A body is suspended on a spring balance when in a ship at the equator. If the ship sails along the equator with a velocity v, show that the scale will read very nearly

$$W_0\left(1 \pm \frac{2v\omega}{g}\right)$$

where W_0 is the reading when the ship is at rest, ω the angular velocity of the earth, and g the acceleration of gravity.

40. A body is hung on a spring balance at the north pole of the earth and the reading of the balance is 64.0 lb. If the same body is hung on the same balance at the equator, what will the reading of the balance be?

CHAPTER VIII

DYNAMICS OF A SYSTEM OF PARTICLES

Except for the principle of conservation of momentum, we have confined ourselves exclusively to the dynamics of a single particle. In problems involving two or more particles we have dealt with each particle separately, applying Newton's laws to it and solving for its motion. The knowledge of the individual motion of each particle in a system of particles is of course sufficient to specify completely the motion of the system. On the other hand, there are certain general laws which give some information as to the motion of a system of particles (such as the conservation of momentum for an isolated system) and it is worth while to investigate some of them. Apart from their own intrinsic value, these laws provide a valuable background for the study of rigid-body motion which we shall start in the next chapter. Our treatment in this chapter will not be exhaustive, and we shall delay the presentation of part of the subject until after our treatment of rigid bodies.

48. Motion of Two Particles; Center of Mass.—We shall first discuss the motion of two particles in a plane, since it is easier to understand the important points involved and our derivation may then be extended immediately to any number of mass points. Consider two mass points m_1 and m_2, free to move in a plane. Suppose external forces F_1 and F_2 act on these particles respectively and let us denote the x- and y-components of these forces by X_1, X_2, and Y_1, Y_2. In addition to these external forces there may be interaction forces between the two particles which we denote by Q_1 and Q_2, the interaction forces acting on particles m_1 and m_2, respectively. For these interaction forces we have the relation, supplied by the third law of motion,

$$Q_1 = -Q_2 \tag{1}$$

or, in component form,

$$Q_{1x} = -Q_{2x}$$
$$Q_{1y} = -Q_{2y} \tag{2}$$

We now apply the second law of motion to each of these particles, writing it in component form. Thus, for the x-component of motion of the first particle we have

$$X_1 + Q_{1x} = \frac{d}{dt}\left(m_1\frac{dx_1}{dt}\right)$$

and similarly, for the second particle,

$$X_2 + Q_{2x} = \frac{d}{dt}\left(m_2\frac{dx_2}{dt}\right)$$

In these equations we have written the x-components of the velocities of the particles as dx_1/dt and dx_2/dt. If we now add these two equations and remember that according to Eq. (2) $Q_{1x} + Q_{2x} = 0$, it follows that

$$X_1 + X_2 = \frac{d}{dt}\left(m_1\frac{dx_1}{dt}\right) + \frac{d}{dt}\left(m_2\frac{dx_2}{dt}\right)$$

$$X_1 + X_2 = \frac{d}{dt}\left(m_1\frac{dx_1}{dt} + m_2\frac{dx_2}{dt}\right) \tag{3}$$

An exactly similar set of equations holds for the y-component of motion of the two particles, so that we obtain

$$Y_1 + Y_2 = \frac{d}{dt}\left(m_1\frac{dy_1}{dt} + m_2\frac{dy_2}{dt}\right) \tag{4}$$

Equations (3) and (4) state that the vector sum of the external forces is equal to the rate of change of the total momentum of the system. This law is true, independent of the nature of the internal forces in the system. Furthermore, these equations contain the principle of conservation of momentum. For, if there are no external forces acting on the particles,

$$X_1 = X_2 = Y_1 = Y_2 = 0$$

and we have

$$m_1\frac{dx_1}{dt} + m_2\frac{dx_2}{dt} = \text{constant}$$

and

$$m_1\frac{dy_1}{dt} + m_2\frac{dy_2}{dt} = \text{constant}$$

so that the vector sum of the momenta of the two particles is constant in the absence of external forces (the case of an isolated system).

The fundamental Eqs. (3) and (4) may be written in a more convenient fashion. Consider the right-hand side of Eq. (3); in it the expression $m_1\dfrac{dx_1}{dt} + m_2\dfrac{dx_2}{dt}$ may be written $\dfrac{d}{dt}(m_1x_1 + m_2x_2)$, so that Eq. (3) may be written

$$X_1 + X_2 = \frac{d^2}{dt^2}(m_1x_1 + m_2x_2) \tag{3a}$$

and similarly for Eq. (4),

$$Y_1 + Y_2 = \frac{d^2}{dt^2}(m_1y_1 + m_2y_2) \tag{4a}$$

If we now denote the total mass of the system by $M = m_1 + m_2$ and define a point in the plane whose x- and y-coordinates are given by the relations

$$\bar{x} = \frac{m_1x_1 + m_2x_2}{M} = \frac{m_1x_1 + m_2x_2}{m_1 + m_2} \tag{5}$$

and

$$\bar{y} = \frac{m_1y_1 + m_2y_2}{M} = \frac{m_1y_1 + m_2y_2}{m_1 + m_2} \tag{6}$$

Equations (3a) and (4a) take the simple form

$$X_1 + X_2 = M\frac{d^2\bar{x}}{dt^2} \tag{3b}$$

$$Y_1 + Y_2 = M\frac{d^2\bar{y}}{dt^2} \tag{4b}$$

We call the point whose coordinates are $\bar{x}$ and $\bar{y}$ the *center of mass* of the system, and we can state Eqs. (3b) and (4b) in words:

The motion of the center of mass of a system of particles is the same as the motion of a single particle of mass equal to the total mass of the system acted on by all the external forces which act on the system of particles.

This is an important law and we shall make much use of it in our study of rigid bodies. In this case we have the simple situation that the position of the center of mass of the rigid body is always fixed with respect to the body. Our equations of motion of the center of mass suggest the following method of considering the motion of any system of mass points; (1) the motion of the center of mass of the system and (2) the motion of the particles with respect to the center of mass of the system.

This particular mode of analysis of the motion turns out to be fundamental. We have already solved part 1 of the motion, and, since this is a problem in the motion of a single mass point, we need not discuss it further.

49. Center of Mass (*Continued*).—We now may generalize the results of the last section for a system of n particles. We proceed as before, writing the equations of motion for each particle. When we add the equations, we find as before that the interaction forces (internal forces) cancel out in pairs, so that we are left with the sum of the external forces only. Thus, for plane motion, the equations of motion are

$$X_1 + X_2 + X_3 + \cdots + X_n =$$
$$\frac{d^2}{dt^2}(m_1 x_1 + m_2 x_2 + m_3 x_3 + \cdots + m_n x_n) \quad (7)$$

and

$$Y_1 + Y_2 + Y_3 + \cdots + Y_n =$$
$$\frac{d^2}{dt^2}(m_1 y_1 + m_2 y_2 + m_3 y_3 + \cdots + m_n y_n) \quad (8)$$

Rather than writing these sums explicitly each time they occur, we shall adopt a shorthand notation which is universally used. For example, we write as the sum of the x-components of the external forces,

$$X_1 + X_2 + X_3 + \cdots + X_n = \sum_{k=1}^{n} X_k$$

The Greek sigma indicates that we are to form a sum, and the subscript k is to have all values starting with $k = 1$ (indicated below the Σ) and ending with $k = n$ (indicated above the Σ). We then rewrite Eqs. (7) and (8) as

$$\sum_{k=1}^{n} X_k = \frac{d^2}{dt^2}\left(\sum_{k=1}^{n} m_k x_k\right) \quad (7a)$$

$$\sum_{k=1}^{n} Y_k = \frac{d^2}{dt^2}\left(\sum_{k=1}^{n} m_k y_k\right) \quad (8a)$$

The definition of the coordinates of the center of mass may now be written

$$\bar{x} = \frac{\sum\limits_{1}^{n} m_k x_k}{\sum\limits_{1}^{n} m_k} = \frac{1}{M} \sum\limits_{k=1}^{n} m_k x_k \tag{9}$$

$$\bar{y} = \frac{\sum\limits_{1}^{n} m_k y_k}{\sum\limits_{1}^{n} m_k} = \frac{1}{M} \sum\limits_{k=1}^{n} m_k y_k \tag{10}$$

where M is again the total mass of the body. The general equations corresponding to Eqs. (3b) and (4b) of the last section now are

$$\sum_{k=1}^{n} X_k = M \frac{d^2\bar{x}}{dt^2} \tag{7b}$$

$$\sum_{k=1}^{n} Y_k = M \frac{d^2\bar{y}}{dt^2} \tag{8b}$$

Now in the case of most bodies, such as a piece of metal or wood, the particles of which it is composed are so numerous and they are so close together that we are justified in considering the body as a continuous distribution of matter. All the theorems which we have developed hold, and we must only rewrite the definition of the position of the center of mass in an appropriate form. If we consider a small volume ΔV of our body containing a mass ΔM, then we define the density ρ of the body at the point where ΔV is situated as

$$\rho = \lim_{\Delta V \to 0} \frac{\Delta M}{\Delta V} = \frac{dM}{dV} \tag{11}$$

and hence the total mass M is given by

$$M = \int \rho \, dV \tag{12}$$

In the important special case of a homogeneous body in which ρ is constant, we have

$$M = \rho \cdot \int dV = \rho V \tag{12a}$$

To define the x- and y-coordinates of the center of mass of such a body, we consider the body as composed of a huge number of small masses each of mass ΔM. Each ΔM has its own x- and y-coordinates, and the coordinates of the center of mass become

$$\bar{x} = \frac{1}{M} \lim_{\Delta M \to 0} \sum x \Delta M = \frac{1}{M} \int x \, dM \qquad (13)$$

$$\bar{y} = \frac{1}{M} \lim_{\Delta M \to 0} \sum y \Delta M = \frac{1}{M} \int y \, dM \qquad (13a)$$

In the case of a homogeneous body we write

$$\bar{x} = \frac{\rho}{M} \int x \, dV = \frac{1}{V} \int x \, dV \qquad (14)$$

$$\bar{y} = \frac{\rho}{M} \int y \, dV = \frac{1}{V} \int y \, dV \qquad (14a)$$

using the relation that $\rho = M/V$ and the fact that ρ is constant.

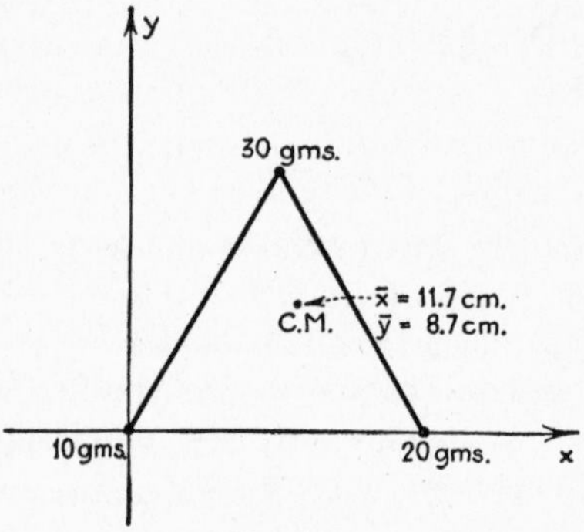

50. Examples.—Let us apply the definitions given in the last section to some actual problems. As the first application, let us suppose that we have three particles of masses 10, 20, and 30 grams, respectively, fixed at the apices of an equilateral triangle of side 20 cm. (Fig. 33). Let us choose x- and y-axes as shown, the origin at the 10-gram mass which we call m_1. We now have as the coordinates of the three bodies,

For $m_1 = 10$ grams:

$$x_1 = 0$$
$$y_1 = 0$$

For $m_2 = 20$ grams:

$$x_2 = 20 \text{ cm.}$$
$$y_2 = 0$$

For $m_3 = 30$ grams:

$$x_3 = 10 \text{ cm.}$$
$$y_3 = 20 \sin 60° \text{ cm.} = 17.3 \text{ cm.}$$

since the angles are all 60°.

FIG. 33.

Thus, from the definition as given by Eqs. (9) and (10),

$$\bar{x} = \tfrac{1}{60}(10 \times 0 + 20 \times 20 + 30 \times 10) = \tfrac{700}{60} = 11.7 \text{ cm.}$$
$$\bar{y} = \tfrac{1}{60}(10 \times 0 + 20 \times 0 + 30 \times 17.3) = \tfrac{519}{60} = 8.7 \text{ cm.}$$

Thus we find the situation of the center of mass 11.7 cm. to the right of the 10-gram mass as shown in the figure and halfway up between the line joining the 10- and 20-gram mass and the 30-gram mass. In connection with this example it should be emphasized that the choice of origin does not affect the result. The student should solve this problem using the position of the 20-gram mass as origin, then using the position of the 30-gram mass as origin, and finally using the center of the triangle as origin.

Turning now to the case of continuous bodies, we shall first consider the case of homogeneous symmetrical bodies, a case of great practical importance. As examples of symmetrical bodies, we may call attention to the sphere which is symmetrical about its center, the hoop which is symmetrical about its center, the circular cylinder which is symmetrical about a point halfway along its long axis, and a uniform stick which is symmetrical about its mid-point. For all these cases we shall prove the following very important result:

The center of mass coincides with the center of symmetry.

We prove this theorem as follows: Let us choose the center of symmetry as an origin. Then, since the body is symmetrical about the origin, there is for every dM with a coordinate x a similar dM with coordinate $-x$, so that, when we add all the $x\,dM$'s, the terms cancel in pairs and the integral in Eq. (13) is zero. A similar situation must exist with respect to the y-axis, so that by the same argument the integral in Eq. (13a) vanishes. Thus we find $\bar{x} = \bar{y} = 0$, so that the center of mass is at the origin. Since we started by placing the origin at the center of symmetry, this completes the proof.

Let us illustrate this proof by considering a homogeneous rod of length l and constant cross section A. The center of symmetry is the center of the rod which we choose as origin, letting the x-axis coincide with the rod (Fig. 34). Now consider a small mass dM at a distance x from O. The mass is

$$dM = \rho A\,dx$$

where ρ is the constant density of the rod.

If we insert this value of dM in the equation defining $\bar{x}$, there follows that

$$\bar{x} = \frac{1}{M} \int_{-\frac{l}{2}}^{+\frac{l}{2}} \rho A x \, dx = \frac{\rho A}{M} \int_{-\frac{l}{2}}^{+\frac{l}{2}} x \, dx$$

The integral yields

$$\left[\frac{x^2}{2}\right]_{x=-\frac{l}{2}}^{x=+\frac{l}{2}} = \frac{l^2}{8} - \frac{l^2}{8} = 0$$

and

$$\bar{x} = 0$$

so that we have found the center of mass at the center of symmetry as expected.

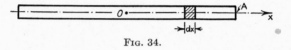

FIG. 34.

The foregoing choice of our origin is convenient but not necessary. Any other origin will lead to the same result. Thus let us take the origin at one end of the rod, and now let x denote the distance of a volume element $A \, dx$ from this end. We have as before

$$dV = A \, dx$$

and furthermore

$$M = A \rho l$$

so that Eq. (14) yields

$$\bar{x} = \frac{1}{Al} \int_0^l A x \, dx$$

where now the limits of integration are 0 to l, corresponding to a summation starting at the origin $x = 0$ and ending at the end of the rod $x = l$. Thus we obtain

$$\bar{x} = \frac{1}{l} \int_0^l x \, dx = \frac{1}{l}\left[\frac{x^2}{2}\right]_0^l = \frac{l}{2}$$

so that we again find the center of mass of our rod at its geometrical center, *i.e.*, halfway along the rod.

As a third and final example, let us consider a right circular cone of altitude h. We now choose the vertex of the cone as origin and the y-axis as shown in Fig. 35. From the symmetry about the y-axis we know that the center of mass lies somewhere on the y-axis so that we need only calculate $\bar{y}$.

Consider a horizontal disk of thickness dy, and radius r at a height y above the origin. Its mass is

$$dM = \rho \pi r^2 dy$$

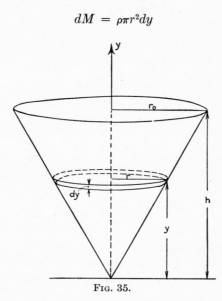

Fig. 35.

where ρ is the constant density of the material of which the cone is made, and the radius r depends on y. From the figure it is clear that r is proportional to y, and we have

$$r = ky$$

Now at the top $y = h$ and $r = r_0$, so that

$$r_0 = kh \qquad \text{or} \qquad k = \frac{r_0}{h}$$

and we have

$$r = \frac{r_0}{h}y$$

Substituting this value of r in the expression for dM, it follows that

$$dM = \frac{\rho \pi r_0^2}{h^2} y^2 dy \qquad\qquad (a)$$

We have now expressed dM as a function of y and are prepared to integrate. $\bar{y}$ is defined by

$$\bar{y} = \frac{1}{M}\int y\,dM = \frac{\rho\pi r_0^2}{Mh^2}\int_0^h y^3dy$$

The value of the integral is $h^4/4$, so that

$$\bar{y} = \frac{\rho\pi r_0^2 h^2}{4M}$$

We must still express M in terms of ρ, r_0, and h. Now

$$M = \int dM = \frac{\rho\pi r_0^2}{h^2}\int_0^h y^2dy$$

using Eq. (a). The integral has the value $h^3/3$, so that we obtain

$$M = \frac{\rho\pi r_0^2 h}{3}$$

Substituting this value of M in our expression for $\bar{y}$, it follows that

$$\bar{y} = \frac{\rho\pi r_0^2 h^2}{4} \times \frac{3}{\rho\pi r_0^2 h} = \frac{3}{4}h$$

so that center of mass is on the axis of the cone one-fourth the altitude from the base.

51. Kinetic Energy of a System of Particles.—We now turn to a discussion of the kinetic energy of a system of particles in preparation for a formulation of the work-energy theorem. Suppose we have an automobile moving in a straight line with a velocity of 20 ft./sec. and a man in the automobile projects a stone of mass m with a speed of 10 ft./sec. with respect to the automobile in the direction of its motion. If the man throwing the stone were fixed in space, he would say that the stone acquires a kinetic energy of $\frac{1}{2}m(10)^2$, or $50m$, and he would identify this increase of kinetic energy as the work done in throwing the stone. If he takes his motion into account, however, he might calculate the work done in the following manner: Initially the stone has a velocity of 20 ft./sec. due to the motion of the automobile, and after projection it has a velocity of 30 ft./sec. in the same direction. Hence the work done in throwing the stone is the change of kinetic energy, $\frac{1}{2}m(30)^2 - \frac{1}{2}m(20)^2$, which is equal to $250m$, or five times the work necessary if he were at rest. This is obviously a ridiculous conclusion, and the purpose of the following argument is to clear up this type of difficulty.

We can straighten out the trouble in our example if we remember that according to the third law of motion it is impossible for the man in the automobile to exert a force on the stone without exerting an equal and opposite force on the automobile. In fact the change of momentum of the automobile must be just equal to the change of momentum of the stone, according to the law of conservation of momentum. Thus in order to calculate the work done in throwing the stone, we must calculate the change of kinetic energy of the automobile as well as that of the stone. This would seem to be the answer to our problem but we should not stop at this point of the argument. Surely, the automobile cannot have its momentum changed without exerting a force on the earth so that the momentum of the earth is changed, and we should include the change of kinetic energy of the earth. But again the earth exerts forces (due to gravitation) on the moon, sun, etc., so that we might go on indefinitely, and our problem still offers difficulty.

We are thus led to answer the question as to the correct method of calculating the kinetic energy of more than one body. The answer is contained in the theorem:

The kinetic energy of a system of particles is equal to the kinetic energy of motion relative to the center of mass of the system, plus the kinetic energy of a single particle of mass equal to the total mass of the system moving with the center of mass.

We shall prove this theorem for the case of two particles, free to move in a plane. Let the particles m_1 and m_2 have coordinates x_1, y_1 and x_2, y_2, measured with the center of mass as the origin. In this system of reference the velocity components of the particles are v_{x1}, v_{y1}, v_{x2}, and v_{y2}, respectively. Now suppose the center of mass has coordinates x and y with respect to any set of axes (moving or fixed). The components of velocity of the center of mass with respect to these last axes are then v_x and v_y. In this system of reference the coordinates of the particles are

$$\begin{array}{ll} x + x_1, y + y_1 & \text{(of } m_1) \\ x + x_2, y + y_2 & \text{(of } m_2) \end{array} \right\} \tag{15}$$

and the corresponding velocity components are

and
$$\begin{array}{cc} v_x + v_{x1}, & v_y + v_{y1} \\ v_x + v_{x2}, & v_y + v_{y2} \end{array} \right\} \tag{16}$$

The kinetic energy of the system is then

$$K.E. = \tfrac{1}{2}m_1[(v_x + v_{x1})^2 + (v_y + v_{y1})^2] + \tfrac{1}{2}m_2[(v_x + v_{x2})^2 + (v_y + v_{y2})^2] \tag{17}$$

If we now expand and regroup the terms, there follows:

$$K.E. = \tfrac{1}{2}[m_1(v_x^2 + v_y^2) + m_2(v_x^2 + v_y^2)] + \tfrac{1}{2}[m_1(v_{x1}^2 + v_{y1}^2) + m_2(v_{x2}^2 + v_{y2}^2)]$$
$$+ [v_x(m_1 v_{x1} + m_2 v_{x2}) + v_y(m_1 v_{y1} + m_2 v_{y2})] \tag{18}$$

We shall now show that the last term is zero. When the center of mass is taken as the origin, the particles have coordinates x_1, y_1 and x_2, y_2. According to Eqs. (5) and (6) we then have

$$\frac{m_1 x_1 + m_2 x_2}{m_1 + m_2} = 0 \quad \text{and} \quad \frac{m_1 y_1 + m_2 y_2}{m_1 + m_2} = 0$$

If we differentiate these equations with respect to t, we then have

$$m_1v_{x1} + m_2v_{x2} = 0 \quad \text{and} \quad m_1v_{y1} + m_2v_{y2} = 0$$

which proves the result.

The first term in Eq. (18) may be written in the form

$$\tfrac{1}{2}(m_1 + m_2)(v_x^2 + v_y^2)$$

which is the kinetic energy of a particle of mass $(m_1 + m_2)$ moving with the center of mass. The second term in Eq. (18) is just the sum of the kinetic energies of the two particles referred to the center of mass as origin, and thus our proof is complete. Thus Eq. (18) can be written

$$K.E. = \tfrac{1}{2}Mv^2 + \tfrac{1}{2}m_1v_1^2 + \tfrac{1}{2}m_2^2v_2 \tag{19}$$

where $M = m_1 + m_2$, $v = \sqrt{v_x^2 + v_y^2}$ the speed of the center of mass, and v_1 and v_2 are the speeds of the two particles measured with respect to the center of mass.

The extension of the foregoing argument to a system of n particles (and to motion in space) is left as an exercise for the student. The result may be stated as follows:

$$K.E. = \tfrac{1}{2}Mv^2 + \sum_{k=1}^{n} \tfrac{1}{2}m_kv_k^2 \tag{20}$$

where m_k is the mass of the kth particle and v_k its speed.

52. Work-energy Theorem for a System of Particles.—The theorem of the last section shows the fundamental significance of the statement of Sec. 48, that the motion of a system may be considered as compounded of the motion of the center of mass and the motion with respect to the center of the mass. We shall now derive the work-energy theorem for a system of particles. Again we shall restrict ourselves to two particles free to move in a plane, leaving the generalization of the proof as an exercise. Let the resultant force acting on particle m_1 have components X_1, Y_1; and similarly for particle m_2 we have the force components X_2 and Y_2. Using the notation of the previous section, the position of particle m_1 in a fixed system of reference is given by

$$x + x_1 \quad \text{and} \quad y + y_1$$

and the work done by the external forces in a small displacement of this particle is

$$X_1d(x + x_1) + Y_1d(y + y_1)$$

Similarly, for particle m_2 we have as the corresponding expression

$$X_2d(x + x_2) + Y_2d(y + y_2)$$

so that the total work done by all the forces in any small displacement of both particles is

$$X_1d(x + x_1) + X_2d(x + x_2) + Y_1d(y + y_1) + Y_2d(y + y_2)$$

which may be written

$$[(X_1 + X_2)dx + (Y_1 + Y_2)dy] + (X_1dx_1 + X_2dx_2 + Y_1dy_1 + Y_2dy_2) \quad (21)$$

The first term represents the work done by the external forces in a small displacement of the center of mass. Now we have shown in Sec. 48 that the motion of the center of mass is the same as if all the mass of the system were concentrated here and this particle of mass M were acted on by all the external forces. Thus it is clear that this term of Eq. (21) represents the work done in the motion of the particle M and is equal to the change of kinetic energy of this particle moving with the center of mass.

Now the whole expression (21) is equal to the total increase of kinetic energy of the system, and in Sec. 48 we have proved that this can be written as the change of kinetic energy of a particle of mass M moving with the center of mass, plus the change of kinetic energy of the particles with respect to the center of mass. The first part of this kinetic-energy change, as we have seen, is equal to the first term of Eq. (21), so that the latter part must be equal to the second term of Eq. (21).

Thus the increase of kinetic energy relative to the center of mass is

$$X_1dx_1 + X_2dx_2 + Y_1dy_1 + Y_2dy_2$$

and is hence equal to the work done by the forces, calculated as if the center of mass were at rest. This gives us the result we set out to obtain, since in any problem we need only place our origin at the center of mass of the system and then calculate work and kinetic energy using this origin, *i.e.*, the system behaves just as if the center of mass were at rest. We now see that in our example of the man throwing a stone out of a moving automobile, if the mass of the stone is small compared with that of the automobile, the motion of the center of mass of the system, stone plus automobile, is practically that of the automobile. The work done in throwing the stone is practically equal to that done if the automobile were at rest. Incidentally, a similar consideration holds for all motion on the surface of the earth. Because of the huge mass of the earth, we may, for all practical purposes, take the center of mass of any accelerated body and the earth coincident with the center of mass of the earth. This justifies our earlier procedure of using the work-energy principle in which we considered the velocity of the body measured with respect to the earth.

Problems

1. Masses of 2, 3, and 4 lb. are located, respectively, at the vertices A, B, and C of a triangle. The side AB is 10 ft. long, AC is 15 ft. long, and the angle BAC is 37°. Find the center of mass of this system with respect to the point A.

2. Masses of 10, 10, 20, and 40 grams are located, respectively, at the corners A, B, C, and D of a rectangle $ABCD$. The sides AB and CD are each 80 cm. long and the sides BC and AD are each 40 cm. long. Find the position of the center of mass of this system.

3. Masses of 2, 4, 6, and 10 lb. are located, respectively, at the corners A, B, C, and D of a quadrilateral. The sides AB and AD are perpendicular to each other and of lengths 6 and 8 in., respectively. BC is parallel to AD and is 20 in. long.   Find the position of the center of mass of this system.

4. A beam of constant density is 1 ft. long and has the cross section shown in Fig. 36a.   Find the position of the center of mass of this beam.

5. A flat piece of wood has the shape shown in Fig. 36b.   Find the position of its center of mass.

6. The cross section of a wedge is a right triangle of base 10 cm. and altitude 5 cm.   Assuming constant density, find the position of the center of mass.

7. If the sharp end of the wedge in Prob. 6 is cut away so that the base becomes 8 cm. long, find the position of the center of mass of the blunt wedge.

8. A flat thin board has as its boundaries the horizontal x-axis, the vertical line $x = 10$ in., and the curve $y = 0.2x^2$.   Find the position of the center of mass of the board.

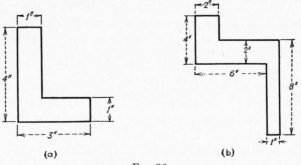

(a)   (b)

Fig. 36.

9. A slim rod of length L has a variable density, the density increasing proportional to the distance from one end according to the relation $\rho = \rho_0[(1 + x/L)]$.   Find the position of the center of mass of the rod.

10. A truncated right circular cone of constant density has its smaller base one-half the area of the top base and is of altitude h.   Calculate the position of the center of mass of this cone.

11. A slim homogeneous wire is bent into a semicircle of radius 10 cm. Calculate the position of its center of mass using the center of the circle as an origin.

12. A slim homogeneous wire is bent into the arc of a circle of radius r. The arc subtends an angle θ_0.

   a. Find the position of the center of mass of the wire.

   b. Find the angle θ_0 if the center of mass is a distance $r/2$ from the center of the circle.

13. A 10-lb. uniform rod of length 4 ft. has a 4-lb. mass point fixed at one end, a 6-lb. mass point at the other end, and an 8-lb. mass 1 ft. from the 4-lb. mass.   Find the position of the center of mass of the system.

14. A horizontal uniform rod 10 cm. long, of mass 10 grams, has small bodies of masses 10 grams and 20 grams at its ends, A and B, respectively.

   a. Find the position of the center of mass of the entire system.

b. If a resultant upward force of 400 dynes, constant in magnitude and direction, is applied at A, find the position of the center of mass after 3 sec.

c. If two equal and opposite vertical forces, each of 400 dynes, are applied at A and B, calculate the position of the center of mass after 3 sec.

15. Two particles of masses 100 and 200 grams, respectively, attract each other with a constant force of 500 dynes. Initially they are 100 cm. apart and each is at rest.

a. Calculate the position of the center of mass of the system from their initial positions.

b. Calculate the position of each mass at the end of 2 sec.

c. Using the positions calculated in *b*, find the position of the center of mass. How should this answer be related to that found in *a*?

16. An 8-lb. body and a 20-lb. body both free to move along a straight line attract each other with a force proportional to their separation. They are initially 4 ft. apart; the 8-lb. body to the left of the other has an initial velocity of -20 ft./sec., the 20-lb. body an initial velocity of $+4$ ft./sec. Where do they collide, if this collision takes place at the end of 20 sec.?

17. Two particles 1 and 2, of equal mass, are on the x-axis initially; particle 1 at the origin, and particle 2 at the point $x = -10$ cm., $y = 0$. The latter particle has an initial velocity of 10 cm./sec. in an upward direction making an angle of 30° with the x-axis, and the former has an initial velocity of 20 cm./sec. downward at an angle of 60° with the x-axis. The particles attract each other with forces depending on the distance between them. If particle 1 passes through the origin at $t = 4$ sec., find the position of particle 2 at this time.

CHAPTER IX

STATICS OF RIGID BODIES

We now turn our attention to the behavior of rigid bodies. We remember that the definition of a rigid body is that it is a system of particles in which the distance between any two particles does not change. It is this constancy of distance between any two particles which makes the rigid body the simplest sort of system of particles. In the last chapter we have seen that a fundamental mode of description of the motion of a system of particles consists of combining the motion of the center of mass of the system with the motion relative to the center of mass. In the case of a rigid body this latter motion is simple. In the first place, the mass points of which the body is composed cannot move toward, or away from, the center of mass without deforming the body. Thus the only motion possible for a particle of the body is one in which its distance from the center of mass stays constant. This is motion on a sphere, or rotation. Furthermore, any two lines in the rigid body which pass through the center of mass must maintain their angular separation unchanged (otherwise the distance between a mass point on one straight line and another on the second line would change, violating the definition of a rigid body) so that the body may rotate as a whole about the center of mass. Thus the most general motion of a rigid body may be built up of the motion of the center of mass plus the rotation of the body about the center of mass. In this chapter we shall consider the statics of rigid bodies and investigate the conditions which must be satisfied if a rigid body stays at rest under the action of external forces.

53. Plane Motion of a Rigid Body; Degrees of Freedom.—For the time being we shall restrict our discussion to a simple type of rigid-body motion, *viz.*, the plane motion of such a body. This means that the center of mass of the body is free to move in a plane, and also that the axis of rotation of the body maintains a fixed direction which is perpendicular to this plane. In fact, if these conditions are fulfilled every point of the rigid body stays in one plane. As familiar examples of such motion, we bring to mind the rolling of a wheel or of a sphere, or the rotation of a flywheel about its axis. To describe uniquely the position of a rigid body capable of plane motion we must determine three independent quantities. For example, we must know (a) the x-coordinate of the center of mass, (b) the y-coordinate of this point, and (c) the direction (angle) which any straight line passing through the center of mass makes with the x-axis. Thus it is evident that our rigid body has three degrees of freedom. If (a) and (b) change with time and (c) is fixed, we say that the body moves in pure translation. Every point of the body moves in an identical manner to the center of mass, so that the motion of the body as a whole is described when the motion of the center of mass (or of any other point of the body) is given. If (a) and (b) are fixed, and (c) changes with time, we say that the body moves in pure rotation about the center of mass, or, more exactly, about an axis through the center of mass and perpendicular to the plane of the motion. It is of course possible to have the case of pure rotation about any fixed axis perpendicular to the plane, and we shall have occasion to investigate such motions. We are now ready to formulate the conditions governing the statics of rigid bodies.

54. Equilibrium Conditions for Rigid Bodies; Moments of Forces.—We now proceed to set up the conditions which must be satisfied if a rigid body is in equilibrium. These will be three in number, corresponding to the three degrees of freedom of the body. In the first place we note that, if the body is in equilibrium, there must be no acceleration of the center of mass. We have already shown in the last chapter that the center of mass of any system of particles (and this certainly includes rigid bodies) moves as if all the mass of the system were concentrated at this point and all the external forces act on this mass point. Thus the equilibrium conditions for the motion of the center of mass (i.e., for translation) are identical with those for a particle free to move in a plane, and these are

$$\left.\begin{array}{l} X_1 + X_2 + \cdots + X_n = 0 \\ Y_1 + Y_2 + \cdots + Y_n = 0 \end{array}\right\} \tag{1}$$

if $X_1, X_2, \ldots, X_n$ are the x-components of the external forces which act on the body and $Y_1, Y_2, \ldots, Y_n$ are the y-components of these forces. In words, the sum of the x-components of all the external applied forces and the sum of the y-components of all the external applied forces must be zero. Thus, there remains only the equilibrium condition for motion relative to the center of mass, *i.e.*, for rotation about an axis through this point. In pure rotation, every mass point must move in a circle about the center of rotation. If the body is in equilibrium there can be no tangential acceleration of any mass point, or, what is the same thing, there can be no angular acceleration of the body. We now must ask the question: How does the angular acceleration of the body depend on the applied forces? The answer to this question may be obtained as follows: The tangential acceleration of a mass point moving in a circle is proportional to the component of the applied force tangent to the circle, *i.e.*, perpendicular to the radius of the circle. Thus we see that the angular acceleration of a rigid body will be propor-

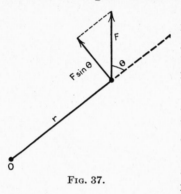

FIG. 37.

tional to the component of applied force perpendicular to the line joining the center of rotation to the point of application of the force, or to $F \sin \theta$ (Fig. 37). Furthermore it is clear that the angular acceleration produced by this force will depend on the distance r from the center O to the point of application and will increase as r increases. Certainly if the force is applied at O, it can produce

no angular acceleration about O. It is a matter of simple experience that the angular acceleration produced by a given force increases proportional to the distance r. A simple experiment will illustrate this fact. If we have a seesaw originally balanced horizontally and place a body at a distance r to one side of the point of support, the seesaw will start to rotate. If we now take a body of half the mass of the first, we find that by placing it at a distance $2r$ to the other side of the point of support the seesaw stays at rest.

The net result is that the angular acceleration of a rigid body is proportional to the product $Fr \sin \theta$, or to a sum of such products if there is more than one force acting. The expression $Fr \sin \theta$ is called the *moment** of the force F or the

---

* Strictly speaking, the moment of a force is a vector since one must specify a direction, that of the axis about which the moment is taken, as well as a magnitude. The same is true of angular velocity, but we shall not stress this point here as it is not essential for our present purposes (see Sec. 70).

torque about the center of rotation O. Now, since for equilibrium the angular acceleration of the body about its center of mass
is zero, it follows that the sum of the moments of the applied
forces about this point must be zero. Thus we write as our third
and final condition

$$F_1r_1 \sin \theta_1 + F_2r_2 \sin \theta_2 + \cdots + F_nr_n \sin \theta_n = 0 \qquad (2)$$

We shall call the moment of a force *positive* if, when acting alone,
it starts the body rotating in a counterclockwise direction and
negative if it produces a clockwise rotation.

55. Analytic Representation of Moments of Forces.—Let us
consider the expression for the moment of a force more closely.
We have written it as

$$Fr \sin \theta$$

and have shown that it is the product of the radius and the component of the force per-
pendicular to the radius.
There is another mode of
interpreting this expression.
Consider the expression r
$\sin \theta$ (Fig. 38). If we drop a
perpendicular from O to the
line of action of the force, we
form the right triangle OPQ.
From this triangle we see that
the line $OQ = r \sin \theta$, so that
we may thus say:

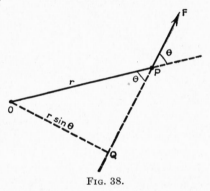

FIG. 38.

The moment of a force about a center O is the product of the
force and the perpendicular distance from the center to the
line of action of the force.

This proves to be a very useful definition in many applications
and we shall now make use of it.

There is another method of representing the moment of a force
in terms of the components of the force. We construct a set of
coordinate axes through the center of rotation O and replace
the force F by its x- and y-components X and Y, respectively.
The point of application of the force P is at a distance r from
O and has the coordinates x and y. From the definition of the
last paragraph the moment of the Y-force is $+Yx$ and that of the

X-force is $-Xy$. Thus we may write the moment of the force F whose components are X and Y as

$$Fr \sin \theta = Yx - Xy \qquad (3)$$

In the following applications we shall make use of all the above expressions for the moment of a force.

56. Equilibrium Equations.—Let us recapitulate our three conditions for equilibrium. We have seen that (1) the sum of the x-forces and (2) the sum of the y-forces each must be zero, and also that (3) the sum of the moments about the center of mass must be zero. We shall now prove the exceedingly important theorem:

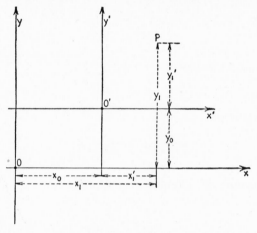

Fig. 39.

If the above conditions for equilibrium are satisfied, the sum of the moments about *any* point in the plane is zero.

This theorem will allow us to replace the third condition of equilibrium by the condition that the sum of the moments of the applied forces about any point in the plane is zero. By this means a great practical advantage is gained, as it is usually easier to calculate moments about some point other than the center of mass.

To prove the theorem let us consider a point P whose coordinates are x_1 and y_1 with respect to a set of coordinates with the origin O at the center of mass (Fig. 39). The first step is to calculate the coordinates of P measured from another origin O'. Let the origin O' have the coordinates x_0 and y_0, measured with respect to the origin O.   If the coordinates of P with respect to O' are called x_1' and y_1', it is clear from the figure that

$$x_1 = x_1' + x_0$$

and

$$y_1 = y_1' + y_0$$

Now suppose the force F_1 (components X_1, Y_1) acts at the point P.   Then according to Eq. (3) the moment of this force about the center of mass is

$$Y_1 x_1 - X_1 y_1$$

Similarly, if a force F_2 (components X_2, Y_2) acts at a point whose coordinates are x_2 and y_2, its moment about the center of mass is

$$Y_2 x_2 - X_2 y_2$$

Thus the sum of the moments of all the forces about the center of mass may be written

$$(Y_1 x_1 - X_1 y_1) + (Y_2 x_2 - X_2 y_2) + \cdots + (Y_n x_n - X_n y_n)$$

or more concisely

$$\sum_{k=1}^{n} (Y_k x_k - X_k y_k)$$

For equilibrium this expression must be zero.

If we now substitute the expressions

$$x_1 = x_1' + x_0$$
$$y_1 = y_1' + y_0$$
$$x_2 = x_2' + x_0$$
$$y_2 = y_2' + y_0$$
Etc.

in the above expression for the moments, we obtain for equilibrium

$$0 = \sum_{k=1}^{n} [Y_k(x_k' + x_0) - X_k(y_k' + y_0)] \tag{4}$$

We may now rewrite the right-hand side of this expression as

$$\sum_{k=1}^{n} (Y_k x_k' - X_k y_k') + x_0 \sum_{k=1}^{n} Y_k - y_0 \sum_{k=1}^{n} X_k \tag{5}$$

Now, since for equilibrium

$$\sum_{k=1}^{n} X_k = X_1 + X_2 + \cdots + X_n = 0$$

and

$$\sum_{k=1}^{n} Y_k = Y_1 + Y_2 + \cdots + Y_n = 0$$

there follows

$$\sum_{k=1}^{n} (Y_k x_k' - X_k y_k') = 0 \tag{6}$$

This is just the sum of the moments of the forces about the point O', which is any point in the plane, and our proof is complete. We must particularly emphasize the fact that this theorem is valid only if $\Sigma X = 0$ and $\Sigma Y = 0$, and hence is true only for equilibrium. We shall have occasion to refer to this in the next chapter when we study the general translational motion of a rigid body.

As a final summary we repeat: A rigid body free to move in a plane is in equilibrium, if

(*a*) The sum of the *x*-components of the applied forces is zero⎫
(*b*) The sum of the *y*-components of the applied forces is zero⎬ (7)
(*c*) The sum of the moments of the applied forces about any⎭
     point in the plane is zero.

Of course, the algebraic sum is meant in all the three conditions.

A very useful corollary of the above laws is the following. If the lines of action of all the applied forces go through the same point in the plane, the moments of all the forces around this point are zero and the third condition *c* is automatically fulfilled. In this case we have only to apply the first two conditions.

57. Examples.—The following examples may help to illustrate the meaning and method of applying the laws which we have derived. Suppose a rigid body of any shape be allowed to fall freely. Every particle of the body acquires an acceleration *g*, so that the whole body performs translatory motion. We now ask the question: Is it possible to apply a single force to the body which will hold the body in equilibrium? If so, at what point must this force be applied and how large must it be? We choose an arbitrary origin and choose the x-axis horizontal. Now we divide the body into a huge number of vertical slices, of thickness dx and mass dm. The pull on one of these slices due to the earth is $-g \cdot dm$ (Fig. 40) and is vertically downward on each slice (although it may be different in magnitude for different slices). Let us now apply our conditions of equilibrium. If F is the unknown force, we have for equilibrium:

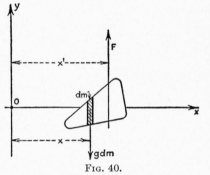

FIG. 40.

1. The sum of the x-components of all the forces is zero, and, since all the forces due to the earth are vertically downward, this condition can be satisfied only if the force F is vertical so that its x-component vanishes.

2. The sum of the y-components of all the forces is zero. Here we have as the sum of all the forces due to the pull of the earth

$$-\int g\, dm = -g\int dm = -Mg$$

if M is the total mass of the rigid body. Thus this condition of equilibrium demands that

$$-Mg + F = 0$$

or

$$F = Mg$$

so that we have found that the force F must be directed vertically upward and must be equal to the weight of the body.

3. The sum of the moments of all the forces about any point is zero. Let us take moments about the origin (which is arbitrary). The earth pull on the slice dm which is located at a distance x from O has a moment

$$-g\, dm\, x$$

and the total moment due to the earth pull on all the slices is

$$-g\int x\, dm$$

The moment of the force F is

$$+Fx'$$

if x' is the distance from the origin to the line of action of F. Thus the sum of the moments is

$$Fx' - g\int x\,dm = 0$$

or

$$x' = \frac{g}{F}\int x\,dm$$

and, since $F = Mg$, this becomes

$$x' = \frac{1}{M}\int x\,dm$$

This is just the x-coordinate of the center of mass, so that we have proved that a rigid body may be held in equilibrium under the action of the earth pull by a single vertical force equal to the weight of the body whose line of action passes through the center of mass of the body. Our proof holds no matter what the orientation of the body in space, and, since the force F always passes through the center of mass (and not through any other points of the body for two or more different orientations), we may replace the whole body by a single particle of mass M at the center of mass and consider the pull of the earth on this particle. In doing this we take account of the weight of the body and also of the moments of the weights of all the particles of which the body is composed. Because of the importance of the center of mass in this connection it is usual to call this point the *center of gravity* of the body. In the following discussion we shall use the terms interchangeably.

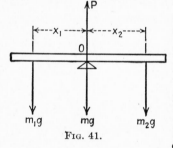

FIG. 41.

As a second example let us consider a uniform rigid rod of mass m supported on a knife edge at its center O (Fig. 41) and suppose two masses m_1 and m_2 are suspended from it at distances x_1 and x_2 from O. According to our discussion in the last paragraph we may represent the pull of the earth on the rod by a single force acting at the center of gravity O. If this system is in equilibrium, we must satisfy the three conditions of Eq. (7).

a. Since there are no x-components of force acting on the rod, this condition is automatically satisfied.

b. In the y-direction there are the weights of the two masses and of the rod acting downward, and the push of the support up on the rod. If this push is P, we must have

$$mg + m_1g + m_2g = P$$

c. If we take as a center of rotation the point of support O, we have as the sum of the moments

$$m_1gx_1 \sin (90°) - m_2gx_2 \sin (90°) = 0$$

or

$$m_1x_1 = m_2x_2$$

This gives us a simple and practical method of comparing masses and is usually done with an equal-arm balance for which $x_1 = x_2$. In this case the condition for equilibrium demands that $m_1 = m_2$, so that the mass of any body may be thus obtained by comparing it with a set of standard bodies.   It is impossible to obtain the weight of the body by these measurements alone, as one must also determine the acceleration g of a freely falling body at the place where the measurement is made.   It is to be noticed that the value of g is immaterial to the above measurement; the only assumption made is that it is the same for all bodies at the same place on the earth's surface, and this assumption is well borne out by measurement.

Consider a ladder 40 ft. long which leans up against a wall making an angle of 60° with the floor. It weighs 40 lb., and its center of gravity is 15 ft. from the bottom.   If the reaction of the wall is horizontal, find the forces exerted on the ladder at both its ends.

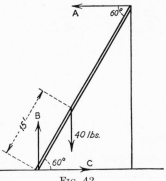

Fig. 42.

The first thing to do in such a problem is to make a proper diagram such as Fig. 42 and to draw all the forces acting *on* the body in their proper positions. We then apply the conditions of equilibrium.

a. The sum of the forces in the x-direction must equal zero:

$$-A + C = 0, \qquad \text{or} \qquad A = C$$

b. The sum of the y-forces must be zero:

$$B - 40 = 0, \qquad \text{or} \qquad B = 40 \text{ lb.}$$

c. The sum of the moments of all the forces about any point must be zero. Here we can save a lot of work by choosing the center of rotation skilfully. If we choose it at the point of application of one of the forces, then the moment of this force about this point is zero. Therefore we choose the bottom point of the ladder as the point about which we are to take moments.
We have

$$40 \cdot 15 \cdot \sin 30° - A \cdot 40 \cdot \sin 60° = 0$$
$$300 - 35A = 0$$
$$A = 8.6 \text{ lb. to the left}$$

From the first condition, we now find

$$C = 8.6 \text{ lb. to the right}$$

Thus all the unknown forces have been obtained.

Problems

1. A 500-lb. body is suspended by a bar and a rope. The body hangs at one end of the 4-ft. bar which is horizontally fixed to a wall. The free end of the rope is attached to a point on the wall 3 ft. above the bar.
Find the tension in the rope and the compression in the bar.

2. A body weighs 10.0 grams when placed on one side of an "equal"-arm balance and 10.5 grams when placed on the opposite side. The beam is horizontal with no weights in the pans. Find the true weight of the body.
Prove that the ratio of the arm lengths of the balance is $\sqrt{10.5/10}$.

3. A tapering pole has its center of gravity one-third of its length from the thick end and weighs 50 lb. It is carried by two men supporting it at each end. Where must a 25-lb. weight be hung so that each of the men supports the same load? What is the upward force exerted by each man on the pole?

4. A 20-ft. uniform plank weighing 80 lb. rests on a horizontal plane with 5 ft. of its length protruding over the edge of the plane. How far out can a 150-lb. man walk without tipping the plank?

5. A cube 3 ft. on an edge weighing 100 lb. rests on a floor with one edge touching a cleat in the floor. At what height above the floor must a 60-lb. horizontal force be applied to just tip the cube? What is the force (magnitude and direction) exerted by the cleat on the cube?

6. A uniform ladder 20 ft. long and weighing 40 lb. leans against a smooth vertical wall and is inclined at an angle of 53° with the horizontal. The coefficient of static friction between ladder and floor is 0.60. How far up the ladder can a 160-lb. man climb before it slips?

7. Two uniform similar ladders 10 ft. long, each weighing 20 lb., are hinged together at the top and stand on a smooth floor with their ends 12 ft. apart. They are connected by a rope 3 ft. above the floor.

a. Find the push of the floor on each ladder.

b. Find the tension in the rope.

c. Find the force (direction and magnitude) exerted by one ladder on the other at the hinge.

8. If in Prob. 7 a 50-lb. weight is placed on a step halfway up one of the ladders, find

a. The push of the floor on each ladder.

b. The tension in the rope.

c. The force exerted by one ladder on the other at the hinge.

9. The top of a ladder that weighs 100 lb. rests against a smooth vertical wall and the ladder makes an angle of 60° with the horizontal. What is the force of friction at the foot of the ladder?

10. A door 3 ft. wide and 8 ft. high is supported by hinges 1 ft. from the top and bottom. If $\frac{3}{4}$ of the weight of 200 lb. is supported by the lower hinge, what is the resultant force exerted by the door on each hinge?

11. One end of a uniform rod weighing 20 lb. rests on a frictionless surface and the other end is supported by a nail. What are the magnitude and direction of the force exerted by the nail?

12. A ladder, length 10 ft. and weighing 50 lb., rests against a smooth vertical wall and is inclined at an angle of 60° with the horizontal. If the coefficient of static friction between the ladder and the horizontal surface on which it rests is 0.40, how far can a man weighing 150 lb. climb up the ladder before it starts to slip at the bottom? Assume center of gravity of ladder is 4 ft. from lower end.

13. A derrick boom is hinged at one end and supports a weight of 2,000 lb. at the other end. At the same end as the weight is a supporting cable which makes an angle of 60° with the vertical and in such a direction that the stress in the boom is a compression. If the boom is inclined at an angle of 30° with the horizontal, what is the tension in the supporting cable? Find the magnitude and direction of total force exerted on the boom by the hinge.

14. A 50-lb. table, 4 ft. high and 8 ft. between its front and rear legs, is dragged lengthwise up a 30° inclined plane at constant velocity by a rope attached to the center of the top edge of the table. The center of gravity of the table is 1 ft. below the center of its top, the rope is parallel to the surface of the inclined plane, and the coefficient of friction between the legs and the plane is 0.3.

Calculate the pull of the rope on the table and the components of the forces exerted by the plane on the legs of the table parallel to the plane and perpendicular to the plane. What are the direction and magnitude of the resultant force exerted by the plane on each leg?

15. One end of a 40-lb. uniform beam 6 ft. long is hinged to a vertical wall. To the other end is fastened a 6-ft. rope which itself is fixed to the wall at a point 6 ft. above the hinge. A 60-lb. weight hangs from the beam at a point 4 ft. along the beam from the wall end.

a. Calculate the tension in the rope.

b. Calculate the resultant force exerted on the hinge by the wall.

16. A circular ring weighing 12 lb. rests upon three supports 120° apart. Find the least downward force which will cause the ring to leave one of the supports and where must it be applied?

17. A derrick boom is hinged at one end and supports a weight of 4,000 lb. at the other end. A supporting cable is attached to the end carrying the weight and makes an angle of 30° with the vertical in such a direction that the boom is under compression. If the boom is inclined at an angle of 45° with the horizontal, what is the tension in the supporting cable? What is the resultant force exerted on the boom by the hinge?

18. A bar *AB* is 10 ft. long, weighs 30 lb., and has its center of mass 4 ft. from *A*. The bar rests with one end (*A*) on a smooth inclined plane making an angle of 30° with the horizontal and end *B* rests on a similar inclined plane making an angle of 45° with the horizontal.

Calculate the force exerted by each plane on the bar and the angle which the bar makes with the horizontal.

19. A 100-lb. table 6 ft. long and 4 ft. high slides down a 30° inclined plane with constant velocity. The center of mass of the table is 1 ft. below the center of the table top.

a. Calculate the coefficient of friction between the table legs and the plane.

b. Calculate the magnitude of the force exerted by the plane on the front legs of the table.

20. An 80-lb. table is dragged along a floor at constant velocity by a horizontal rope attached to a point on the table 3 ft. above the floor. The distance between the legs is 8 ft., and the center of mass of the table is midway between the front and rear legs, 2 ft. above the floor. The coefficient of friction between the legs and floor is 0.20.

a. What is the tension in the rope?

b. What are the normal components of the push of the floor on each leg?

21. A 15-ft. uniform ladder weighing 28 lb. is dragged along a horizontal floor by a man who pulls on one end 2.8 ft. above the floor, the other end resting on the floor. The coefficient of friction between ladder and floor is 0.2. If the man drags the ladder with a constant velocity of 5 ft./sec., find:

a. The horizontal and vertical components of the pull exerted by the man.

b. The pull exerted by the man (magnitude and direction).

c. The *upward* push of the floor on the ladder.

22. A uniform beam 20 ft. long, weighing 50 lb., stands on one end leaning 30° to the vertical, with a horizontal rope attached to the top end to maintain equilibrium.

a. Make a force diagram showing the forces acting *on* the beam.

b. Compute the unknown forces.

23. A uniform bar 4 ft. long, weighing 10 lb., has two weights hung from its ends. One, a 10-lb. weight, is hung on a string 1 ft. long and the other, a 20-lb. weight, is hung on a string 2 ft. long.

a. Where must the bar be supported if it is to maintain a horizontal equilibrium position?

b. How far below the bar is the center of mass of the system?

24. One end of a uniform 12-lb. rod is hinged to a horizontal surface, and the other end rests on a smooth 60° inclined plane. The rod makes an angle of 30° with the horizontal. Find the force exerted by the inclined plane on the rod.

25. A 10-ft. uniform horizontal boom weighing 100 lb. is hinged at one end to a vertical wall. The other end is attached to a 12.5-ft. cable which is fastened to the wall at a point above the hinge.   Weights of 200 and 50 lb. are hung from the boom 3 and 8 ft. from the wall, respectively.

a. Find the tension in the cable.

b. Find the magnitude and direction of the force exerted by the hinge on the boom.

26. A 2,000-lb. truck of 120-in. wheel base has its center of mass at a point 50 in. back of the front wheels.   The truck is at rest.

a. Find the upward forces at the front and rear wheels.

b. How far forward of the rear axle should a load of 3 tons be placed in order that the upward forces at front and rear wheels be equal?

27. A uniform ladder 20 ft. long weighing 50 lb. rests against a smooth wall with its base 12 ft. from the wall.   A horizontal rope is attached to the ladder and wall and is 4 ft. above the floor.   The coefficient of static friction between ladder and floor is 0.2.

If a 150-lb. man stands on the ladder 15 ft. from the bottom, find the tension in the rope and the push of the wall on the ladder.

28. A 40-lb. chair is pulled along a floor with constant velocity by a horizontal force acting at a point midway between the rear legs at the height of the seat.   The seat is 18 in. from the floor, and the center of mass of the chair is at the center of the seat.   The distance between front and rear legs is 2 ft., and the coefficient of friction between the legs and the floor is 0.20.

a. What force is needed?

b. Find the horizontal and vertical components of the push exerted by each leg on the floor.

c. What is the maximum height at which the force can be applied without tipping the chair over?

29. A light rigid frame is in the form of a right triangle of base 15 cm. and altitude 5 cm.   Small masses of 20 and 10 grams are placed at the ends of the 15-cm. side, the 20-gram mass at the corner where the angle is 90°.

If the frame is supported so that it can swing freely about the corner of the frame to which no mass is attached, find the angle which the hypotenuse will make with the vertical when the frame is in equilibrium.

CHAPTER X

PLANE DYNAMICS OF RIGID BODIES

In the last chapter we confined ourselves to a study of the conditions which must be fulfilled if a rigid body free to move in a plane is held in equilibrium. Now we are prepared to extend our discussion to include the case of accelerated motion of such bodies. Again we remind ourselves that the most general plane motion of a rigid body may be compounded of a motion of the center of mass of the body plus a rotation about the center of mass. The motion of the center of mass is calculated by replacing the whole body by a mass point of mass equal to the total mass of the body and calculating the motion of this particle under the action of all the external forces which act on the rigid body. Furthermore we have seen that it is convenient to think of two typical kinds of motion which a rigid body may perform: (1) pure translation in which the body moves as a whole, every point of the body performing the identical motion of every other point; and (2) rotation of the body about an axis perpendicular to the plane of the motion. We shall adopt the procedure of first discussing problems of pure translation, then turning to the study of pure rotation of a rigid body about a fixed axis, and finally combining these results to develop the general scheme for solving problems involving the general motion of the rigid body.

58. Translation of a Rigid Body.—When a rigid body moves in pure translation, the motion of any point of the body describes the motion of the whole body. In particular the motion of the center of mass of the body (coordinates $\bar{x}$, $\bar{y}$) is in any case determined by the equations of motion:

$$\left. \begin{aligned} \Sigma X &= M\frac{d\bar{v}_x}{dt} \\ \Sigma Y &= M\frac{d\bar{v}_y}{dt} \end{aligned} \right\} \tag{1}$$

where ΣX and ΣY denote the sum of the x- and y-components of all the external forces acting on the body, M the mass of the body, and $\bar{v}_x$ and $\bar{v}_y$ the x- and y-components of the velocity of the center of mass. If the body moves in pure translation then there must be no rotation about the center of mass (every point of the body performs a motion identical with that of the center of mass), and hence the sum of the moments of the forces taken about an axis passing through the center of mass must be zero. Thus, for translation alone, we must satisfy the condition that the sum of the torques about an axis passing through the center of mass vanishes.

$$\Sigma \bar{T} = 0 \qquad (2)$$

It must be emphasized that Eq. (2) refers to the moments of the forces about the center of mass and about no other point in the

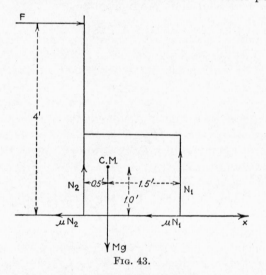

Fig. 43.

plane. As we have seen in Eq. (5) of Chap. IX, if the sum of the moments about the center of mass is zero, then this sum is zero when taken about another point if, and only if, there is no acceleration of the center of mass, *i.e.*, if the body is in equilibrium and hence $\Sigma X = \Sigma Y = 0$.

To illustrate the use of the above equations let us consider a chair on a floor pushed by a horizontal force applied to the back at a point 4 ft. above the floor. Suppose the front and rear legs are 2 ft. apart and the center of mass is located at a point $\frac{1}{2}$ ft. in front of the rear legs and 1 ft. above the floor. The coefficient of friction between chair legs and floor is 0.25. We wish to find the greatest acceleration possible for the chair without tipping. Let the normal components of the push of the floor on the front and rear legs be N_1 and N_2, respectively (Fig. 43). According to our equations of motion

$$\Sigma X = F - \mu N_1 - \mu N_2 = M\bar{a}_x$$
$$\Sigma Y = N_1 + N_2 - Mg = 0$$

and taking moments about the center of mass,

$$1.5N_1 - 1\mu N_1 - 1\mu N_2 - 3F - 0.5N_2 = 0$$

whence

$$3F = 1.5N_1 - 0.5N_2 - \mu(N_1 + N_2)$$

From the second equation of equilibrium,

$$N_1 = Mg - N_2; \qquad N_1 + N_2 = Mg$$

and, using the value $\mu = \frac{1}{4}$, there follows for F,

$$F = \frac{1.5Mg - 1.5N_2 - 0.5N_2 - 0.25Mg}{3} = \frac{1.25Mg - 2N_2}{3}$$

and we see that, as the force F is increased from zero, the push on the rear legs decreases. Since the smallest value possible for N_2 is zero, the maximum force we may apply and still produce pure translation is

$$F_{max} = \tfrac{5}{12}Mg$$

Inserting this value in our first equation of motion there follows

$$(\bar{a}_x)_{max} = \frac{(\tfrac{5}{12} - \tfrac{1}{4})Mg}{M} = \tfrac{16}{3} \text{ ft./sec.}^2$$

Thus we see that it is possible to accelerate the chair with any acceleration up to $\tfrac{16}{3}$ ft./sec.^{2} without producing tipping. From this example we see that the weight of the chair does not influence this conclusion. A much smaller acceleration is possible if the force F is reversed in direction, everything else staying the same. The solution of this problem is left as an exercise for the student.

59. Rotation of a Rigid Body about a Fixed Axis.—If a rigid body moves in pure rotation about a fixed axis, every mass point of the body performs circular motion about the axis. The linear velocities and accelerations of the various particles differ one from another, but as a consequence of the rigidity of the body the angular velocity and the angular acceleration of every particle in the body are the same. Thus the motion of the whole body is described by the angle ϕ which some line of the body passing through the center of rotation makes with a fixed axis, *e.g.*, the x-axis, the angular velocity $\omega = d\phi/dt$, and the angular acceleration is $\alpha = d\omega/dt$. We now proceed to a derivation of the equations of rotational motion. Consider any mass point m_1 of the body at a distance r_1 from the axis of rotation O. Let the resultant force F_1 acting on it

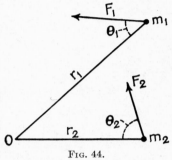

Fig. 44.

make an angle θ_1 with r_1 (Fig. 44). The component of the acceleration of the point toward O is caused by the internal forces which hold the body together and does not interest us further. The tangential acceleration is determined by the external force. Since this acceleration is perpendicular to r_1, we have

$$F_1 \sin \theta_1 = m_1 a_{1t}$$

and, since the tangential acceleration a_{1t} is related to the angular acceleration of the body by the equation

$$a_{1t} = r_1\frac{d\omega}{dt} = r_1\alpha$$

we may rewrite our equation of motion as

$$F_1 \sin \theta_1 = m_1 r_1\frac{d\omega}{dt}$$

Similarly, for another point m_2,

$$F_2 \sin \theta_2 = m_2 r_2\frac{d\omega}{dt}$$

In exactly the same manner we may write an equation of motion for each mass point of the body, *e.g.*, for a mass point m_k,

$$F_k \sin \theta_k = m_k r_k\frac{d\omega}{dt}$$

If we now multiply both sides of the first equation by r_1, of the second by r_2, etc., and then add all the resulting equations, it follows that

$$F_1r_1 \sin \theta_1 + F_2r_2 \sin \theta_2 + F_3r_3 \sin \theta_3 + \cdots$$
$$= (m_1r_1^2 + m_2r_2^2 + m_3r_3^2 + \cdots)\frac{d\omega}{dt} \quad (3)$$

or, written more concisely,

$$\sum Fr \sin \theta = \left(\sum mr^2\right)\frac{d\omega}{dt} \quad (4)$$

Or, in words:

The sum of the moments of all the forces taken about the axis of rotation is proportional to the angular acceleration of the body; the proportionality factor is the sum of the mass of each mass point each multiplied by the square of its distance from the axis of rotation.

It is customary to give special names to the terms in Eq. (4): the moments of the forces are also called the *torques* which we denote by the symbol T, and the term (Σmr^2) is called the *moment of inertia* of the body about the axis in question and is denoted by the symbol I. Thus we may write the equation of motion, Eq. (4), as

$$T = I\frac{d\omega}{dt} \quad (5)$$

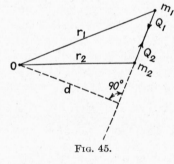

FIG. 45.

We shall now prove the important theorem that the left-hand side of Eq. (5) is equal to the sum of the external torques, since the torques due to the interaction forces between the various mass points of the body add up to zero as a consequence of the third law of motion. Consider any two mass points m_1 and m_2 at distances r_1 and r_2 from the rotation axis O. Let Q_1 be the force which m_2 exerts on m_1 and Q_2 be the force which m_1 exerts on m_2. The sum of the moments of these two forces about O is (Fig. 45)

$$-Q_1d + Q_2d = d(Q_2 - Q_1)$$

and since according to the third law $Q_1 = Q_2$, this sum is zero.

Thus we see that the sum of the internal torques cancel in pairs, so that, when we add all the torques due to all the forces acting, we are left with the sum of the torques of the external forces only. Thus we may state: **The rotational motion of a rigid body is determined completely by the external torques and is independent of the nature and magnitudes of the internal torques.** This statement is valid (according to the above proof) for any system of particles whether they form a rigid body or not.

60. Calculation of Moment of Inertia; Radius of Gyration.— The moment of inertia of a rigid body about a specified axis is a quantity dependent only on the body, independent of its motion, and for rotational motion plays the same part as that of the mass of a particle in translation. For a number n of discrete particles held together in a rigid structure, the moment of inertia about an axis is defined as

$$I = \sum_{k=1}^{n} m_k r_k^2 \qquad (6)$$

and, if the positions of these masses with respect to the axis of rotation are known, the evaluation of the moment of inertia becomes a matter of simple (although perhaps very tedious) addition. Just as in the case of the calculation of the position of the center of mass of a body, it is convenient to treat most rigid bodies as continuous distributions of matter, of given shape and density. To calculate the moment of inertia of such a body about some axis, we imagine the body divided into a huge number of tiny elements, each of mass ΔM. If the mass ΔM is at a perpendicular distance r from the axis of rotation, we have (in the limit as $\Delta M \to 0$)

$$I = \lim_{\Delta M \to 0} \Sigma r^2 \Delta M = \int r^2 dM \qquad (7)$$

where the integration is to be extended over the whole rigid body. In order to carry out this integration, we place

$$dM = \rho \, dV \qquad (8)$$

where dV is the volume occupied by the mass dM, and ρ is the density of the body at that point. In the special but extremely important case where the body is homogeneous, $i.e.$, the density is constant, we have, besides Eq. (8),

$$M = \rho V \qquad (9)$$

so that Eq. (7) may be written

$$I = \rho \int r^2 dV = \frac{M}{V} \int r^2 dV \tag{10}$$

This is the form which we shall generally use in the actual evaluation of moments of inertia.

To illustrate the procedure which must be followed, let us calculate the moment of inertia of a homogeneous slim rod of length L and mass M about an axis at right angles to the rod and passing through one end. We choose this end of the rod as an origin and let the x-axis lie along the rod. The essential point in the calculation is to choose dV so that all points in it lie at the same distance from the axis. Thus, in this case, if we proceed along the rod a distance x from O, at this distance we take a volume element of length dx and cross section A (A is the constant cross section of the rod). If the cross-section dimensions are small compared to the length of the rod (and this is the case we are considering), we may say that every point in the volume element $dV = A\,dx$ lies at the same perpendicular distance x from the axis O. Inserting this value of dV in Eq. (10), we have

$$I = \frac{M}{V} \int x^2 A\,dx = \frac{AM}{LA} \int_0^L x^2 dx$$

where we have used $V = AL$ and have inserted the limits of integration $x = 0$ to $x = L$. The value of the integral is $L^3/3$, so that we obtain

$$I = \frac{ML^2}{3} \tag{11}$$

as the moment of inertia of the rod about this axis.

From our derivation it is clear that this holds only for a rod of small cross section, and in the case of a large cross section we would have to further subdivide the body into smaller volume elements since different points of the same cross section would then lie at different distances from the axis O.

As a second example let us calculate the moment of inertia of a homogeneous solid cylinder of mass M and radius R about its

axis of symmetry.   This axis passes through the center of mass
of the body.   We must now subdivide the cylinder into volume
elements such that all the points in each element lie at the same
distance r from the axis of rotation.   It is clear that such points
lie in a cylindrical shell whose
axis is coincident with that of
the solid cylinder.   In fact, we
may think of the solid cylinder
as composed of a huge number
of cylindrical shells of different
radii fitting tightly one over the
other, the outermost shell having
a radius R and the innermost a
radius zero.   Thus our procedure
is to calculate the moment of
inertia of one of these shells, and
then add these up (integrate) for
all the shells.   For this purpose,

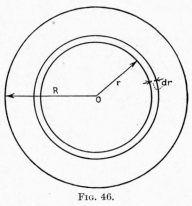

Fig. 46.

consider a cylindrical shell of radius r and thickness dr (Fig. 46).
The volume of this shell is the area of its base times l, if l is the
altitude of the cylinder.   Thus

$$dV = 2\pi rl \, dr$$

and the total volume of the solid cylinder is

$$V = \pi R^2 l$$

Inserting these values in Eq. (10) and integrating from $r = 0$
to $r = R$, there follows that

$$I = \frac{M}{\pi R^2 l}\int_0^R 2\pi l r^3 dr = \frac{2M}{R^2}\int_0^R r^3 dr$$

The value of the integral is $R^4/4$, and hence

$$I = \frac{MR^2}{2} \tag{12}$$

so that the moment of inertia is one-half the mass of the cylinder
times the square of its radius.   For convenience we give without

proof as the moment of inertia of a solid homogeneous sphere of mass M and radius R about an axis passing through its center,

$$I = \frac{2MR^2}{5} \tag{13}$$

It is often convenient to introduce a quantity known as the *radius of gyration* of a body about a specified axis. The meaning of this quantity is best described as follows: Consider a hoop or cylindrical shell of mass M and radius k. Since all the mass of the body is at a common distance k from an axis passing through the center of mass, the moment of inertia about this axis is simply Mk^2. Now suppose we consider some arbitrary rigid body whose moment of inertia about a specified axis is I. The radius of gyration of this body about this axis is denoted by k and is defined by the relation

$$Mk^2 = I \tag{14}$$

where M is the mass of the body. From the above discussion we immediately see the significance of the radius of gyration. If we were to imagine a hoop or ring of mass equal to the mass of the body and radius equal to the radius of gyration, this hoop would have the same moment of inertia about its center as the original body has about its axis of rotation. Thus the radius of gyration is that distance from the axis of rotation where we could concentrate all the mass of the body and obtain the same moment of inertia as the actual body possesses about this axis.

For the slim rod free to rotate about an axis through one end, we have

$$Mk_{\text{rod}}^2 = I = \frac{ML^2}{3}$$

according to Eq. (11), so that

$$k_{\text{rod}} = \frac{L}{\sqrt{3}} \tag{15}$$

For a solid cylinder about its axis of symmetry according to Eq. (12),

$$Mk_c^2 = \frac{MR^2}{2}$$

so that

$$k_c = \frac{R}{\sqrt{2}} \tag{16}$$

and for a solid sphere about an axis through its center

$$k_s = \sqrt{\tfrac{2}{5}}R \qquad (17)$$

61. Relation of Moments of Inertia about Different Axes.—
According to the definition of moment of inertia, its value
depends on both the rigid body and the axis about which the body
may rotate.   There is an important relation between the moment
of inertia of a body about an axis which passes through its center
of mass and the moment of inertia of the same body about any
other axis parallel to the first.   This relation may be stated as
follows:

 **The moment of inertia of a rigid body about any axis is equal
to its moment of inertia about a parallel axis passing through its
center of mass, plus the product of the mass of the body and the
square of the distance between the axes.**

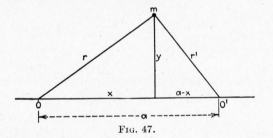

Fig. 47.

Let a be the distance between the axes and let us choose our
origin O at the center of mass and the x-axis along the line joining
O and O'.   Since our origin is the center of mass we have the
relations

$$\Sigma mx = 0 \qquad \text{and} \qquad \Sigma my = 0 \qquad (18)$$

which follow from the definition of center of mass in Sec. 49.   If
we now fix our attention on any mass point m of the body at a
distance r from O and r' from O', then, from the definition of
moment of inertia,

$$I_0 = \Sigma mr^2$$
$$I_0' = \Sigma mr'^2 \qquad (19)$$

where I_0 and I_0' are the moments of inertia about the axes at O
and O', respectively.   From Fig. 47 we see that

$$r'^2 = (a - x)^2 + y^2 = a^2 - 2ax + x^2 + y^2 = a^2 + r^2 - 2ax$$

Inserting this value of r'^2 in the expression for I_0', there follows that

$$I_0' = \Sigma ma^2 + \Sigma mr^2 - \Sigma 2amx$$

and, since a is a constant length, this may be written as

$$I_0' = a^2 \Sigma m + \Sigma mr^2 - 2a \Sigma mx$$

In the first term Σm is the sum of the masses of all the mass points in the body and hence is the total mass M. The second term is just I_0 according to Eq. (19), and because of the fact that O is the center of mass the last term is zero (Eq. 18). Thus we have

$$I_0' = Ma^2 + I_0 \tag{20}$$

which completes the proof. This theorem allows us to calculate the moment of inertia about any axis parallel to one through the center of mass in a simple manner if the moment of inertia about the latter is known.

We may also express the result embodied in Eq. (20) in terms of the radius of gyration of the body. Let k_0 be the radius of gyration referred to the axis through the center of mass, and k' the radius of gyration of the body referred to the other axis. By definition,

$$I_0' = k'^2 M \qquad \text{and} \qquad I_0 = k^2 M$$

from which follows that

$$k'^2 = k_0^2 + a^2 \tag{21}$$

There is one more point which should be mentioned in connection with the calculation of moments of inertia. Suppose we consider a rigid body as made up of several parts, let us say, three parts, which we label I, II, and III. Since the moment of inertia of the whole body is obtained by adding the quantities mr^2 for all the mass points in the body, it is clear that we may first perform this addition for part I, then for part II, and finally for part III. Let the results of this calculation be I_I, I_II, and I_III. If we now add these three quantities together we obtain the total moment of inertia I, so that

$$I = I_\mathrm{I} + I_\mathrm{II} + I_\mathrm{III}$$

or, in general, **the moment of inertia of any rigid body may be obtained by adding the moments of inertia of the various parts**

of which the body is composed. This is a convenient rule which may be illustrated in the case of a solid disk of mass M, radius R, with projecting hubs each of mass m and radius r. We may think of this body composed of three cylinders; the first a solid cylinder of mass M and radius R, and of two other solid cylinders, each of radius r and mass m. Thus the moment of inertia of the disk and hubs about the axis is given by

$$I = I_\mathrm{I} + I_\mathrm{II} + I_\mathrm{III} = \frac{MR^2}{2} + \frac{mr^2}{2} + \frac{mr^2}{2} = \frac{MR^2}{2} + mr^2$$

An example of pure rotation follows.

Example.—As an example of the application of the laws of rotational motion of rigid bodies, let us consider a uniform cylinder weighing 128 lb., 4 ft. in diameter, which is free to rotate about its own axis which is held fixed in a horizontal plane (Fig. 48). A weight hanging on a string which is wrapped tightly around the cylinder falls a distance of 16 ft. in 3 sec., starting from rest. Required are the weight hanging on the cord, the tension in the cord, the torque acting on the cylinder, and the angular velocity of the cylinder at the end of 2 sec.

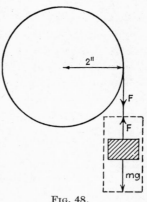

FIG. 48.

First consider only the falling weight. It is acted on by two forces, the pull of the earth and the constant tension F in the cord. For a body starting from rest and moving with constant acceleration, we have

$$s = \tfrac{1}{2}at^2$$

so that

$$16 = \tfrac{1}{2}a \cdot 9$$

or

$$a = 32/9 \text{ ft./sec}^2$$

According to Newton's second law, we have for this body

$$mg - F = ma \tag{1'}$$

where a is the constant downward acceleration of $32/9$ ft./sec². In this equation both m and F are as yet unknown.

Now consider the cylinder. If we neglect friction in the bearings, the torque acting on it about its axis is $T = Fr$, where r is the radius of the cylinder. Note that the cord leaves the surface of the cylinder tangentially and hence at right angles to a radius. Thus we have

$$T = Fr = I\alpha$$

or

$$F = \frac{I}{r}\alpha \tag{2'}$$

In this equation F and α are as yet unknown. r is known and I can be calculated from the given data.

In Eqs. (1') and (2') we have three unknowns, F, m, and α, and we need one more equation to effect a solution.   This is a geometrical relation between the angular acceleration of the cylinder and the acceleration of the falling weight.   If the cord does not slip, the acceleration of a point on the cord must equal the tangential acceleration of a point on the circumference of the cylinder, and, furthermore, the acceleration of the weight is equal to that of any point of the cord.   Thus, since $a_t = r\alpha$,

$$a = r\alpha \tag{3'}$$

Using this relation, Eq. (2') can be written as

$$F = \frac{I}{r^2}a \tag{2''}$$

and, adding Eqs. (1') and (2''), we eliminate F.   This yields

$$mg = ma + \frac{I}{r^2}a \tag{4'}$$

The moment of inertia of the cylinder about its axis is

$$I = \frac{Mr^2}{2} = \frac{128}{2 \times 32} \times (2)^2 = 8 \text{ slug-ft.}^2$$

and hence Eq. (4') becomes

$$32m = \frac{32m}{9} + 2 \times \frac{32}{9}$$

from which

$$m = \tfrac{1}{4} \text{ slug}$$

and the falling weight is

$$mg = \frac{32}{4} = 8 \text{ lb.}$$

The tension in the cord is most easily calculated from Eq. (2'') as

$$F = \frac{8}{4} \cdot \frac{32}{9} = \frac{64}{9} = 7.1 \text{ lb.}$$

and the torque acting on the cylinder is

$$T = Fr = 7.1 \times 2 = 14.2 \text{ lb.-ft.}$$

To calculate the angular velocity when $t = 2$ sec., we remember that the angular acceleration is constant and that the cylinder starts from rest. Then

$$\omega = \alpha t$$

so that

$$\omega = \frac{16}{9} \times 2 = 3.55 \text{ radians/sec.}$$

62. Energy Relations for Rotation.—We now shall investigate the expressions for the kinetic energy and for the work done by the forces acting on a rigid body which is free to rotate about a fixed

axis. Consider a particle m_1 of the rigid body at a distance r_1 from the axis of rotation. Its speed is

$$v_1 = r_1\omega$$

where ω is the angular velocity of the rigid body about this axis (the common angular velocity of all the points of the body). Its kinetic energy is by definition

$$(K.E.)_1 = \tfrac{1}{2}m_1v_1^2 = \tfrac{1}{2}m_1r_1^2\omega^2$$

Similarly, for a second particle m_2 at a distance r_2,

$$(K.E.)_2 = \tfrac{1}{2}m_2v_2^2 = \tfrac{1}{2}m_2r_2^2\omega^2$$

with a similar expression for each mass point in the body. Now the total kinetic energy of the body is equal to the sum of the kinetic energies of all the particles of which it is composed, so that we have

$$K.E. = \tfrac{1}{2}\omega^2(m_1r_1^2 + m_2r_2^2 + m_3r_3^2 + \cdots)$$

or more concisely

$$K.E. = \tfrac{1}{2}(\Sigma mr^2)\omega^2 = \tfrac{1}{2}I\omega^2 \tag{22}$$

We now are in a position to derive the work-energy theorem for rotating rigid bodies. We start with the equation

$$T = I\frac{d\omega}{dt}$$

where T is the resultant torque (sum of all the torques) and I the moment of inertia about the axis of rotation. In time dt, the body turns through an angle $d\phi$. Multiply both sides of this equation by $d\phi$, and it becomes

$$T\,d\phi = I\frac{d\omega}{dt}d\phi = Id\omega\frac{d\phi}{dt}$$

Now $d\phi/dt = \omega$ from the definition of angular velocity so that we have

$$T\,d\phi = I\omega\,d\omega \tag{23}$$

The left-hand side of the equation is the work done by the external torques when the body rotates through a small angle $d\phi$. If we wish the total work done by these torques when the body rotates from an initial angle ϕ_0 to an angle ϕ, we must integrate Eq. (23) from ϕ_0 to ϕ. Thus

$$W = \int_{\phi_0}^{\phi} T \, d\phi = \int_{\omega_0}^{\omega} I\omega \, d\omega = I\int_{\omega_0}^{\omega} \omega \, d\omega$$

where ω_0 is the initial angular velocity (at ϕ_0) and ω the angular velocity at the position ϕ. Carrying out the integration on the right-hand side, we find

$$W = \int_{\phi_0}^{\phi} T \, d\phi = \tfrac{1}{2}I\omega^2 - \tfrac{1}{2}I\omega_0^2 \tag{24}$$

which is the work-energy theorem since the right-hand side is the increase of kinetic energy of the body. In the special case of a constant torque Eq. (24) takes the form

$$T(\phi - \phi_0) = \tfrac{1}{2}I\omega^2 - \tfrac{1}{2}I\omega_0^2 \tag{24a}$$

We can use these results to check the answers we obtained to the example of the last section. There we found that the falling weight had an acceleration of $\tfrac{32}{9}$ ft./sec.^{2}, and hence, in 2 sec. from rest, it descended a distance

$$s = \tfrac{1}{2} \cdot \tfrac{32}{9} \cdot 2^2 = 7.1 \text{ ft.}$$

Thus 7.1 ft. of the string are unwrapped from the cylinder in this time. When the cylinder turns through an angle $d\phi$, a length of string $ds = R \, d\phi$ becomes unwrapped so that we have

$$s = R(\phi - \phi_0)$$

or

$$\phi - \phi_0 = \frac{s}{R} = \frac{7.1 \text{ ft.}}{2 \text{ ft.}} = 3.55 \text{ radians}$$

Since the system starts from rest, $\omega_0 = 0$ and the torque is

$$T = 14.2 \text{ lb.-ft.}$$

and the moment of inertia $I = 8$ slug-ft.^{2}. Since the torque is constant, we may apply Eq. (24a) and obtain

$$(14.2)(3.55) = \frac{8\omega^2}{2}$$

$$\omega^2 = \frac{(7.1)^2}{4}$$

$$\omega = 3.55 \text{ radians/sec.}$$

which checks the result found by other methods.

Another method of finding this result is as follows: The sum of all the forces which may do work on the system (cylinder and hanging body) is just the weight of the hanging body. In descending a distance of 7.1 ft. this force of 8 lb. does an amount of work equal to (7.1)(8) ft.-lb. Now this must be equal to the total gain of kinetic energy of the system, so that

$$(7.1)(8) = \tfrac{1}{2}mv^2 + \tfrac{1}{2}I\omega^2$$

Now, $v = at = (\tfrac{32}{9})2$ ft./sec., where v is the velocity of the falling body at the end of 2 sec., so that

$$(7.1)8 = \tfrac{1}{2} \cdot \tfrac{8}{32} \cdot (\tfrac{64}{9})^2 + 4\omega^2$$
$$\omega^2 = 12.6$$
$$\omega = 3.55 \text{ radians/sec.}$$

as before.

63. Combined Translation and Rotation.—We are now prepared to examine the most general plane motion of a rigid body. As we have repeatedly emphasized, the most general motion can be thought of as a combination of translation of the center of mass in a plane and of rotation about an axis perpendicular to this plane and passing through the center of mass. We have already discussed in some detail each of these motions separately and there remains only the task of combining our results. The motion of the center of mass is determined by Eqs. (1), Sec. 58, and these are

$$\left.\begin{array}{l} \sum X = M\dfrac{d\bar{v}_x}{dt} \\[2ex] \sum Y = M\dfrac{d\bar{v}_y}{dt} \end{array}\right\} \tag{25}$$

and the equation for rotation about an axis through the center of mass is given in Eq. (5) which we now write as

$$\sum T = I_0\frac{d\omega}{dt} \tag{26}$$

using I_0 to indicate that the rotation is taken about the center of mass.

Equations (25) and (26) form the complete set of equations of motion, and we shall now proceed to illustrate their use in discussing the motion of rolling bodies. If a body rolls without slipping, there is a definite relation between the angular motion of the body about its center of mass and the linear motion of its center of mass.   Let us formulate the condition for rolling for the case of a symmetrical body such as a cylinder or sphere rolling on a horizontal plane.   If the body rolls without slipping, then each point of the circumference comes in contact with a different point of the horizontal plane.   Thus, while the body makes one complete revolution about O, the point of contact P progresses to the right a distance equal to the circumference of the circle, or $2\pi R$.   Now the center of mass O is always located directly above the point of contact so it also moves to the right a distance $2\pi R$.   In general if the body rotates through an angle $d\phi$ in time dt, a point on its circumference moves a distance $ds = R\,d\phi$ and this is equal to the distance moved by the center of mass in this same time dt.   Thus we have as the general condition for rolling (without slipping)

$$ds = R\,d\phi \tag{27}$$

where ds is the distance the center of mass moves parallel to the surface on which the body rolls and $d\phi$ is the angle turned through by the body in the same time.   If we divide each side of Eq. (27) by the time dt, it follows that

$$\left.\begin{aligned} \frac{ds}{dt} = v = R\frac{d\phi}{dt} = R\omega \\[2ex] v = R\omega \end{aligned}\right\} \tag{28}$$

or

Finally, if we differentiate this equation with respect to t,

$$\left.\begin{aligned} \frac{dv}{dt} = R\frac{d\omega}{dt} \\[2ex] a = R\alpha \end{aligned}\right\} \tag{29}$$

or

so that the center of mass has an acceleration equal to the radius R times the angular acceleration of the rolling body.   Any one of the three conditions as expressed by Eq. (27), (28), or (29) is sufficient to establish the fact that the body rolls without slipping.

Let us take as an example the case of a homogeneous cylinder rolling on a horizontal plane under the action of a horizontal force F whose line of action passes through the center of the cylinder, and the friction force necessary to cause rolling.   If we take the direction of F as the $+x$-axis, then the friction force f

acts in the negative x-direction (Fig. 49). The equation of motion for the translation of the center of mass is, according to Eq. (25),

$$F - f = M\frac{d\bar{v}_x}{dt} \qquad (30)$$

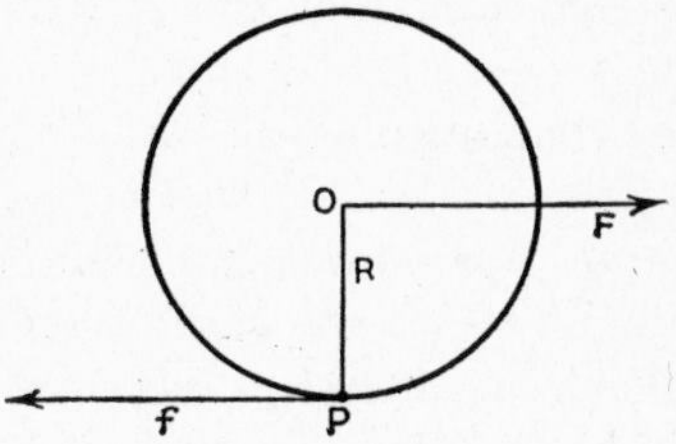

and, since there is no y-component of acceleration, we need not write the other equation for translation.

The equation for the rotational acceleration about O is, according to Eq. (26),

FIG. 49.

$$T = f \times R = I_0\frac{d\omega}{dt} \qquad (31)$$

and, since $I_0 = \frac{1}{2}MR^2$, this equation may be written as

$$f \times R = \frac{1}{2}MR^2\frac{d\omega}{dt}$$

or

$$f = \frac{1}{2}MR\frac{d\omega}{dt}$$

The condition for rolling [Eqs. (29)], however, is

$$\frac{d\bar{v}_x}{dt} = R\frac{d\omega}{dt}$$

so that

$$f = \frac{1}{2}M\frac{d\bar{v}_x}{dt} \qquad (32)$$

If we now insert this value of the friction force in Eq. (30) we find

$$F - \frac{M}{2}\frac{d\bar{v}_x}{dt} = M\frac{d\bar{v}_x}{dt}$$

or

$$F = \frac{3}{2}M\frac{d\bar{v}_x}{dt} \qquad (33)$$

so that the translational acceleration of a rolling cylinder is two-thirds as large as it would be on a perfectly smooth surface under the action of the same force F, since then we would have pure translation.

64. Instantaneous Axis for Rolling Bodies.—In the last section we have discussed the motion of a rolling body as a translation of its center of mass plus a rotation about this center.   There is another important method of discussing the motion of a rolling body (or, in fact, of any rigid-body motion) which depends on the fact that at any instant of time the body is rotating about a definite axis.   To show that this is so, let us fix our attention on the cylinder of the last section and calculate the velocity of the point P, a point on the circumference of the cylinder which is in contact with the plane at the instant of time under consideration. Relative to the moving center of mass O, this point has a velocity $-\omega R$ (in the same direction as f), and, since the center of mass itself has a velocity in space equal to v, the velocity of the point P in space is

$$v_P = v - R\omega$$

and from our condition for rolling without slipping [Eq. (28)] this is zero.   Thus we have shown that, when any point P on the circumference of the cylinder comes in contact with the plane, its velocity in space is zero.   It is easy to see that only those points which are in contact with the plane have zero velocity, and these lie in a straight line perpendicular to the paper at P (Fig. 49).   Thus we have the situation that all the points on one straight line in a rigid body have zero velocity while all other points in the body have velocities other than zero.   Clearly this is a rotation about the straight line through P.   Thus we have shown that the rolling of a cylinder is a pure rotation about an axis passing through the point of contact of cylinder and plane. Since this point of contact is not fixed in space during the motion, we call the axis of rotation an *instantaneous axis of rotation.*

We shall now prove the important result that the angular velocity (and angular acceleration) of the body about the instantaneous axis P is equal to the angular velocity (and angular acceleration) about O.   Let ω' be the angular velocity about the instantaneous axis P at any instant of time.   The linear velocity of the point O, which is a distance R from this axis, is

$$v_0 = R\omega'$$

Now from Eq. (28) the linear velocity of the point O is related to the angular velocity ω of the body about an axis through O by the equation

$$v_0 = R\omega$$

so that

$$\omega = \omega'$$

If we differentiate this equation with respect to t, it follows that

$$\alpha = \alpha'$$

Let us apply these considerations to calculate the acceleration of the cylinder in the last section, considering the motion as pure rotation about P. We then have

$$\sum T_P = I_P \frac{d\omega}{dt} \qquad (34)$$

i.e., the sum of the torques about P is equal to the moment of inertia about P times the angular acceleration. The sum of the torques is

$$\sum T_P = FR$$

and we can calculate the moment of inertia about P with the help of Eq. (20). Since the distance between P and O is R, this yields

$$I_P = I_0 + MR^2 = \tfrac{1}{2}MR^2 + MR^2 = \tfrac{3}{2}MR^2$$

Inserting these values in Eq. (34), it follows that

$$F \times R = \frac{3}{2}MR^2\frac{d\omega}{dt}$$

and, since $R\dfrac{d\omega}{dt} = \dfrac{d\bar{v}_x}{dt}$, the linear acceleration of O along the x-axis,

$$F = \frac{3}{2}M\frac{d\bar{v}_x}{dt}$$

which is identical with the result of our calculations of Sec. 63, as expressed in Eq. (33).

65. Energy Relations for Combined Translation and Rotation. We shall now derive an expression for the kinetic energy of a rigid body. Let $\bar{v}$ be the velocity of its center of mass at any instant of time and let us take its direction as that of the x-axis. Furthermore, at this instant let the angular velocity of the rigid body be ω. Consider any particle of the body m at a distance r from O. The velocity of this particle with respect to the center of mass O is $v' = r\omega$, and this vector makes an angle ϕ with the

y-direction as shown in Fig. 50. This velocity vector has components

$$v'_x = r\omega \sin \phi$$
$$v'_y = -r\omega \cos \phi$$

Now the particle m has a velocity v in space, which is the sum of the velocity of O ($\bar{v}$) and its velocity (v') with respect to O. In

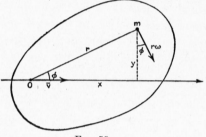

FIG. 50.

component form this is

$$v_x = \bar{v} + v'_x = \bar{v} + r\omega \sin \phi$$
$$v_y = 0 + v'_y = -r\omega \cos \phi$$

The kinetic energy of this particle is, by definition,

$$\tfrac{1}{2}m(v_x^2 + v_y^2) = \tfrac{1}{2}m\bar{v}^2 + \tfrac{1}{2}mr^2\omega^2(\sin^2 \phi + \cos^2 \phi) + m\omega\bar{v}r \sin \phi$$

To get the total kinetic energy of the body we add up over all particles in the body, obtaining

$$K.E. = \tfrac{1}{2}\bar{v}^2(\Sigma m) + \tfrac{1}{2}\omega^2(\Sigma mr^2) + \omega\bar{v}(\Sigma mr \sin \phi)$$

Now

$$\Sigma m = M$$

the total mass of the body; and

$$\Sigma mr^2 = I_0$$

the moment of inertia about the center of mass O;

$$\Sigma mr \sin \phi = \Sigma my = 0$$

since the origin O is the center of mass, and our expression reduces to

$$K.E. = \tfrac{1}{2}M\bar{v}^2 + \tfrac{1}{2}I_0\omega^2 \tag{35}$$

Or, in words:

The kinetic energy of a rigid body is equal to the kinetic energy of a particle of mass equal to the mass of the body moving with the center of mass plus the kinetic energy of rotation about the center of mass.

The work-energy theorem and the principle of conservation of mechanical energy hold unchanged if we use Eq. (35) for the kinetic energy. To understand this we must remember that the most general displacement of a rigid body in a plane is the sum of a displacement ds of the center of mass and an angular displacement $d\phi$ of the body about an axis through the center of mass. The work done in the displacement ds is

$$(\Sigma F_s)ds$$

and that done in the displacement $d\phi$ is, according to Eq. (23),

$$(\Sigma T)d\phi$$

Since the first expression equals the change in translational kinetic energy, and the second equals the change in rotational kinetic energy, it follows that the total work done by all the external forces equals the change in the total kinetic energy of the body.

In the special case of rolling without slipping these relations become much simpler. Consider a symmetrical body such as a wheel rolling on a plane (inclined or horizontal). Let R be the distance from the center of mass to the plane. Its kinetic energy is, according to Eq. (35),

$$K.E. = \tfrac{1}{2}M\bar{v}^2 + \tfrac{1}{2}I_0\omega^2$$

and, since it rolls without slipping,

$$\omega = \frac{\bar{v}}{R}$$

Inserting this value of ω in the expression for kinetic energy, it becomes

$$K.E. = \frac{1}{2}M\bar{v}^2 + \frac{1}{2}I_0\frac{\bar{v}^2}{R^2} = \frac{1}{2}\bar{v}^2\left(M + \frac{I_0}{R^2}\right) \qquad (36)$$

and, if k_0 is the radius of gyration about the center of mass, this is

$$K.E. = \frac{1}{2}M\bar{v}^2\left(1 + \frac{k_0^2}{R^2}\right) \qquad (36a)$$

We shall now show that for a rolling body the friction force necessary to produce rolling is not a dissipative force and that

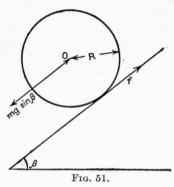

FIG. 51.

it acts as a converter of translational into rotational energy. To fix our ideas, let us suppose the rigid body rolls down an inclined plane making an angle β with the horizontal (Fig. 51). Choosing the x-axis parallel to the plane, there are two x-forces acting: $mg \sin \beta$ down the plane and the friction force f up the plane. The sum of the y-components of all the forces is zero, so we need not consider them further. Suppose the center of mass O moves a distance ds down the plane. During this displacement the body rotates through an angle $d\phi = ds/R$. The work done in the displacement ds is

$$(mg \sin \beta - f)ds$$

and that done in the displacement $d\phi$ is

$$Td\phi = (fR)d\phi = f \, ds$$

so that the total work done on the body is the sum of these two expressions

$$dW = mg \sin \beta \, ds - f \, ds + f \, ds = mg \sin \beta \, ds$$

an expression which no longer contains the friction force f. If the body rolls a distance s down the plane, the total work done on it is

$$mg \sin \beta \, s = mgh$$

where $h = s \sin \beta$ is the vertical distance through which the body falls and is the decrease in potential energy of the body. Suppose now that the body starts from rest. After moving this distance s, its kinetic energy is equal to the gain of kinetic energy so that we have

$$mg \sin \beta \, s = \frac{1}{2}m\bar{v}^2\left(1 + \frac{k_0^2}{R^2}\right)$$

Hence its velocity $\bar{v}$ at any point s from the start is given by

$$\bar{v}^2 = \frac{2g \sin \beta}{1 + \dfrac{k_0^2}{R^2}} s \tag{37}$$

If we compare this expression with that for the velocity of a mass point moving with a constant acceleration $d\bar{v}/dt = a$, and starting from rest

$$\bar{v}^2 = 2as$$

we see that the body rolls down the plane with an acceleration

$$\frac{g \sin \beta}{1 + \dfrac{k_0^2}{R^2}} \tag{38}$$

For a cylinder where $k_0^2 = \frac{1}{2}R^2$, this becomes

$$a_c = \tfrac{2}{3}g \sin \beta \tag{39}$$

and for a sphere where $k_0^2 = \frac{2}{5}R^2$, we have

$$a_s = \tfrac{5}{7}g \sin \beta \tag{40}$$

Thus we see that we may apply the principle of conservation of mechanical energy to such a motion and hence that the friction force which produces rolling does not dissipate mechanical energy.

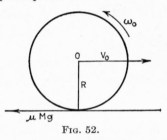

FIG. 52.

66. Rolling and Sliding.—In this paragraph we shall consider an example of rigid-body motion in which both sliding and rolling occur. Suppose a sphere or wheel is projected along a horizontal surface with an initial linear velocity v_0 and with an initial angular velocity ω_0, so that it starts sliding along the surface (Fig. 52). We consider the case when ω_0 tends to produce rolling opposite to the direction of motion. The friction force is $-\mu Mg$ and is the only unbalanced force acting. Hence

$$-\mu Mg = M\frac{d\bar{v}}{dt}$$

or

$$\frac{d\bar{v}}{dt} = -\mu g \tag{41}$$

Furthermore the friction force exerts a torque action about an axis through the center of mass O. This torque is

$$T = -\mu MgR$$

and, if the radius of gyration about the axis in question is k,

$$-\mu MgR = k^2 M \frac{d\omega}{dt}$$

whence

$$\frac{d\omega}{dt} = -\mu g \frac{R}{k^2} \tag{42}$$

or

$$R\frac{d\omega}{dt} = -\mu g \frac{R^2}{k^2} \tag{42a}$$

Adding Eqs. (41) and (42a) we find

$$\frac{d}{dt}(\bar{v} + R\omega) = -\mu g\left(1 + \frac{R^2}{k^2}\right) \tag{43}$$

Sliding ceases when $\bar{v} + R\omega = 0$, since $\bar{v} + R\omega$ is the forward velocity of the lowest point of the body. Integrating Eq. (43), we find

$$\bar{v} + R\omega = (v_0 + R\omega_0) - \mu g\left(1 + \frac{R^2}{k^2}\right)t$$

and this is zero when

$$t = \frac{v_0 + R\omega_0}{\mu g\left(1 + \dfrac{R^2}{k^2}\right)} \tag{44}$$

After this interval of time, sliding ceases. For this value of t we obtain the velocity of the body by integrating Eq. (41)

$$\bar{v} = v_0 - \mu g t$$

$$= v_0 - \frac{v_0 + R\omega_0}{1 + \dfrac{R^2}{k^2}}$$

which may be written

$$\bar{v} = \frac{R^2}{k^2 + R^2}\left(v_0 - \frac{k^2\omega_0}{R}\right) \tag{45}$$

so that the motion may be either ·backward or forward after sliding stops. If $v_0 > k^2\omega_0/R$, the body continues to roll in the same direction with the velocity $\bar{v}$, and if $v_0 < k^2\omega_0/R$, it returns to its starting point with this velocity $\bar{v}$.

For a ring, $k^2 = R^2$ and we have

$$\bar{v}_{\text{ring}} = \tfrac{1}{2}(v_0 - R\omega_0)$$

as the velocity of the center of mass when slipping stops.

For a sphere

$$k^2 = \tfrac{2}{5}R^2$$

so that

$$\bar{v}_{\text{sphere}} = \tfrac{5}{7}(v_0 - \tfrac{2}{5}R\omega_0)$$

The case where ω_0 tends to produce rolling in the direction of v_0 is left as an exercise for the student.

Problems

1. The center of mass of an automobile is 2 ft. above the ground and 4 ft. back of the front axle. The brakes when applied lock the front wheels without affecting the rear wheels. It is stated that the automobile can be brought to rest in a distance of 50 ft. without having the rear wheels leave the ground. What is the maximum speed for which this statement is true?

2. A 2-ton automobile has a wheel base of 11 ft. and its center of mass is halfway between the front and rear wheels and 3 ft. off the ground.

a. What is the maximum acceleration which the car may attain without having the front wheels leave the ground?

b. What is the traction force?

c. What is the minimum value of the coefficient of friction between the wheels and the ground which will allow this motion?

d. Calculate the upward push on each of the rear wheels and also the total force exerted by the road on these wheels.

3. A 100-lb. bench 3 ft. high with its legs 4 ft. apart has its center of gravity at the center of the top of the bench. It is pulled up a 30° incline at constant velocity by a horizontal force F acting at the center of mass. The coefficient of friction is 0.20.

a. Calculate the force F.

b. Calculate the normal force on each leg.

c. Calculate the *total* force exerted by the incline on each leg.

4. Prove by means of a direct integration that the moment of inertia of a thin rod of length L and mass M free to rotate about an axis perpendicular to the rod and passing through the center of mass is $\tfrac{1}{12}ML^2$. If the axis passes through one end of the rod, prove that the moment of inertia is $\tfrac{1}{3}ML^2$.

5. Find the moment of inertia of a hollow cylinder of mass M, inner radius R_1 and outer radius R_2.

6. A 2,400-lb. automobile is driven at a speed of 48 ft./sec. around a curve on a horizontal road, the curve being an arc of a circle of 128-ft. radius. The lateral distance between wheels is 5 ft., and the center of mass of the car is situated in a vertical plane halfway between the left and right wheels and is 2.5 ft. off the ground.

a. Calculate the vertical component of the push of the road on the wheels nearer the center of the curve.

b. What is the maximum speed with which this car can round the curve without tipping over, assuming sufficient friction to prevent skidding?

7. A slim rod has a density which varies proportionally to the distance from one end. The density at one end is twice that at the other end. Thus the density at a point x is $\rho = \rho_0\left(1 + \dfrac{x}{L}\right)$.

By integration calculate an expression for the moment of inertia of this rod about an axis passing through one end (the one of smaller density) and perpendicular to the length of the rod.

Express your answer in terms of M, the mass of the rod, and L, its length.

8. A flywheel weighs 64,000 lb. and has a radius of gyration of 10 ft.

a. What constant torque will bring it up to a speed of 300 r.p.m. in 2 min. from rest?

b. What is the angular acceleration?

c. How much work is done in getting it up to speed?

d. How many revolutions does the wheel make in the 2 min.?

9. A vertical steel tank used as a centrifuge is to be set in rotation about a vertical axis through its center. The radius of the tank is 2 ft. The top and bottom weigh 96 lb. each, and the cylindrical portion weighs 192 lb. About how long a time is required to bring it up to a speed of 1,200 r.p.m. by a 10-hp. motor?

10. A 10-lb. block is pulled up a frictionless 37° inclined plane by a string parallel to the plane. The string passes over a pulley weighing 28 lb. whose radius of gyration is $1/\sqrt{2}$ times its radius and a weight of 16 lb. hangs on the free end of the string.

a. Calculate the acceleration of the hanging weight.

b. Calculate the tension in the part of the string between the hanging weight and the pulley.

c. Calculate the tension in the part of the string between the block on the plane and the pulley.

11. Two solid disks A and B are mounted on a light shaft free to rotate about a fixed horizontal axis. Disk A weighs 6 lb. and is of radius 8 in., and disk B weighs 4 lb. and has a radius of 4 in. Strings are wrapped tightly around the surfaces of the disks leaving the disks on opposite sides of the shaft. On each string is hung a weight of 2 lb. These two suspended weights start from rest, and both are initially 4 ft. above the floor.

a. Which weight will descend?

b. How long does it take for one of the weights to reach the floor?

c. How fast is each moving at this instant of time?

12. The moment of inertia of a wheel and axle is 20 slug-ft.^{2}. When acted on by a constant external torque it speeds up from 600 to 1,200 r.p.m. in 1 min. If the external torque is then removed the wheel comes to rest in 15 min.

a. Find the angular acceleration and the angular deceleration of the wheel.

b. Find the external torque acting for the first minute and the value of the torque due to friction. (Assume the latter constant.)

c. How many revolutions does the wheel make in the first minute? in the last 10 min.?

d. How much work is done by the friction torque in bringing the wheel to rest?

13. A wheel is mounted on an axle weighing 32 lb. and 4 in. in diameter. A rope is wrapped around the axle and a weight of 40 lb. hangs at the end of the rope. If the weight descends a distance of 150 ft. from rest in 5 sec., what is the moment of inertia of the wheel?

14. A solid cylinder 8 in. in diameter and weighing 30 lb. is free to rotate about a fixed horizontal axis. A rope is wrapped around the cylinder and a weight of 5 lb. hangs freely at the end of the rope. If the system is initially at rest, what will be the angular velocity of the cylinder when the 5-lb. weight has fallen a distance of 25 ft.?

15. An Atwood's machine consists of a pulley in the form of a solid disk of mass M. When masses m_1 and m_2 are attached to the ends of the string running over the pulley, show that m_1 descends with an acceleration

$$a = \frac{m_1 - m_2}{m_1 + m_2 + \dfrac{M}{2}} g$$

16. Masses of 200 and 400 grams are connected by a light cord which passes over a frictionless pulley of radius 10 cm. The downward acceleration of the 400-gram weight is found to be 100 cm./sec.² Assuming that the cord does not slip, calculate the moment of inertia of the pulley.

17. An Atwood's machine consists of a frictionless pulley of radius 10 cm. Masses of 60 and 40 grams are attached to the ends of the string running over the pulley. The larger mass is observed to descend 49 cm. in 2 sec. from rest.

a. What is the moment of inertia of the pulley?

b. Find the pull of the string on the 40-gram mass.

18. A uniform rod 6 ft. long rotates about an axis through one end. It is held in a horizontal position and then released. Find the linear velocity of the free end when it passes through the lowest point.

19. A pencil 8 in. long is stood on end on a table and allowed to tip over. If the bottom point does not slip, find the velocity of the tip of the pencil when it hits the table.

20. A 64-lb. sphere 3 in. in radius rolls along a horizontal floor with a constant velocity of 8 ft./sec.

a. Find its translational and its rotational kinetic energy.

b. How far would this sphere roll up a 30° incline?

c. How long would it be on the inclined plane?

21. A 3-kg. uniform solid cylinder rolls on a horizontal table under the action of a horizontal force whose line of action passes through the center of the cylinder. The force is exerted by a rope which passes over a light frictionless pulley, and a 400-gram body hangs at the end of the rope. If the system starts from rest, what is the velocity of the center of mass of the cylinder when the 400-gram body has descended a distance of 40 cm.? What is the tension in the rope?

22. A uniform solid cylinder rolls up a 30° inclined plane. If its translational velocity is 16 ft./sec. at the bottom of the plane, how far from the bottom of this plane does the cylinder come to rest? What is the time required to travel this distance?

23. On a loop-the-loop apparatus a sphere is released at a height h above the lowest point of the circle. Show that the smallest value of h, such that the sphere does not leave the framework at the highest point of the circle, is $\frac{27}{10}R$, where R is the radius of the circle minus the radius of the sphere.

24. A sphere, mass 100 grams, rolls without slipping on the inside of a vertical circle. If the sphere is released from rest at the end of a horizontal diameter, what are the magnitude and direction of the force exerted on the circular framework by the sphere at the lowest point of the circle?

25. A thin uniform rod of mass 600 grams and length 1 meter is free to rotate about a fixed horizontal axis through one end of the rod. Two mass points, each of mass 250 grams, are attached to the rod, one at a position 20 cm. from the axis and the other 80 cm. from the axis. The rod is held in a horizontal position and released. Calculate the speed of each particle when the rod makes an angle of 30° with the horizontal.

26. A hoop of radius 20 cm. is free to rotate about a horizontal axis perpendicular to the plane of the hoop and passing through its rim. The mass of the hoop is 1 kg.

a. Find the moment of inertia of the hoop about this axis.

b. If the hoop is at rest when its center is directly above the axis, find its angular velocity and acceleration when the center is at the same level as the axis, and find the force exerted on the axis when the center is directly below it.

27. Two solid spheres are fixed at opposite ends of a slim rod of length 100 cm. and mass 500 grams. The rod is free to rotate in a vertical plane about an axis passing through its center. The spheres are 10 and 20 cm. in diameter and have masses of 2 and 8 kg., respectively.

a. Calculate the position of the center of mass of the system.

b. If the rod is held in a horizontal position and released, calculate the speed of the center of each sphere when the rod makes an angle of 37° with the vertical.

28. A solid homogeneous cylinder and a hollow cylinder of the same radius start rolling together from rest at the top of an inclined plane 24 ft. high and 40 ft. long.

a. Which cylinder reaches the bottom of the plane first? How long does it take?

b. What is the separation of the cylinders when the faster one reaches the bottom?

29. A 10-lb. uniform disk of 1-ft. radius is mounted so that it is free to rotate in frictionless bearings about a horizontal axis perpendicular to the plane of the disk and passing through its center. A 1-lb. small mass is rigidly attached to the rim of the disk and is initially held at rest in a position such that the radius from the center to the 1-lb. body lies above the horizontal at an angle of 30°. The system is released from rest.

a. Calculate the speed of the 1-lb. body as it passes through the lowest point of its path.

b. Calculate the force exerted by the bearings on the rotating system when the 1-lb. body is at the lowest point of its path.

30. A sphere rolls on the inside of a vertical circular track and rolls completely around the track. If the normal push of the track on the sphere is

F_2 at the bottom point of the circle and is F_1 at the top point, show that $F_2 - F_1 = \frac{3}{7}mg$, where mg is the weight of the sphere.

31. A sphere of mass M rolls on the inside of a vertical circular framework. If it starts from rest at the end of a horizontal diameter, show that the normal component of the force exerted on the sphere by the framework when the sphere is at the end of a diameter making an angle ϕ with the vertical is

$$N = \tfrac{17}{7}Mg \cos \phi$$

32. How much work is done by a horizontal force applied to an axle passing through the center of a solid cylinder weighing 10 lb. in rolling it up a plane 12 ft. long inclined 30° with the horizontal? The velocity of translation of the center of mass is 6 ft./sec. at the bottom of the plane and 10 ft./sec. at the top of the plane.

33. A sphere rolls down a 30° inclined roof. If it starts from rest at a point 17.5 ft. from the edge of the roof and the edge of the roof is 26 ft. above the ground, where is the point where it strikes the ground?

34. A brass disk is 1 in. thick and 6 in. in diameter and has projecting hubs 2 in. in diameter, each 2 in. long. Two strings are wrapped about the hubs and their ends fastened to a ceiling. The disk is then allowed to fall and starts rotating as the string unwinds. What is the downward velocity of the disk 3 sec. after it starts to fall? How far does it fall in the next second?

35. A cylindrical spool of mass M has a cylindrical axle d cm. in diameter, l cm. long, and disks D cm. in diameter and L cm. thick. Its moment of inertia about its figure axis is I. A string is wound about the axle and leaves the bottom of the axle at an angle ϕ with the horizontal. The spool is rolled along by exerting a force F on the string. Discuss the ensuing motion, distinguishing among the various possibilities.

36. A wheel rolls along the ground with a constant velocity of its center of mass of 10 ft./sec. Find the velocity of the points on the rim at both ends of the vertical diameter and the horizontal diameter

a. Relative to the center of the wheel.

b. Relative to the ground.

Sketch the path of a point on the rim during a complete revolution of the wheel.

37. A uniform rod 2 ft. long rotates freely in a vertical plane about an axis through one end. On the other end is a fixed body of mass equal to that of the rod. If the velocity of this body at the bottom point of its path is three times as great as its velocity at the top point, calculate this latter velocity.

38. A spool consisting of two disks each of mass 100 grams and radius 10 cm., connected by an axle of mass 20 grams and radius 5 cm., rests on a 30° inclined plane. A string is wrapped around the axle, leaving the axle on its top side and passing over a frictionless pulley of negligible moment of inertia at the top of the plane. On the end of the string hangs a 100-gram body. If the spool rolls, calculate how long it takes for the hanging weight to descend a distance of 70 cm. from rest.

39. Solve Prob. 38, if the string leaves the axle on its bottom side.

40. A 4-lb. block is pulled on a horizontal table by a string which passes over a smooth pulley and is wrapped around the rim of a 16-lb. wheel of radius 8 in. The radius of gyration of the wheel is 4 in., and the coefficient of friction between the block and table is 0.5. The system starts from rest, and the string unwinds from the wheel starting it rotating as it falls. How fast is the block moving when the wheel has fallen a distance of 5 ft.? How far has the block gone in this time?

41. The fixed pulley of an Atwood's machine has a mass of 600 grams, a radius of 8 cm., and a radius of gyration about its axis of 6 cm. One end of the string passing over this pulley is wrapped around the surface of a 500-gram thin hollow cylinder. A 200-gram body is hung on the other end of the string. What is the acceleration of the center of the hollow cylinder? What is the acceleration of the 200-gram weight?

42. Two inclined planes stand back to back. On the plane of angle θ_1 is a cylinder of mass M, radius R; on the plane of angle θ_2 is a block of mass m. They are connected by a string passing over a frictionless pulley of negligible moment of inertia at the top of the planes, and the line of action of the string passes through the center of mass of the cylinder. The cylinder rolls, and the coefficient of friction between block and plane is μ. Prove that, if

$$m \sin \theta_2 > \mu m \cos \theta_2 + M \sin \theta_1$$

the block will descend, and that, if

$$M \sin \theta_1 > \mu m \cos \theta_2 + m \sin \theta_2$$

the cylinder will roll down the plane.

43. A spool with wheels of radius R_2 and an axle of radius R_1 rests on a horizontal table. A string wrapped around the axle leaves the underside at an angle of θ above the horizontal. Prove that, if $\cos \theta > R_1/R_2$, the string will unwind and, if $\cos \theta < R_1/R_2$, it will wind up.

44. A homogeneous sphere of radius R is projected up along an inclined plane of angle α with an initial angular velocity ω_0 and initial linear velocity v_0. The coefficient of friction is μ. Discuss the motion following the argument of Sec. 66.

45. A homogeneous sphere of radius r is placed on top of a large fixed sphere of radius R and rolls on it without slipping. If the rolling sphere starts from rest at the top point:

a. Find an expression for the speed of the center of the rolling sphere when it is a distance h below the starting point.

b. Find an expression for the angular velocity of the sphere at the above position.

c. For what value of h will the small sphere leave the surface of the large one?

CHAPTER XI

SPECIAL RIGID-BODY MOTIONS

In this chapter we shall bring to a conclusion our study of rigid-body motions, and, although we shall confine our attention to certain special kinds of motion, it will be necessary in so doing to generalize the concepts introduced in the previous chapter. The first part of our study will take up certain problems of pure rotation about a fixed axis under the action of a variable torque, leading us to so-called *angular* harmonic motion which is the rotational analogue of simple harmonic motion. The second part of the work will be concerned with the simplest kind of rigid-body motion in which we drop the restriction that we have plane motion of the body. It is in this latter connection that it will be necessary to extend our definition of torque and angular velocity so that the vector nature of these quantities is brought to light.

67. The Physical Pendulum.—We have already discussed the motion of a simple pendulum from the standpoint of simple harmonic motion, and have found that for small oscillations the period T is given by

FIG. 53.

$$T = 2\pi\sqrt{\frac{l}{g}} \qquad (1)$$

If we now wish to consider the pendulum motion of a rigid body suspended on a fixed horizontal axis, the so-called physical pendulum, it is simplest to consider pendulum motion as a pure rotation about the axis of suspension.

For a simple pendulum (Fig. 53), we write, as the torque τ acting on the body,

$$\tau = -mgl \sin \theta \qquad (2)$$

If we take θ positive for counterclockwise rotation about a fixed axis we may write

191

$$\tau = I\alpha = I\frac{d^2\theta}{dt^2} \tag{3}$$

where we have

$$I = ml^2 \tag{4}$$

Inserting Eq. (2) in Eq. (3) we find, as the differential equation of the motion,

$$\frac{d^2\theta}{dt^2} + \frac{g}{l}\sin\theta = 0 \tag{5}$$

For angles small enough so that we may replace $\sin\theta$ by θ we know that the motion is simple harmonic with the period given by Eq. (1).

For a physical pendulum Eq. (3) is of course still valid, and Eq. (2) may be used if we replace l by L, the distance from the axis of support to the center of mass C (Fig. 54). If I denotes the moment of inertia of the body about the fixed axis, we have

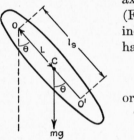

$$\tau = -mgL\sin\theta = I\frac{d^2\theta}{dt^2}$$

or

$$\frac{d^2\theta}{dt^2} + \frac{mgL}{I}\sin\theta = 0 \tag{6}$$

Fig. 54.

which is exactly the same form as Eq. (5) if we replace l by I/mL. Hence, for small oscillations, a physical pendulum oscillates with the period

$$T = 2\pi\sqrt{\frac{I}{mgL}} = 2\pi\sqrt{\frac{k^2}{gL}} \tag{7}$$

where k is the radius of gyration of the body about the axis through O. Comparison of Eq. (7) with Eq. (1) shows that the period is the same as that of a simple pendulum of length

$$l_s = \frac{I}{mL} = \frac{k^2}{L} \tag{8}$$

l_s is known as the length of the equivalent simple pendulum. The point O', which lies a distance l_s from O, is known as the *center of oscillation* of the physical pendulum with respect to O. The point O' is the point where we may concentrate all the mass and retain the same oscillatory motion about O.

68. Center of Oscillation.—Let us denote the period of a physical pendulum oscillating about an axis through O by T_0, and its period when oscillating about an axis through O' by T_0'.

If O' is the center of oscillation with respect to O, then

$$T_0 = T_0' \tag{9}$$

From Eq. (7) we have

$$T_0 = 2\pi\sqrt{\frac{k^2}{gL}} = 2\pi\sqrt{\frac{l_s}{g}} \tag{10}$$

and

$$T_0' = 2\pi\sqrt{\frac{k'^2}{g(l_s - L)}} \tag{11}$$

Let us call the radius of gyration about an axis through the center of mass k_0. We then have by virtue of Eq. (21), Chap. X,

$$k^2 = k_0^2 + L^2 \qquad \text{and} \qquad k'^2 = k_0^2 + (l_s - L)^2$$

and, by Eq. (8),

$$k^2 = Ll_s$$

so that

$$k_0^2 = L(l_s - L)$$

Inserting this into the expression for k'^2, we find

$$k'^2 = (l_s - L)l_s$$

so that Eq. (11) becomes

$$T_0' = 2\pi\sqrt{\frac{l_s(l_s - L)}{g(l_s - L)}} = 2\pi\sqrt{\frac{l_s}{g}} = T_0 \tag{12}$$

which completes the proof.

O and O' are known as *conjugate points* of the pendulum. It is clear that the length of the equivalent simple pendulum is equal to or greater than the distance from the axis to the center of mass, *i.e.*, $l_s \geq L$. The proof is left to the student.

69. The Torsion Pendulum.—Consider a rigid body suspended by a wire. If a torque τ is applied which twists the wire about its axis, it is found experimentally that when the wire comes to rest it has twisted through an angle θ which is proportional to τ,

$$\tau = k'\theta \tag{13}$$

If the external torque is removed, a restoring torque equal to $-k'\theta$ acts on the body and it performs rotatory harmonic motion. Such a device is known as a *torsion pendulum*.

If the moment of inertia of the body about an axis coincident with that of the wire is I, we may write (neglecting the small moment of inertia of the wire)

$$I\alpha = -k'\theta$$

or

$$I\frac{d^2\theta}{dt^2} + k'\theta = 0 \qquad (14)$$

Equation (14) is identical with Eq. (6) if in the latter we replace sin θ by θ. Hence we have simple harmonic motion with period

$$T = 2\pi\sqrt{\frac{I}{k'}} \qquad (15)$$

k' is called the *coefficient of torsional stiffness* of the wire and we shall learn how to calculate its dependence on the dimensions of the wire later.

The torsion pendulum may be used to determine the moment of inertia of complicated bodies experimentally. The suspended body may be in the form of a platform. With the platform alone, the period may be found to be T_1. A body of known moment of inertia A (such as a solid disk) may then be placed on the platform and the period again determined as T_2.

Finally the disk is replaced by the body whose moment of inertia B is to be found, and the period of vibration T_3 is measured.

We are thus led to the three equations

$$T_1 = 2\pi\sqrt{\frac{I}{k'}}$$

$$T_2 = 2\pi\sqrt{\frac{I+A}{k'}}$$

$$T_3 = 2\pi\sqrt{\frac{I+B}{k'}}$$

which contain the three unknowns I, k', and B. Of course, this result refers to moments of inertia about an axis coincident with that of the wire.

70. Angular Velocity and Torque as Vectors.—We have thus far treated angular velocities and torques as algebraic quantities, and this has been sufficient as long as we confined ourselves to studies of rotation about an axis whose direction in space remains unaltered during the motion. We must now extend these defini-

tions to take care of more general motions. The complete specification of either an angular velocity or a torque involves both a
magnitude and a direction (the direction of the axis about
which the body rotates or about which the moment of a force is
taken). This suggests strongly that these quantities are vectors,
and it turns out that this is the case.

Consider a rigid body rotating about an axis, *e.g.*, a wheel
spinning on its axle. We define the angular velocity ω of the body
as a vector drawn along the axis of rotation, of magnitude
$d\phi/dt$, where $d\phi$ is the angle through which the body turns in
time dt. Furthermore, the vector is drawn in the direction in
which a right-handed screw would move if rotated in the same
sense as the body rotates.

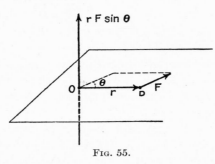

Fig. 55.

The definition of a vector torque is as follows: Consider a force
F acting at a point P (Fig. 55). If we wish the moment of this
force about a point O, we construct the vector $r = OP$. The
vectors r and F determine a plane, and the axis about which the
torque is taken is the perpendicular to this plane through the
point O. The moment of F is then a vector of magnitude

$$T = Fr \sin \theta \qquad (16)$$

where θ is the angle between the direction of r and that of F,
and it is drawn along the axis at right angles to both r and F.
The sense of the vector is determined by rotating the vector r
about the axis until its direction coincides with that of F, the
rotation to take place through the smallest angle possible. The
direction in which a right-handed screw would move when so
rotated is then the direction of the vector T.

The above definition of moment of a force as a vector can
obviously be extended to vectors other than forces.

71. Angular Momentum and Its Conservation.—In Chap. VIII we have seen that a direct application of Newton's second law to systems of particles led to theorems concerning the motion of the center of mass of such systems. In effect the fundamental law states that the sum of the external forces equals the rate of change of linear momentum of the system. There is a similar fundamental law concerning the rotational motion of a mechanical system, and we shall develop this law and examine some of its consequences in this section.

First, let us examine the motion of a single particle of mass m. We define the *angular momentum* of this particle about a point O as the moment of the momentum vector of the particle about this point, and this is a vector directed at right angles to the momentum vector and to the radius vector r drawn from O to the point where the particle is situated, as explained in the previous section. The fundamental theorem for rotation may be stated as follows: *The torque about any point of the resultant force acting on the particle is equal to the rate of change of angular momentum of the particle about the same point.*

If we denote the angular momentum by p, then this theorem can be symbolically written as

$$T = \frac{dp}{dt} \tag{17}$$

This is a vector equation and really represents three inde-

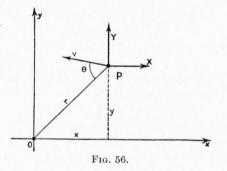

Fig. 56.

pendent equations, one for each degree of freedom of the particle. Applied to a system of particles or to a rigid body, the same form of the equation still holds where T represents the vector sum of the external torques acting on the system and p the vector sum of the angular momenta of all the particles of which the system is composed, or, briefly, the resultant angular momentum of the system.

We shall now indicate the derivation of Eq. (17). Consider a particle of mass m located at point P and moving with a velocity v as shown in Fig. 56. We choose an arbitrary origin O and let the x-y plane be the plane containing the vectors r and v, as shown. The x- and y- components of the resultant force F acting on m will be denoted by X and Y, respectively, and those of r by x and y. The second law of motion requires that

$$\left. \begin{array}{l} X = \dfrac{d}{dt}(mv_x) \\[2ex] Y = \dfrac{d}{dt}(mv_y) \end{array} \right\} \tag{18}$$

If we multiply the first equation by y, the second by x, and subtract the first from the second, the left-hand side of the resulting equation becomes $xY - yX$. From Eq. (3) of Chap. IX, we see that this is the torque about O or, more precisely, the component of the torque of the force F at right angles to the x-y plane which we shall call the z-component of the torque. The right-hand side of the same equation is

$$x\frac{d}{dt}(mv_y) - y\frac{d}{dt}(mv_x) = \frac{d}{dt}[x(mv_y) - y(mv_x)]$$

The expression inside the square bracket is just the z-component of the angular momentum which we denote by p_z, so that we have

$$T_z = xY - yX = \frac{d}{dt}[x(mv_y) - y(mv_x)] = \frac{d}{dt}(p_z) \tag{19}$$

In exactly the same way one can show that equations similar to Eq. (19) hold for the x- and y-components so that Eq. (17) has been derived for a single particle.

For a system of particles or for a rigid body we have an equation identical with Eq. (19) for each particle; upon adding them the left-hand side becomes the sum of the z-components of the external torques (the torques due to internal forces add up to zero), and the right-hand side equals the rate of change of the z-component of the resultant angular momentum of the system. Thus the proof is complete.

If the system of particles performs plane motion, the above results take a more familiar form. Referring back to Fig. 56, we have for the angular momentum of the particle m,

$$p = mvr \sin \theta \tag{20}$$

and since $v \sin \theta$ is the component of velocity perpendicular to r, it can be written as $r\omega$, where ω is the angular velocity about O. Thus Eq. (20) becomes

$$p = mr^2\omega \tag{21}$$

and the total angular momentum of the system becomes

$$p = \Sigma mr^2\omega \tag{22}$$

For rigid bodies performing plane motion, ω is the same for all particles, and Eq. (22) takes the simpler form

$$p = \omega(\Sigma mr^2) = I\omega \tag{23}$$

so that for this case the angular momentum of the rigid body about the axis through O is equal to the product of the moment of inertia and the angular velocity taken about the same axis. Inserting this expression for p into Eq. (17) and remembering that I is a constant for a rigid body, we obtain the familiar equation

$$T = \frac{d}{dt}(I\omega) = I\frac{d\omega}{dt} = I\alpha \tag{24}$$

We now are in a position to state an important consequence of Eq. (17): **If a system of bodies is acted on by no external forces, its angular momentum about any axis is constant.** This theorem is known as the conservation of angular momentum. For a system of particles performing motion in a plane, it can be written as

$$p = \Sigma mr^2\omega = \text{constant} \tag{25}$$

and for the special case of a common angular velocity ω of all the particles it takes the simpler form

$$p = I\omega = \text{constant} \tag{26}$$

As an example of an application of the theorem of the conservation of angular momentum, we may consider the sun as practically free from external forces. The sun is supposed to be constantly shrinking in size; if this is so, its angular velocity about its axis must continually increase to keep its angular momentum constant.

72. Angular Impulse—Angular-momentum Theorem.—For translational motion we have the theorem that the impulse of a force which acts for a time t is equal to the change of linear momentum of the body on which the force acts during that time. There is an analogous theorem for rotation. According to Eq. (17) we have

$$T = \frac{dp}{dt} \tag{27}$$

where T is the resultant of the external torques. Integrating this equation from $t = 0$ to $t = t$, we obtain

$$\int_0^t T dt = p_t - p_0 \tag{28}$$

or, in words, *the impulse of a torque (angular impulse) acting for time t equals the change in angular momentum during this time interval. It must not be forgotten that p is a vector.*

For plane motion of a rigid body or of a system of particles of common angular velocity ω, this becomes

$$\int_0^t T dt = (I\omega)_t - (I\omega)_0 \tag{29}$$

73. Center of Percussion.—If a rigid body held fixed at a point is struck a blow, there will be, in general, a transfer of momentum to the body which holds the rigid body fixed.

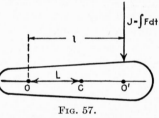

Fig. 57.

This transfer of momentum will just equal the impulse of the force exerted on the rigid body at the point of support. Suppose the fixed axis is through O, the center of mass at C, the blow of impulse J is struck at O', and the impulse of the axis on the rigid body is J' (Fig. 57).

From the impulse-momentum theorem, we have

$$J + J' = m\bar{v} = mL\omega$$

if the body is initially at rest and the angular velocity about O produced by the blow is ω. The angular momentum produced by the blow is

$$Jl = I\omega$$

so that the impulse J' is

$$J' = mL\omega - \frac{I\omega}{l} = \frac{m\omega L}{l}\left[l - \frac{I}{mL}\right]$$

and this will be in the same direction as J or opposite to it depending on whether l is greater or less than I/mL.   If the axis absorbs no momentum, then $J' = 0$, and hence

$$l = \frac{I}{mL} = \frac{k^2}{L}$$

which is identical with Eq. (8) and shows that O' is the center of oscillation with respect to O. O' is also known as the *center of percussion* with respect to O.

Anyone who has played baseball knows the "sting" experienced if the ball is not hit at the center of percussion of the bat.

74. The Gyroscope; Precession.—In our study of rigid-body motions up to this point, we have restricted ourselves to motions involving rotations about axes of *fixed* direction, *i.e.*, we have considered only changes of magnitude of the vector angular momentum and not changes of direction of this vector.   The situation is entirely analogous to the study of the motion of a mass point in a straight line, where only changes in speed could occur.   In considering motions of a mass point in a plane, we saw that the most general acceleration (and hence motion derived from it) could be compounded of a rate of change of magnitude of the velocity vector (tangential acceleration) and a rate of change of direction of the velocity vector (normal acceleration).   Similarly, to study the most general motion of a rigid body we must consider changes in the direction of the angular-momentum vector as well as changes in the magnitude thereof.   Such a study would take us far beyond the scope of this book, and we shall restrict our attention to the simplest sort of rigid-body motion which illustrates the effect of a torque changing only the *direction* of the angular momentum.   This motion is entirely analogous to the motion of a mass point in a circle with constant speed where the velocity changes only in direction at a constant rate and is known as the *steady precession of a gyroscope.*

By a gyroscope we shall understand a symmetrical rigid body rotating about its axis of symmetry *which is free to change its direction.*   The steady precession of such a gyroscope is a motion in which every point of the *axis* performs circular motion with constant angular velocity.   Such a motion can be obtained by setting a wheel into rotation about an axle (the axis of symmetry) and supporting *one* end of the axle on a vertical post (Fig. 58).

The steady precession of this gyroscope consists of a circular motion of the axis OP in a *horizontal* plane with a constant angular velocity ω' about the vertical axis OA. In order that such a motion occur we must have a constant external torque such as is provided by the pull of the earth on the gyroscope (in Fig. 58, $T = MgL$). The axis about which this torque acts, *i.e.*, the direction of the torque, is perpendicular to the plane of the paper through O.

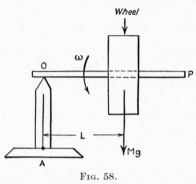

Fɪɢ. 58.

Let us consider the precessing gyroscope at the instant of time when it is in the position shown in Fig. 58. The angular momentum of the system at this instant is very nearly a vector of length $I\omega$ in the direction OP, and the torque T is a vector at right angles to $I\omega$ in a horizontal plane (Fig. 59).

Here I represents the moment of inertia about the axis OP and ω the angular velocity about this axis. During the next dt

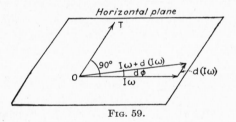

Fɪɢ. 59.

sec., the impulse of the torque is Tdt and produces a *change* in angular momentum $d(I\omega)$ which is at right angles to $I\omega$. The final angular momentum $I\omega + d(I\omega)$ is the vector shown in Fig. 59, and from the triangle we see that the angle $d\phi$ through which the axis turns in dt sec. is

$$d\phi = \frac{d(I\omega)}{I\omega} = \frac{Tdt}{I\omega} \tag{30}$$

which upon division by dt becomes

$$\omega' = \frac{d\phi}{dt} = \frac{T}{I\omega} \tag{31}$$

or

$$T = I\omega\omega' \tag{32}$$

so that we see that a constant torque acting at right angles to the already existing angular momentum produces a constant angular velocity of precession about an axis perpendicular to the axes of torque and angular momentum.   The magnitude of the angular momentum about the axis must remain constant since no torques act about this axis.

In particular, if the torque is due to gravity, then

$$T = MgL$$

where L is the distance from the vertical axis to the center of mass of the gyroscope.   Equation (32) then becomes

$$MgL = I\omega\omega' \tag{33}$$

It must be pointed out that the constant torque can only maintain the steady precession of the gyroscope but cannot alone produce such a motion.   For example, if a gyroscope, such as is shown in Fig. 58, is supported at the center of mass and suddenly released, a precession will occur, but it will not be of the steady type described above.   At the first moment the axis will drop a little, and then as precession ensues, the end of the axis OP oscillates up and down about the position it occupies during steady precession.   This latter oscillation, which is usually very fast, is called *nutation*, and there is nothing analogous to it in particle dynamics.   Since there is no component of torque about the vertical axis, the component of angular momentum about this axis must stay constant.   Thus as the gyroscope axis drops, the precession velocity increases and *vice versa*.   The steady precession of a gyroscope is a *stable* motion, and if it is disturbed the forces act in such a direction as to restore this motion.   This is analogous to static stability, as exemplified by a marble at the bottom of a bowl.   If disturbed, it oscillates about its equilibrium position.   In the gyroscopic case, steady precession is a state of *dynamic stability*, and when disturbed an oscillation takes place about this stable motion.   It is just this oscillation which we call nutation.

Problems

1. An annular disk of inner radius R_1 and outer radius R_2, mass M, is hung on a knife-edge perpendicular to the plane of the disk and performs small oscillations.

  a. What is the moment of inertia of the disk about the axis of suspension?

  b. Where is the center of oscillation?

  c. What is the period of the oscillations?

2. Show that the center of oscillation of a sphere of radius R hung on a string of length L lies a distance $\dfrac{2}{5}\dfrac{R^2}{L+R}$ below the center of the sphere.

3. A connecting rod 30 cm. long suspended from one end oscillates with a period of 1.00 sec. When suspended from the other end, it oscillates with a period of 0.896 sec. Find the radius of gyration of the rod referred to an axis through its center of mass. Where is the center of mass? What are the lengths of the equivalent simple pendulums for these two oscillations?

4. A thin rod 3 ft. long is held 6 in. from one end by a boy. If he hits a ball with this rod, where along the rod must he hit it if he is to feel no "sting"?

5. A torsion pendulum consists of a platform in the form of a circular disk 20 cm. in diameter suspended by a thin rod perpendicular to the plane of the disk. Alone it has a period of 0.75 sec. If an annular ring of outer radius 9 cm. and inner radius 8 cm. of mass 2 kg. is placed symmetrically on the disk, the period of the .pendulum is doubled. The annular ring is removed, and two homogeneous cylinders, each 4 cm. in diameter and 15 cm. high, are placed on the disk so that the axes of the cylinders intersect a common diameter of the disk and the surfaces of the cylinders are tangent to the edge of the disk. The period is found to be 1.60 sec. Find the density of the material of which the cylinders are made.

6. A flat circular disk, 20 cm. in radius, performs small oscillations as a pendulum about a horizontal axis perpendicular to the plane of the disk and 1 cm. from the center of the disk. Find the length of the simple pendulum which will have the same period.

7. A physical pendulum is constructed of a slim rod 28 cm. long at the end of which is fastened a disk of radius 14 cm. and mass equal to the mass of the rod. The center of the disk is placed at the free end of the rod, the plane of the disk being vertical.

  a. Find the radius of gyration of the pendulum about its axis of suspension.

  b. Find the period of this pendulum for small oscillations.

8. A slim rod of length 1 meter hangs vertically, supported by a string 40 cm. long. If the system is set into oscillation as a pendulum, calculate the period of small oscillations. Where is the center of oscillation of this system? (Assume that the string stays lined up with the rod during the motion.)

9. A man weighing 160 lb. runs around the edge of a horizontal turntable which is free to rotate about a vertical axis through its center. The man runs with a constant speed of 4 ft./sec. with respect to the ground, and the turntable is rotating in a direction opposite to that of the man with an angular velocity of 0.2 radian/sec. The turntable has a moment of inertia about the axis of rotation of 320 slug-ft.² and a radius of 8 ft.

If the man comes to rest with respect to the turntable, calculate the final angular velocity of the system.

10. A uniform slim rod, initially at rest on a smooth horizontal table, is struck a blow at one end of the rod in a direction perpendicular to the length of the rod. Prove that the kinetic energy gained by the rod will be greater in the ratio of 4:3 than if the other end were fixed in frictionless bearings.

11. A uniform slim rod is spinning freely with an angular velocity ω about an axis through its center and perpendicular to its length. If one end be suddenly held fixed so that the rod rotates about this end, find the new angular velocity.

12. A cylinder of mass M and radius r rolls on a horizontal table, with one end of the cylinder extending beyond the edge of the table. A long string is attached to a point on the surface of the projecting part, the string being pulled vertically downward with a constant force F. Show that the cylinder oscillates back and forth on the table with a period of $2\pi\sqrt{3Mr/2F}$ for small amplitude oscillations.

13. A man weighing 160 lb. stands on a rotating platform of negligible mass holding a pair of dumb-bells, each weighing 8 lb., at a distance of 1 ft. from his vertical axis. If the man is given an angular velocity of 2 r.p.s. about his vertical axis, calculate his angular velocity if he raises his arms and holds the dumb-bells each at a distance of 3 ft. from the axis. The radius of gyration of the man about his vertical axis is 0.45 ft. and does not change appreciably when he raises his arms. What is the change of kinetic energy?

14. A turntable in the form of a solid disk of radius 10 ft. and mass 480 lb. turns about a fixed vertical axis, making one complete revolution in 5 sec. A 160-lb. man standing at the center runs out along a radius of the table and then runs around the circumference, all at a constant speed of 5 ft./sec. relative to the turntable.

a. Calculate the torque exerted by the man on the table as he runs out along the radius.

b. What is the angular velocity of the turntable when he reaches the rim?

c. What is the angular velocity of the turntable when he runs along the circumference?

15. Calculate the change in diameter of the earth due to shrinking, necessary to produce a change of 1 sec. per day. Assume the earth is a sphere of radius 6.3×10^8 cm.

16. Two spheres, each having a radius of 2.5 cm. and a mass of 200 grams, are mounted on a uniform rod 20 cm. long having a mass of 30 grams. Initially the centers of the spheres are 5 cm. from the center of the rod (but on opposite sides), and the whole system rotates in a horizontal plane about a vertical axis through the center of the rod. Without otherwise changing the system, the catch holding the spheres in position is released, and the spheres slide out until their centers are 10 cm. from the center of the rod. If initially the rod of rotation was 12 r.p.m., what is the rate of rotation when the spheres are in the new position?

17. A slender homogeneous rod of length 60 cm., resting on a perfectly smooth horizontal surface, is struck a blow at right angles to the length of the rod at one end of the rod. Find the distance through which the center of the rod moves while it makes one complete revolution.

18. A uniform rod of mass 400 grams and length 60 cm. is pivoted at one end so that it may oscillate as a pendulum. When hanging in equilibrium it is hit at the bottom end by a horizontal blow with a hammer. Calculate the impulse of the blow, if

a. The rod rises to a horizontal position.

b. The rod just reaches a vertical position with its free end up.

c. The rod rotates in a complete circle and its angular velocity at the top position is 2 radians/sec.

19. An airplane motor weighs 320 lb. and has a radius of gyration of 1 ft. The propeller weighs 30 lb. and has a radius of gyration of 2.5 ft. The motor rotates with an angular velocity of 3,000 r.p.m. The airplane moves in a horizontal circle of radius 280 ft. with a speed of 120 miles/hr. Find the torque tending to make the airplane rotate in a vertical circle.

20. A heavy pendulum of mass M at rest is struck by a bullet of mass $m(m < < M)$, moving with a velocity v at a point p units of length below the point of support. Show that, if the pendulum swings through an angle θ,

$$v = \frac{2Mk}{mp} \sin \frac{\theta}{2} \sqrt{Lg}$$

if k is the radius of gyration about the axis and L the distance from the axis to the center of mass.

CHAPTER XII

PLANETARY MOTION; GRAVITATION

The dynamical problem of the motion of the planets about the sun properly belongs to the realm of particle dynamics. We have, however, deferred the discussion of these motions to this point since it provides a valuable historical background to the law of universal gravitation. The interpretation of the latter in terms of the idea of field of force and its properties constitutes not only a new and fundamental concept but also a valuable basis for our future discussion of the mechanics of continuous bodies. In this manner we can most clearly understand the unity of method underlying the application of Newton's laws of motion both to particles and to continua, such as liquids and gases.

75. Kepler's Laws.—The motion of the planets around the sun provided Newton with the experimental material from which he derived his law of gravitation. Kepler, using the data collected by the Danish astronomer Tycho Brahe, found empirically that the motion of the planets could be described by the following three laws:

LAW I. The planets move in ellipses and the sun is at one of the foci.

LAW II. The radius vector drawn from the sun to a planet sweeps out equal areas in equal times.

LAW III. The squares of the periods are proportional to the cubes of the semimajor axes.

These ellipses are very nearly circles and in the following discussion we shall treat the orbits as circular. In this case the sun is situated at the center of the circle and the semimajor axes of the ellipses become the radii of the circles. Our main results are valid for elliptical motion, although we shall not prove this in the discussion which follows.

For a particle moving in a circle, the area swept out by the radius in time dt, as the radius turns through an angle $d\theta$, is (Fig. 60)

$$dA = \tfrac{1}{2}R^2 d\theta \tag{1}$$

so that the rate at which the radius vector sweeps out area is

$$\frac{dA}{dt} = \frac{1}{2}R^2\frac{d\theta}{dt} = \frac{1}{2}R^2\omega \qquad (2)$$

Kepler's second law tells us that this is constant, so that the angular velocity is constant. There is no tangential acceleration, so that the force exerted on a planet by the sun is directed along a radius toward the sun.

The central acceleration is

$$a_r = -\omega^2 R \qquad (3)$$

The third law states that

$$T^2 = CR^3 \qquad (4)$$

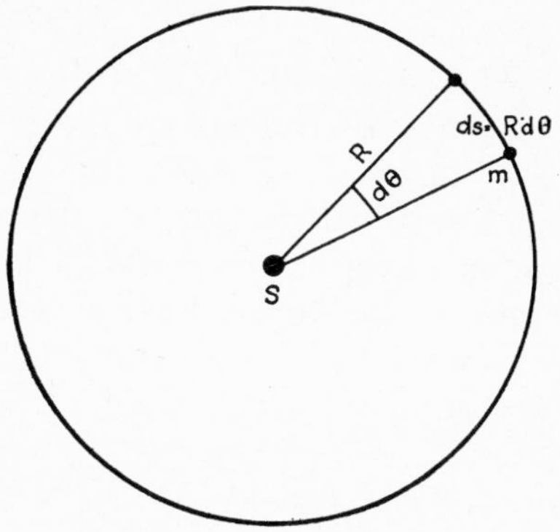

Fig. 60.

where the constant C is the same for all planets. From the definition of the period T, we have

$$T = \frac{2\pi}{\omega} \qquad \text{or} \qquad \omega = \frac{2\pi}{T}$$

so that Eq. (4) becomes

$$\omega^2 = \frac{4\pi^2}{CR^3}$$

Inserting this value of ω^2 in Eq. (3), we find for the acceleration

$$a_r = -\frac{4\pi^2}{C} \cdot \frac{1}{R^2} = -\frac{k}{R^2} \qquad (5)$$

The acceleration of a planet toward the sun is inversely proportional to the square of the distance between planet and sun, and the proportionality factor depends only on the sun since $k = 4\pi^2/C$ is the same for all the planets. The force with which the sun pulls on a planet of mass m is then

$$F = -\frac{km}{R^2} \qquad (6)$$

Newton generalized this result by placing the constant k proportional to the mass of the sun M and postulating the resulting law as valid for all mass points in the universe.

Thus, every particle in the universe attracts every other particle with a force varying directly as the product of the two masses and inversely as the square of the distance between them.

$$F = -\frac{\gamma M m}{R^2} \tag{7}$$

where γ is a universal constant of dimensions

$$[\gamma] = \frac{l^3}{mt^2}$$

and whose numerical value is

$$\gamma = 6.66 \times 10^{-8}\frac{\text{cm.}^3}{\text{gram-sec.}^2} \tag{8}$$

Of course, Newton's third law of motion requires that the planets pull on the sun with equal and opposite forces, but because of the huge mass of the sun we can neglect its acceleration caused by these forces.

76. Field of Force; Gravitational Potential.—Consider a single fixed mass point of mass M, such as the sun. This mass will exert a force on any other particle m, according to Eq. (7), no matter where the latter particle is situated. We can think of all space being affected by the mass M, and we say that a *field of force* is set up by this mass. The same general statement is valid for a system of bodies, and we can investigate the field of force by measuring the magnitude and direction of the force exerted on a small test body of mass m as it is moved from point to point of space. At each point of space we can imagine the force vector drawn, and we can construct curves whose directions, *i.e.*, the tangents to these curves, give the direction of the force exerted on the test mass at every point. The curves are known as *lines of force*, and they map out the field.

For the case of our single particle M the lines of force consist of straight lines radiating in all directions from M as a center (Fig. 61). In other cases the lines will be more complicated curves. The lines of force yield information as to the direction but not as to the magnitude of the gravitational forces. We specify the latter by introducing the idea of the *intensity* of the field. *This is defined as the force per unit mass exerted on a particle at a given point P.* The intensity of a field of force does not

depend on the mass of the test body used to explore the field but
only on the positions and masses of the attracting bodies. We
shall denote the intensity of a
gravitational field of force by G,
and for a *single* particle of mass M
we have, from Eq. (7),

$$G = \frac{F}{m} = -\frac{\gamma M}{R^2} \qquad (9)$$

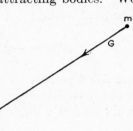

G is a vector whose magnitude is
given by the above equation and
whose direction is inward along the

FIG. 61.

line connecting M and the point P at which we calculate the field.

For a system of particles the intensity of the field may be
calculated by *vector* addition, the resultant intensity being the
vector sum of the intensities due to the individual particles. If
the lines of force form a set of parallel straight lines and if the
intensity is the same at all points, we say that the field is *uniform*.

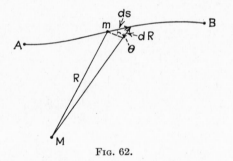

FIG. 62.

Such a uniform field exists in a limited region near the surface
of the earth, and its intensity is equal to g since the attractive
force of the earth on a particle of mass m is mg.

Gravitational forces are conservative, and it is usual to call
the field conservative. To see this for the case of a single particle,
let us calculate the work done by the force given by Eq. (7) on
m as it moves from A to B along an arbitrary curve. The work
done by this force as m moves a distance ds along the curve is
(Fig. 62)

$$dW = -\frac{\gamma mM}{R^2} ds \sin \theta$$

Now $ds \sin \theta = dR$, and we obtain

$$dW = -\gamma Mm\frac{dR}{R^2}$$

The total work is

$$W_{AB} = -\gamma Mm \int_{R_A}^{R_B} \frac{dR}{R^2} = \gamma Mm\left(\frac{1}{R_B} - \frac{1}{R_A}\right) \qquad (10)$$

and this depends only on the positions of A and B and not on the path connecting them. Thus the potential energy of the mass m in the field of a single particle M is

$$V = -\frac{\gamma Mm}{R} + \text{constant} \qquad (11)$$

If we agree to call the potential energy of m zero when it is infinitely far from M, Eq. (11) becomes

$$V = -\frac{\gamma Mm}{R} \qquad (12)$$

and is the work one must do to remove the particle m from its position to infinity.

We thus see that the equipotential surfaces are the surfaces of concentric spheres with M as center. The lines of force are everywhere at right angles to these surfaces. If we imagine two neighboring equipotential spheres and the particle m moving from a point on one of them to a point on the other, it is evident that, for a given change of potential energy dV, the shortest distance necessary is along a radius and hence along a line of force. In this direction the rate of change of potential energy with distance is greatest, and this maximum rate of change of potential energy is called the *gradient* of the potential energy. We then may state that the force acting on m is the negative gradient of the potential energy and is at right angles to the equipotential surface.

For the case under discussion the above statement in symbols becomes

$$F = -\frac{dV}{dR} = -\frac{\gamma Mm}{R^2} \qquad (13)$$

using Eq. (12), and this agrees with Eq. (7). For the general case of a field due to an arbitrary distribution of matter, it is also true that one can construct equipotential surfaces (they will not be spherical surfaces in general), and the lines of force will be normal to these surfaces everywhere. The force is given by the negative gradient of the potential energy just as in the above example.

It is convenient to introduce, not only the potential energy of a particle in the field of force, but also a gravitational potential Φ which is defined as the *potential energy per unit mass*. For the case of the field of a single particle the gravitational potential is

$$\Phi = -\frac{\gamma M}{R} \tag{14}$$

and the intensity G is the negative gradient of the potential Φ, *i.e.*,

$$G = -\frac{d\Phi}{dR}. \tag{15}$$

For the case of the field of a system of bodies, the potential is obtained by adding expressions similar to Eq. (14) for each body. The addition is algebraic (not vector) since Φ is a scalar.

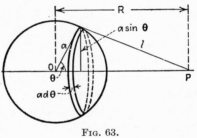

Fig. 63.

77. The Potential of a Sphere.— In the previous paragraph we have discussed the field of force and gravitational potential of a single mass point, and for further application we must discuss the field and potential of extended bodies. We consider first a very thin spherical shell of radius a and thickness t. Let us calculate the potential due to such a shell of mass M at a point P outside the shell.

Consider the ring of width $a\,d\theta$ (Fig. 63). It has a volume

$$dV = 2\pi a \sin \theta \cdot a\,d\theta \cdot t$$

and a mass

$$dM = 2\pi t\rho a^2 \sin \theta\,d\theta \tag{16}$$

if ρ is the density of our spherical shell of thickness t. This ring of mass dM consists of particles all at the same distance l from P so that the potential due to it at P is [Eq. (14)]

$$d\Phi = \frac{-\gamma\,dM}{l} = \frac{-\gamma\,dM}{\sqrt{R^2 + a^2 - 2aR \cos \theta}} \tag{17}$$

and the total potential

$$\Phi = -2\pi\rho t\gamma a^2 \int_0^\pi \frac{\sin \theta\,d\theta}{\sqrt{R^2 + a^2 - 2aR \cos \theta}} \tag{18}$$

The total mass of the spherical shell is

$$M = 4\pi a^2 t\rho$$

so that Eq. (18) becomes

$$\Phi = \frac{-\gamma M}{2} \int_0^\pi \frac{\sin \theta \, d\theta}{\sqrt{R^2 + a^2 - 2aR \cos \theta}} \qquad (19)$$

In order to integrate this, we place

$$R^2 + a^2 - 2aR \cos \theta = x$$

and differentiating

$$dx = 2aR \sin \theta \, d\theta$$

when

$$\theta = 0; \quad x = (R - a)^2$$
$$\theta = \pi; \quad x = (R + a)^2$$

Substituting these values in Eq. (19) we find

$$\Phi = -\frac{\gamma M}{4aR} \int_{(R-a)^2}^{(R+a)^2} x^{-\frac{1}{2}} dx = -\frac{\gamma M}{2aR} \left(x^{\frac{1}{2}} \right)_{(R-a)^2}^{(R+a)^2}$$

or

$$\Phi = -\frac{\gamma M}{2aR} (R + a - R + a) = -\frac{\gamma M}{R} \qquad (20)$$

which is just the same as Eq. (14).

We have thus proved that a thin hollow sphere attracts just as if all its mass were concentrated at its center. A solid sphere may be considered as a large number of tightly fitting hollow spheres, and hence a solid sphere attracts matter outside its surface just as if all its mass were concentrated at its center. Thus the lines of force and equipotential surfaces are just the same as for a single mass point.

78. Variations of g with Altitude.—The acceleration of a freely falling body at the surface of the earth is due to the gravitational pull of the earth, which we shall consider spherical and which hence, according to Eq. (20), behaves like a mass point situated at the center of the earth. The potential energy of a mass point of mass m at the earth's surface is

$$V = m\Phi = -\frac{\gamma M_E m}{R} \qquad (21)$$

where M_E is the mass of the earth and R its radius. The force which the earth exerts on this mass point is then given by

$$F = -\frac{dV}{dR} = -\frac{\gamma M_E m}{R^2} \qquad (22)$$

By the second law of motion the acceleration $-g_0$ caused by this force is given by

$$F = -\frac{\gamma M_E}{R^2} m = -mg_0$$

or

$$g_0 = \gamma \frac{M_E}{R^2} \qquad (23)$$

At a height h above the surface of the earth the acceleration g is given by

$$g = \gamma \frac{M_E}{(R + h)^2} = \gamma \frac{M_E}{R^2} \cdot \frac{1}{\left(1 + \dfrac{h}{R}\right)^2} \tag{24}$$

Dividing Eq. (24) by Eq. (23), we find

$$g = g_0 \frac{1}{\left(1 + \dfrac{h}{R}\right)^2} \tag{25}$$

as the relation giving the variation of g with altitude h.

For all heights small compared with the earth's radius, we can write, instead of Eq. (25),

$$g = g_0\left(1 - \frac{2h}{R}\right) \tag{26}$$

The radius can be determined by measurements on the earth's surface and is found to be

$$R = 6.4 \times 10^8 \text{ cm.}$$

With these data we can find the mass of the earth with the help of Eq. (23).

We have $g_0 = 980$ cm./sec.^{2}, so that

$$M_E = \frac{980 \times (6.4 \times 10^8)^2}{6.7 \times 10^{-8}} = 6 \times 10^{27} \text{ grams}$$

As a final example we shall investigate the motion of a body falling from rest from a height h above the earth's surface, considering the variation of g with altitude.   Neglecting air friction, we have, according to the energy principle,

$$K.E. + V = \text{constant}$$

or

$$\frac{1}{2}mv^2 - \frac{\gamma M_E m}{x} = \text{constant} \tag{27}$$

where x is the distance of the body from the center of the earth. When $v = 0$, $x = R + h$ so that

$$\frac{mv^2}{2} - \frac{\gamma M_E m}{x} = -\frac{\gamma M_E m}{(R + h)} \tag{28}$$

From Eq. (23) we have

$$\gamma M_E = g_0 R^2$$

so that Eq. (28) becomes

$$v^2 = 2g_0 R^2 \left(\frac{1}{x} - \frac{1}{R+h} \right) \tag{29}$$

The velocity with which a body falling freely from a height h would hit the earth's surface ($x = R$) is given by

$$v_0^2 = 2g_0 R \left(1 - \frac{1}{1 + \dfrac{h}{R}} \right) \tag{30}$$

If h is large compared to R, *i.e.*, from very great heights, Eq. (30) becomes

$$v_0^2 = 2g_0 R$$

or

$$v_0 = \sqrt{2g_0 R}$$

which is about 7 miles/sec.

Problems

1. Prove that Kepler's second law would be obeyed no matter what the law of attraction of sun for planet. Under what conditions would this law become invalid?

2. With what horizontal velocity must a projectile 50 miles above the surface of the earth be projected so that it performs motion in a circle about the earth? The radius of the earth is 4,000 miles. What will be the period of rotation?

3. The mass of the earth is 6.1×10^{27} grams (or 7.2×10^{21} tons), and its average distance from the sun is 93,000,000 miles. Assuming that the orbit is a circle, find the central acceleration and the force required to produce it.

4. Two equal masses are fastened to the ends of a light rod 200 cm. long which is supported at its mid-point by a torsion fiber. When the system is allowed to vibrate as a torsion pendulum the period is 400 sec. Two large masses of 10 kg. each are placed in positions of the Cavendish set-up with the center of each large mass 10.0 cm. from the center of the nearer small mass. It is observed that, when this is done, the rod rotates through an angle of 2.70×10^{-4} radian. From these data calculate the gravitational constant.

5. The earth's orbit about the sun can be considered as a circle with a radius of 1.5×10^{13} cm. with the sun at the center. From these data, the value of the gravitational constant and the time required for a complete revolution of the earth about the sun, calculate the mass of the sun.

6. The distance from the earth to the moon is found by triangulation to be 239,000 miles (or 3.84×10^{10} cm.). Assuming that the orbit of the moon is a circle with the earth at the center, and using the data for the mass of the earth and the gravitational constant from the text, calculate the angular velocity of the moon and the time required for a complete revolution. (This is the method used by Newton to check his assumed form for the law of gravitation.)

7. What measurements would it be necessary for an astronomer to make to determine the mass of Jupiter?

8. Masses of 500, 250, 1,000 grams are placed at the three vertices of an isosceles right triangle with the 500-gram body at the right angle. The length of each of the shorter sides of the triangle is 20 cm. What is the total force on the 500-gram body? How much work would be required to move the 500-gram body to a point 50 cm. from the 1,000-gram body and 30 cm. from the 250-gram body?

9. The distance between an 800-kg. mass and a 450-kg. mass is 50 cm. Find the gravitational field intensity due to these two masses at a point which is 40 cm. from the 800-kg. mass and 30 cm. from the 450-kg. mass. Find the gravitational potential due to these two masses at the same point.

10. In a rectangular coordinate system, masses of 12 grams each are located at the points (4 cm., 0) and (0, 3 cm.). Find:

a. The gravitational intensity and potential at the origin.

b. The gravitational intensity and potential at the point midway between the two masses.

c. The work required to carry a 10-gram mass from the origin to the point midway between the masses.

11. Two mass points lie in a plane as follows: a 3,600-gram body at the origin; a 3,200-gram body at the point $x = 8$ cm., $y = 6$ cm. Find the intensity and potential of the gravitational field produced by these masses at the point $x = 0$, $y = 6$ cm. What force in dynes would be exerted on a 10-gram mass placed at this point?

12. What is the length of a simple pendulum whose period is 2.00 sec.? Given that the mass of the moon is one eighty-first that of the earth, and the moon's diameter is 0.27 that of the earth, what is the length of the simple pendulum which would have a period of 2.00 sec. on the moon?

13. Masses of 100 and 400 grams are placed 15 cm. apart. What is the gravitational force on a unit mass at the point P, on the line joining the masses and 5 cm. from the 100-gram mass? What is the potential energy of unit mass at point P? How much work is required to move the unit mass to point P', 10 cm. from each mass?

14. Two mass points of equal mass are held fixed with a distance A between them. Sketch the field of force due to these two mass points. Sketch in the equipotential surfaces on the same diagram. Calculate the potential at any point on the straight line connecting the two points; on the straight line which is the perpendicular bisector of the line of length A connecting the two mass points.

15. Find the potential and field intensity due to a uniform thin circular ring of mass M, and radius R, at the center of the circle. Find the potential and field at a point P along a line perpendicular to the plane of the circle and passing through the center of the circle.

16. Calculate the intensity of the force field produced by a long thin rod of length L and mass M at a point P situated on the long axis of the rod and at a distance A from one end.

17. Two lead spheres, each of radius 25 cm., are placed with their centers 55 cm. apart. Find the force which one exerts on the other. How much work is necessary to separate the spheres infinitely far?

18. The moon has one eighty-first the mass of the earth and is 250,000 miles away from it.

a. At what point is the intensity of the gravitational field, caused by the earth and moon, zero?

b. Write expressions in symbols for the potential energy of a body of mass m due to the field of earth and moon.

(1) When m is on the surface of the earth.

(2) When m is on the surface of the moon.

19. With what velocity must a body be projected upward from the earth's surface so that it reaches a maximum height of 400 miles above its initial position? What percentage of error would be made if this were calculated with a constant value of g? The radius of the earth is 4,000 miles.

20. Given that a body inside a hollow spherical mass is in equilibrium and one outside is attracted toward the center of the sphere by Newton's law of gravitation as if all the mass of the sphere were at the center, prove that a body underneath the earth's surface is pulled toward the center with a force proportional to its distance from the center of the earth.

21. A double star consists of two suns, each of mass 3×10^{37} grams, with their centers 10^{20} cm. apart. The path of a meteorite passes through the mid-point of the line between the suns' centers and is perpendicular to this line. How fast must the meteorite be going at this point for it to escape completely from the double star?

22. What is the acceleration of the earth toward the sun? What is the force with which the sun pulls the earth? Calculate the mass of the sun.

23. How far above the surface of the earth must a body be raised so that its weight is diminished by 1 part in 1,000? Professor Piccard ascended in a balloon to the upper atmosphere, a height of 10 miles above the surface of the earth. If he weighs 150 lb. on the surface of earth, calculate the change in his weight when at the top of his flight.

24. The mass of the sun is 324,000 times the mass of the earth, and the earth is 93,000,000 miles from the sun. How far from the earth must a body be so that the pull of the earth balances the pull of the sun on the body?

25. The moon has $1/81$ the mass of the earth and is 240,000 miles away. Calculate the percentage change in the earth's acceleration toward the sun when there is a total eclipse of the sun as compared to the time when the moon is on the opposite side of the earth.

26. A body is projected vertically from the surface of the earth with a velocity v_0. The radius of the earth is R.

a. Show that, if $v_0 \geq \sqrt{2gR}$, the body will escape from the earth.

b. Show that for the case $v_0 = \sqrt{2gR}$, the time necessary for the body to reach a distance r from the center of the earth is

$$t = \frac{2}{3R\sqrt{2g}}(r^{\frac{3}{2}} - R^{\frac{3}{2}})$$

c. If $v_0^2 < 2gR$, find the greatest height reached and the time of flight of the body.

d. If $v_0^2 < \ < 2gR$, show that the answers to *c* become the same as those derived using a constant acceleration g of a falling body.

CHAPTER XIII

HYDROSTATICS

We now turn to the study of the behavior of deformable bodies in contradistinction to that of rigid bodies. We had defined a rigid body as one whose shape and volume remain unaltered during the process or motion under consideration, or more exactly we said that a body was rigid if the distance between any pair of its mass points remained unaltered. Whether a body is rigid or not depends then on the precision of the measurements employed to determine the volume and shape changes of the body. It is indeed possible to employ measuring devices sensitive enough to show that all bodies depart more or less from perfect rigidity. In studying this departure of bodies from rigidity, we are led to a more or less detailed consideration of the internal forces which hold bodies together, and from this standpoint it is convenient to classify bodies into three classes:

a. Solids. These show large resistance to both changes of shape and volume.

b. Liquids. These show practically no resistance to changes of shape but very great resistance to change of volume.

c. Gases. These show practically no resistance to change of shape and very little to change of volume.

This is a rough classification but it is very helpful, although there are cases where the above criteria fail to distinguish one class from its neighbor.

The resistance shown to changes of shape and size is termed *elasticity*. A complete definition of this word will be given later when we learn how to set up a means of measuring it. For the present we shall merely point out a qualitative difference which is a matter of daily experience. If the same force acts first on a metal and second on a piece of rubber of similar original form and size, the rubber undergoes a much larger deformation than the metal. We say that the metal is more elastic and the rubber is the less elastic body. It should be noticed that this terminology is just the antithesis of that of everyday language. A rigid body is (in physics) perfectly elastic.

217

We have overwhelming evidence from the study of chemical and many other types of phenomena that all bodies are composed of enormously large numbers of minute particles, which we call *atoms* (and *molecules*). A complete knowledge of the structure and laws of interaction of atoms and molecules should allow us to predict the forces which hold bodies together and hence, from this point, to develop a complete theory of a deformable body from the knowledge of the atoms and molecules of which it is composed. This is unfortunately impossible at present, as our knowledge of interatomic and intermolecular forces is so limited that the theory of the behavior of deformable bodies has been built up along entirely different lines. It has used the picture of a deformable body as a continuous distribution of matter—as it indeed seems upon casual observation—and with the help of this picture has developed a powerful and important means of understanding the phenomena displayed by deformable bodies. We shall use this older, more approximate picture very much in our succeeding work, and we shall now show that this type of theory does not necessarily conflict with the more fundamental atomic theory. In the continuous theory we must be able to choose our elements of volume dV so small that they may be considered as infinitesimals, allowing us to use the ordinary methods of calculus, and yet large enough so that each contains many molecules, in which case the forces exerted by such a volume element will be a sort of average over all the molecular and atomic forces caused by this volume element. This choice is actually possible, and we shall illustrate by an example. Let us calculate the number of silver atoms in a cubic centimeter of the metal. Avogadro's principle tells us that each gram-atomic weight of any substance contains 6×10^{23} atoms. Silver has an atomic weight of 108 and a density of 10.6 grams/cm.[3]. Thus the number of atoms of silver per cubic centimeter is

$$\frac{6 \times 10^{23} \times 10.6}{108} = 5.9 \times 10^{22} \text{ atoms/cm.}^3$$

Now suppose we were to choose as a volume element dV a cube, each side of which has a length of 1/10,000 mm.—certainly small enough from a large-scale viewpoint to be considered an infinitesimal—we have for the volume $dV = (10^{-5})^3 = 10^{-15}$ cm.[3]. The number of atoms of silver in this tiny element is about $6 \times 10^{22} \times 10^{-15} = 6 \times 10^7$ or about sixty million atoms.

Thus it is evident that the continuous theory represents a reasonably good picture of the more correct atomic model.

79. Pressure.—We shall start our study by handling the problems of equilibrium of fluids (liquids and gases). We shall define an ideal fluid as one which offers no resistance to change of shape, *i.e.*, it possesses no elasticity of form and pours freely. On the other hand liquids possess great volume elasticity, so that we may consider them as incompressible for most purposes. This property is not possessed by gases, and hence there will be some difference in the special formulas developed for incompressible liquids and the more general ones developed for fluids. Unless explicitly stated, we shall consider the density of liquids constant, independent of the pressure.

In the study of continuous media, it is not convenient to talk about forces but rather of *pressures*, a term which we now define. Consider a small plane area ΔA inside a fluid. The fluid on one side of this surface exerts a force ΔF on the fluid on the other side, and this force is transmitted across the surface ΔA. We define the pressure on this surface as the force per unit area acting on it, thus:

$$p = \frac{\Delta F}{\Delta A} \tag{1}$$

where p is the pressure of the fluid at the point where ΔA is situated. ΔA may be part of the surface of an immersed body, or part of the fluid itself. Strictly the pressure is defined as the limit of the ratio of $\Delta F/\Delta A$, as ΔA approaches zero. Pressure has the dimensions of force per unit area and is measured in dynes per square centimeter, pounds per square foot, or any other system of units derived from these.

A very important consequence of the definition of an ideal fluid is that the force exerted on any area ΔA when the fluid is in equilibrium acts perpendicularly to the area and hence coincides with the direction of the normal to this surface. Consider a cubical element of volume of the fluid such as shown dotted in Fig. 64, and let us imagine that the fluid is slightly changed in shape so that the top face of the cube moves slightly to the right with respect to the bottom face. The final shape is shown in full lines, and it is clear that the original cube and the final slant prism have the same volume so that we have a change of shape with no change of volume. Since, by definition, no work is done by the forces acting on this element of volume during this change of shape, there can be no horizontal component of force acting on the top surface. Thus we have shown that the force on this face is perpendicular to it. In a similar way one may repeat this argument for the other faces of the cube. As a final point we might mention that it can be shown

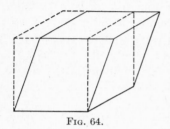

FIG. 64.

that any arbitrary change of shape of a volume element of a fluid can be resolved into a combination of these simple changes of shape we have considered.

Thus the pressure of a fluid depends only on the position of ΔA and not on the orientation of the latter, and the force exerted on ΔA is always normal to it. This independence of pressure of direction is commonly known as Pascal's principle. It is really not an independent principle but rather a logical consequence of the definition of an ideal fluid.

80. Law of Equilibrium.—We now proceed to formulate the law of equilibrium for a fluid. If a fluid is in equilibrium, then any part of the fluid is also in equilibrium and we must express our laws so that they apply to each mass point or volume element of the fluid. For this purpose it is convenient to divide the forces acting on any volume of a fluid into two classes:

a. Surface Forces. These are the forces transmitted across the bounding surface of the fluid volume under consideration, such as those due to the push of the surrounding fluid. These forces may be expressed in terms of the pressure in an ideal fluid, and according to the results found in the preceding section these pressure forces act at right angles to the surface of the volume being studied.

b. Body Forces. These are forces which act on every mass point of the fluid such as those due to a gravitational field of force. For simplicity we shall restrict our attention to the case of the uniform gravitational field at the surface of the earth.

In the absence of body forces the law of equilibrium is simple. It states that the pressure is everywhere the same in a fluid in equilibrium. This may be proved by considering a cubical-volume element of the fluid and adding up the forces on its faces. Thus, if we take the x-axis perpendicular to one pair of faces of this tiny cube and apply the condition that the sum of the x-components of the forces must add up to zero, it follows that the pressure is the same on opposite faces of the cube. Since this is true for any pair of faces, we see that the pressure does not depend on position and hence is constant throughout the whole fluid.

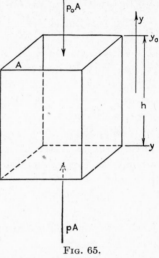

FIG. 65.

In the case of the earth's gravitational field we proceed as outlined above, but now we must add to the pressure forces the pull of the earth on the fluid mass under consideration. Since the gravitational pull is everywhere vertical, it follows that the pressure can vary only in the vertical direction and is constant at all points in any horizontal plane. To find the law expressing the variation of pressure with depth, let us consider a vertical column of fluid of cross section A and height h (Fig. 65). Let us take the y-axis vertically upward, the top face of the column at the height y_0, and the bottom face of the column at the height y, so that

$$h = y_0 - y$$

Since the fluid is ideal the only y-components of the surface forces are those due to the pressure at the top face and at the bottom face. The former force is a downward push and the latter is upward. Besides these surface forces, we have the weight of the column of fluid which is a downward force. It is clear without calculation that the pressure at the bottom face must be larger than that at the top face, if equilibrium is to be maintained.

If we call the pressure at the top face p_0, and that at the bottom face p, the sum of the pressure forces on these faces is

$$pA - p_0A = (p - p_0)A$$

For incompressible liquids the pull of the earth on the column is its volume times its constant density times g, so that the body force is

$$-hA\rho g$$

Thus our equilibrium condition gives

$$(p - p_0)A - hA\rho g = 0$$

or

$$p - p_0 = \rho g h \tag{2}$$

Thus we see that the pressure in an incompressible liquid increases proportional to the depth. For water, as an example, we have $\rho g = 62.5$ lb./ft.^{3}, so that the pressure increases by 62.5 lb./ft.$^2 = 0.434$ lb./in.^{2} for each foot increase in depth. Of course, Eq. (2) only holds for an incompressible liquid in which the density is constant. In the case of a gas in which the density depends on the pressure, we must apply our laws of equilibrium not to a column of finite height h but to a column of infinitesimal height dy, since the pressure, and hence the density, is different at different levels in the column. For this purpose we rewrite Eq. (2) in the form

$$\frac{p - p_0}{h} = -\frac{p_0 - p}{y_0 - y} = \rho g$$

Here $p_0 - p$ is the increase in pressure as we ascend from the face at y to the face at the height y_0. Thus $p_0 - p = \Delta p$ and $y_0 - y = \Delta y$. As $\Delta y \to 0$, the left-hand side of the above equation becomes $-dp/dy$ and the whole equation may be written

$$\frac{dp}{dy} = -\rho g \tag{3}$$

This is the general equation of equilibrium for any fluid in equilibrium under the action of gravity whether it be compressible or not.

It should be added that the conditions for rotational equilibrium are automatically satisfied. Consider again a cubical-volume element. Since the body forces may be considered as acting at the center of mass, and since the surface forces are perpendicular to the surfaces of this volume element, the sum of the torques taken about any axis through the center of mass is zero and this is just the condition necessary for the rotational equilibrium of the volume element.

81. Applications. *a. Hydraulic Press.*—Suppose we may neglect the body forces acting on an incompressible liquid in equilibrium. We then know that the pressure everywhere within the liquid is constant. This situation is realized in the usual hydraulic press (Fig. 66), in which the pressure on the liquid is so large that we may correctly neglect the variations of pressure with depth compared to the pressure in the liquid. If the force exerted on the small piston of area A_1 is F_1 when the piston is in equilibrium, and the force F_2 is exerted on the large piston of area A_2, we have

$$p = \text{constant} = \frac{F_1}{A_1} = \frac{F_2}{A_2}$$

or

$$F_2 = \frac{A_2}{A_1}F_1 \qquad (4)$$

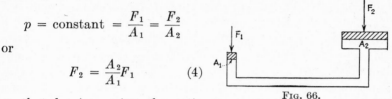

Fig. 66.

so that by increasing the ratio A_2/A_1 one obtains a simple means of amplifying a force.

b. *Archimedes' Principle.*—In the case of the equilibrium of an incompressible liquid, such as water under the action of gravity,

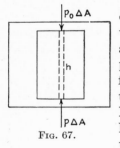

Fig. 67.

we have seen that the pressure increases with depth according to Eq. (2). Furthermore, as we have pointed out, the pressure is the same at all points at the same depth, *i.e.*, the pressure is constant on the equipotential surfaces of the earth's gravitational field. Equation (2), which is a direct consequence of Newton's laws, contains the law commonly known as Archimedes' principle. We may think of any submerged body as composed of a

huge number of vertical columns of cross section ΔA and height h (Fig. 67). Since in this figure $p > p_0$, the upward force exerted on the column has a magnitude

$$\Delta B = (p - p_0)\Delta A$$

Inserting in this equation the value of $p - p_0$ from Eq. (2), we have for the buoyant force acting on our column,

$$\Delta B = \rho g \Delta A \cdot h$$

and hence the total upward force is

$$B = \Sigma \Delta B = \rho g \Sigma \Delta A \cdot h = \rho g V \qquad (5)$$

where V is the total volume of the submerged body. Now, since ρ is the density of the liquid, ρV represents the mass of a volume of liquid just equal to the volume of the submerged body.   Hence the total buoyant force is equal to the weight of a volume of liquid equal to the submerged volume of the immersed body. This is exactly Archimedes' principle.

c. *The Pascal Paradox.*—Consider a vessel whose bottom has an area A containing liquid of height h.   If the pressure at the surface is p_0 (atmospheric), then the pressure on the bottom is $p = p_0 + \rho gh$ and the total force exerted by the liquid on the bottom of the vessel is

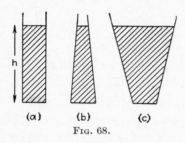

(a)   (b)   (c)

Fig. 68.

$$F = A\rho gh$$

and does not depend on the shape of the container.   Consider three vessels of the following shapes with the same base area containing liquid of the same height (Fig. 68). These vessels contain different amounts of liquids, and it seems at first glance that the bases must support different weights and hence exert different forces on the liquid.   Yet our equation tells us the forces must be equal.   This seeming paradox is known as Pascal's paradox.

Of course our equation is correct, and the complete analysis must include the forces exerted by the walls as well as by the base of the container.   In vessel a the walls push horizontally, so the base supports the whole weight of liquid.   In vessel b the walls exert forces (normal to the walls) which have downward components which add to the weight of the liquid.   In vessel c the forces exerted by the walls on the liquid have upward components which balance part of the weight of the liquid.   In all cases the total force exerted by the base on the liquid is the same.

82. The Free Surface of a Liquid.—In the preceding section we have seen that the pressure in a liquid acted on by gravity is constant in any given horizontal plane, *i.e.*, in an equipotential surface.   It is true, in general, that the surfaces of constant pressure of a liquid coincide with the equipotential surfaces of the field of force which holds it in equilibrium.   Thus, if we consider as large a body of water as the ocean, we may not assume a constant intensity of the gravitational field, but since the equipotential surfaces are spherical, so are the surfaces of constant pressure.

The free surface of a liquid is always one of constant pressure and is always perpendicular to the lines of force whatever the nature of the field of force. Thus, a small body of liquid displays a flat surface (subject to restrictions which we shall discuss in the next section), the ocean displays a spherical surface, and a solution of $FeCl_3$ placed in a magnetic field will form a surface perpendicular to the resultant of the magnetic force and the earth's field.

It is possible by an application of these ideas to calculate the surface assumed by a rotating liquid. Although this is an accelerated motion, we can reduce our problem to a static one by the following scheme. For any accelerated motion we have $F = ma$, and if we rewrite this in the form $F - ma = 0$, this last equation is in the form of an equilibrium equation where we introduce the fictitious force $-ma$ to take into account the actual acceleration of the body.

Suppose we have a liquid in a cylindrical vessel rotating with constant angular velocity about the vertical axis y. Each particle of the liquid rotates in a circle of radius x and has an acceleration equal to $-\omega^2 x$ (Fig. 69). Now we replace this term $ma = -m\omega^2 x$ by the outward force $m\omega^2 x$ and consider the static behavior of the liquid in the earth's field and this fictitious force field. We know that the free surface of the liquid is perpendicular to the resultant of the two forces at every point. If ϕ is the angle whose tangent gives the slope of the curve formed by the surface, we have, from the accompanying figure,

$$\tan \phi = \frac{m\omega^2 x}{mg} = \frac{\omega^2 x}{g}$$

but

$$\tan \phi = \frac{dy}{dx}$$

the slope of the curve, so that

$$\frac{dy}{dx} = \frac{\omega^2 x}{g}$$

and integrating (ω = constant)

$$y = \frac{\omega^2 x^2}{2g} \qquad (6)$$

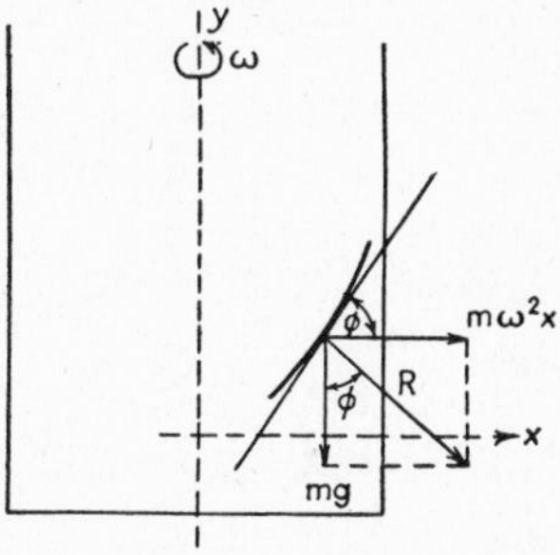

Fig. 69.

if we choose our origin at the point where the curve intersects the y-axis. This is the equation of a parabola, and it holds for the intersection of the surface of the liquid with any vertical plane through the axis of rotation. Hence the free surface is that of a paraboloid of revolution, the axis of revolution being the axis of rotation.

83. Surface Tension.—We have already seen that the free surface of a liquid is one of constant pressure. The free surface displays other properties of great interest. To understand why the surface should behave differently from the body of the liquid, we must think of the liquid as composed of a huge number of molecules which attract each other with large forces. As a rough picture, we may suppose that the molecules are rigid spheres about 10^{-7} cm. in diameter. Now consider a molecule inside the liquid. It is attracted by all its neighbors, but since on the average it is uniformly surrounded by other molecules, the average force exerted on this molecule by all the others will be zero.   On the other hand a molecule in the surface is not uniformly surrounded by other molecules, as there are not so many above as below it.   Hence, on the average, there is a large force pulling the molecules in the surface toward the inside of the liquid, thus imparting unusual properties to the surface layer.*   This layer must be of a thickness of several times 10^{-7} cm.   If we increase the free surface of a liquid (for example, by pouring it from one vessel to another of different shape), it is necessary to move new molecules from the inside of the liquid into the surface.   Work must be done by the internal forces in creating this new surface.   This work has been neglected in our definition of an ideal fluid in Sec. 79.   It is usual to compare the surface layer of a liquid with a tough skin or rubber membrane stretched over the surface of the liquid.   Such an analogy is helpful but must be used with caution as the law of force in the two cases is quite different as we shall see in a later section.

The existence of this surface layer explains many otherwise mysterious phenomena.   The formation of drops is one of the most striking which can be understood with the help of this concept.   As a drop forms on the end of a tube, it assumes a series of definite shapes and stays on the tube as long as the surface force can hold it.   When it breaks off, it is invariably accompanied by a small secondary droplet.   The drop thus formed becomes spherical, as the surface tries to shrink together, *i.e.*, the molecules on the inside pull the surface molecules inward and produce as tight packing as possible.   Since the sphere is the shape which for a given volume has the smallest surface, the drops become spheres.

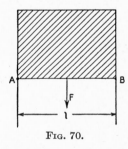

FIG. 70.

84. Coefficient of Surface Tension; Surface Energy.—Suppose we form a soap film as shown in Fig. 70, where the wire AB is free to move.   It is found that it is necessary to apply a force F, as shown, to hold the surface from shrinking together. This force turns out to be independent of the position of the wire AB and proportional to the length of this wire.   Thus, by

* Of course, there is an equally large force pushing outward, since the surface layer is in equilibrium.   Perhaps it would be more exact to state that the surface layer is subject to tremendous compression.

Newton's third law, the surface exerts a force F on the wire, so that we may write

$$F \sim l$$

(If this were a rubber sheet, the force would depend not only on l but also on the area of the sheet, *i.e.*, the larger the area the larger the force necessary to hold it in equilibrium.) We now introduce as a measure of the surface force the force per unit length at the edge of the surface. Since there are two sides to the film, the edge has a length $2l$, and we have

$$F = 2\alpha l \tag{7}$$

where α, the coefficient of surface tension, is the force per unit length on the boundary. In the c.g.s. system of units, α is measured in dynes per centimeter. The following table gives values of α for a few liquids at room temperature.

Liquid	H_2O	Soap solution	Ethyl alcohol	Ether	Hg
α in (dynes/cm.)..........	72	26	22	16	500

The coefficient of surface tension is extremely sensitive to impurities. Minute traces can produce marked changes in α. The reason for this behavior is that the concentration of the impurity is always greater in the surface than in the body of the liquid. Now let us stretch our soap film so that the wire AB moves a distance Δx from position 1 to position 2 (Fig. 71). The work done by the pull of the surface is

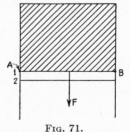

Fig. 71.

$$\Delta W = -F\Delta x = -2\alpha l \Delta x$$

Since F is constant this work can be entirely regained if the wire moves back from position 2 to position 1, so that there is a potential energy of the surface and the change of potential energy is

$$\Delta V = -\Delta W = 2\alpha l \cdot \Delta x$$

We have changed the surface by an amount $\Delta A = 2l\Delta x$, so that the increase of potential energy of the surface is

$$\Delta V = \Delta A \cdot \alpha$$

or

$$\alpha = \frac{\Delta V}{\Delta A} \tag{8}$$

Thus we may interpret the coefficient of surface tension as the potential energy per unit area of the surface of a liquid. Dimensionally we have

$$[\alpha] = \text{dynes/cm.} = \text{dyne-cm./cm.}^2 = \text{ergs/cm.}^2$$

85. Formation of Drops; Capillary Rise.—If we form a drop of liquid from a tube of radius r, the drop breaks off when the surface force can no longer support the weight of the drop (Fig. 72). Just at the point of breaking, we have

FIG. 72.

$$mg = 2\pi r \alpha$$

If, after dropping, the drop becomes a sphere of radius R, we have very nearly

$$mg = \tfrac{4}{3}\pi R^3 \rho g$$

and hence

$$\alpha = \frac{mg}{2\pi r} = \frac{2}{3}\frac{R^3 \rho g}{r} \tag{9}$$

The size of the drops varies with the surface tension and hence is different for different liquids. For liquids of approximately the same density ρ, we see from Eq. (9) that the radii of the drops vary roughly as $\alpha^{\frac{1}{3}}$.

When liquids adhere to the surface of a solid they are said to "wet" the solid, and they rise in capillary tubes made of these solids. Thus water wets glass, and the forces of attraction between the glass and the water are much larger than the forces of cohesion in water. If a capillary tube of glass is placed vertically in a dish of water, the water rises in the tube to a height h above the free surface in the dish. As shown in Fig. 73, a menis-

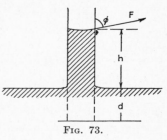

FIG. 73.

cus is formed and the angle ϕ is called the *angle of contact*. To calculate the height h, let us consider the column of liquid in the tube of height $(h + d)$. According to Newton's laws, the sum of the vertical components of all the forces acting on this column must be zero. At the top surface we have the downward force due to atmospheric pressure which is $-p_0\pi r^2$, if r is the radius of the tube. At the bottom surface we have the upward force due to the pressure of the liquid at a depth d. This is, according to Eq. (2),

$$(p_0 + \rho gd)\pi r^2$$

Then we have the pull of the earth on the column of liquid given by

$$-\rho g\pi r^2(h + d)$$

and finally the vertical component of the force F shown in the figure. This is the surface-tension force which the molecules of water clinging to the glass exert on their neighbors, and its vertical component is

$$2\pi r\alpha \cos \phi$$

where α is the coefficient of surface tension of the liquid. Applying the condition of equilibrium, we have

$$-p_0\pi r^2 + (p_0 + \rho gd)\pi r^2 - \rho g\pi r^2(h + d) + 2\pi r\alpha \cos \phi = 0$$

Solving this equation for h, there follows:

$$h = \frac{2\alpha \cos \phi}{\rho gr} \tag{10}$$

If the angle of contact is small, and for water on clean glass it is very nearly zero, we may place $\cos \phi \cong 1$, and Eq. (10) becomes

$$h \cong \frac{2\alpha}{\rho gr} \tag{10a}$$

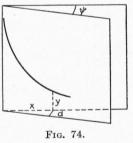

so that height to which a liquid rises in a capillary varies inversely as the radius of the tube.

If we take two plane plates of glass and place them so as to form a small angle ψ between them with one edge of one in contact with an edge of the other, upon

Fig. 74.

partial immersion in a liquid which wets glass the liquid will rise between the plates (Fig. 74). From the figure, we have

$$\tan \psi = \frac{d}{x}$$

and we have seen that the height to which the liquid rises varies as $1/d$.   Hence

$$y = \frac{c}{d} = \frac{c}{\tan \psi} \cdot \frac{1}{x} = \frac{k}{x}$$

where c and k are constants.

Thus we see that the surface of the liquid will form the curve

$$xy = k \tag{11}$$

which is the equation of a rectangular hyperbola.

86. Excess Pressure in Bubbles.—Because of the surface

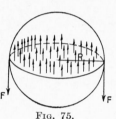

FIG. 75.

tension of liquids, a bubble, *e.g.*, a soap bubble, always tends to contract and diminish the surface.   Hence, to form a soap bubble, we must blow and create an excess pressure inside the bubble to hold it in equilibrium. Let us calculate this excess pressure for a spherical bubble.   Imagine that we slice the sphere into two hemispheres, and consider the forces acting on the upper hemisphere (Fig. 75).   The downward force is

$$(2\pi R\alpha)_{\text{inside}} + (2\pi R\alpha)_{\text{outside}} = 4\pi R\alpha$$

and the total upward force is due to the excess pressure p of the gas in the lower hemisphere on the plane cutting the sphere. This is

$$\pi R^2 p$$

so that for equilibrium

$$\pi R^2 p = 4\pi R\alpha$$

and hence

$$p = \frac{4\alpha}{R} \tag{12}$$

so that the excess pressure is smaller, the larger the bubble. These excess pressures are very small.   A soap bubble of 5 mm. radius has an excess pressure

$$p = \frac{4 \times 25}{0.05} = 200 \text{ dynes/cm.}^2 \cong 0.0002 \text{ atmosphere}$$

If we have a cylindrical shape, we imagine the cylinder (long axis horizontal) split in two by a vertical plane AA, and consider the forces on the back half of the cylinder (Fig. 76). The total force pulling forward is

$$(2\alpha L)_{\text{inside}} + (2\alpha L)_{\text{outside}} = 4\alpha L$$

and the force pushing back is due to the excess pressure in the gas in the front half and is $p \cdot 2RL$, so that, for equilibrium,

$$p \cdot 2RL = 4\alpha L$$

or

$$p = \frac{2\alpha}{R} \qquad (13)$$

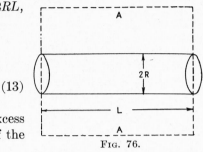

Fig. 76.

which is just one half the excess pressure needed for a sphere of the same radius.

If we have a sphere and cylinder connected, the excess pressures must be equal, so that

$$\frac{4\alpha}{R_s} = \frac{2\alpha}{R_c}$$

or

$$R_s = 2R_c$$

so that the radius of the sphere is twice that of the cylinder.

Problems

1. Calculate the radius of an aluminum sphere which contains about 1,000,000 atoms of aluminum.

2. Calculate the difference in pressure between the top and bottom of a mercury column 76.0 cm. high and 2 cm. in diameter. The density of Hg is 13.59 grams/cm.^{3} Express your answer in dynes per square centimeter and in pounds per square inch. Calculate the height of a water column which produces the same pressure difference.

3. A tank 3 ft. long, 5 ft. wide, and 6 ft. high is filled half full of water. Calculate the total force exerted by the water on each wall (and on the bottom). (HINT: Consider a strip of the wall dy in height at a distance y below the surface. Calculate its area, the force on it, and then integrate to get the total force.)

4. A vertical gate 3 ft. wide by 4 ft. high is hinged along its top edge which is parallel to the water surface and 12 ft. below it. Calculate the total torque in pound-feet acting on the gate about the hinge as an axis.

5. Show that if a body of volume V, density ρ_0, is completely submerged in a liquid of density ρ, there is a resultant force acting on it equal to $gV(\rho_0 - \rho)$ in the downward direction.

6. The cross section of a certain dam is a rectangle, 10 ft. wide and 20 ft. high.   The depth of water behind the dam is 20 ft.

Considering a section of the dam 1 ft. in length, what is the force on a small horizontal element of the upstream face, of width dy, at a depth y below the surface?

What is the torque, due to this force, tending to overturn the dam about the bottom of the downstream face O?

Show that the total torque about O due to the water pressure on the 1-ft. section is 83,500 lb.-ft.   If the material of the dam weighs 100 lb./ft.³, show whether or not the restoring torque about O due to the weight of the dam is greater than the torque due to water pressure.

7. A rectangular tank 10 ft. wide, 16 ft. long, and 12 ft. deep is filled one-third full of water, and the remainder of the tank contains oil of density 56 lb./cu. ft.   What is the total force exerted by the water on one end of the tank?

8. A uniform rod of length l is hinged at one end a distance $l/3$ below the surface of water.   If the rod is in equilibrium at an angle of 60° to the vertical, what is the density of the material of the rod?

9. A hollow cylindrical can 20 cm. in diameter floats in water with 10 cm. of its height above the water line when a 10-kg. iron block hangs from its bottom.   The iron is submerged in the water in which the cylinder floats. If the iron block is placed inside the can, how much of the cylinder's height will be above the water line?   The density of iron is 7.8 grams/cm.³.

10. Archimedes' discovery of the principle bearing his name enabled him to solve a problem equivalent to this one.   A crown consisting of gold and silver weighs 1,000 grams in air and 920 grams in water.   Find the number of grams of gold and of silver it contains.

11. A hollow sphere of inner radius 9 cm. and outer radius 10 cm. floats in water half submerged.   Calculate the density of the material of the sphere. What will be the density of a liquid in which it would just float completely submerged?

12. A cubical block of wood 10 cm. on a side and of density 0.5 gram/cm.³ floats in a jar of water.   Oil, of density 0.8 gram/cm.³, is poured on the water until the top of the oil layer is 4 cm. below the top of the block.   How deep is the oil layer?

13. Prove that, if a body floats, the ratio of the total volume of the body to the volume of the immersed part is equal to the ratio of the density of the liquid to the density of the body.

14. The upper edge of a vertical gate in a dam is along the surface of the water.   It is hinged at the lower end which is 10 ft. below the surface of the water.   The gate is 6 ft. wide.   Calculate the torque about the hinge.

15. A polar bear weighing 1,000 lb. is floating on a cake of ice.   As the ice melts, what will be the least volume so that the polar bear does not get his feet wet.

Specific gravity of salt water = 1.03; specific gravity of ice = 0.92.

16. The density of water at a depth z is given approximately by the formula $\rho = \rho_0(1 + \beta z)$. $\beta = 1.21 \times 10^{-6}$ per foot.   Calculate the pressure at a depth of 10^4 ft. in salt water of specific gravity 1.025.

17. One end of a uniform wooden rod 4 ft. long and 2 in.^{2} in cross section, of specific gravity 0.6 is hinged at a point 2.0 ft. below the water surface. What vertical force applied at the other end would be required to keep the rod completely immersed?

18. A cubical block of steel (density = 7.8 grams/cm.^{3}) floats on mercury (density = 13.6 grams/cm.^{3}). How much of the block is above the mercury surface? If water is poured on the Hg surface, how high must the water layer be so that the water surface just rises to the top of the steel block?

19. A water-soluble crystal weighs 250 grams in air and 120 grams when submerged in oil of density 0.9 gram/cm.^{3} What is the density of the crystal?

20. A barrel of water standing on one arm of an equal-arm balance is balanced by a weight of 200 lb. A steam coil weighing 60 lb. and occupying a volume of 0.33 ft.^{3} is hung from the ceiling and completely immersed in the water without touching the sides of the barrel. Will the apparent weight of the barrel of water increase or decrease? how much? What is the tension in the rope supporting the steam coil?

21. A test tube 2 cm. in diameter partially filled with Hg, the whole weighing 30 grams, floats vertically in water. Show that, if it is depressed and suddenly released, it will perform simple harmonic motion. What will be the period?

22. A U-tube of uniform cross section of 6 in.^{2} contains 96 in.^{3} of water. A force of 0.2 lb. is applied uniformly on one free surface and is suddenly removed. Calculate the period of the ensuing simple harmonic motion. What is its amplitude?

23. A cylindrical vessel 10 cm. in radius contains a liquid standing at a height of 5 cm. It is rotated about its long axis so that the vertex of the paraboloid formed by the surface of the liquid just touches the bottom of the vessel. What is the angular velocity necessary to attain this condition?

24. A clean platinum ring of 2 cm. radius is placed on the surface of clean water of surface tension 72 dynes/cm. and is carefully raised until the film which clings to the ring breaks. What force is necessary to cause the film to break? By measuring this force we have a method for measuring the coefficient of surface tension.

25. Drops of water, alcohol, and mercury are formed from similar pipettes. What is the ratio of the radii of the drops which are thus formed? Calculate the radii of the drops.

26. A U-tube has dissimilar legs, one of 2 mm. radius and the other of 5 mm. radius. If water is poured into this U-tube, what will the difference of level be? What would this difference be for ether?

27. A tube of square cross section 0.04 in.^{2} is dipped vertically into a vessel of water. How high will the water rise in this tube?

28. Mercury stands in an inverted completely evacuated tube to a height of 6 cm. A bubble of air 1 mm. in diameter is formed under the mercury at the bottom of the tube. What is the total pressure of air in this bubble? If it rises very slowly to the surface, how large is it just as it reaches the mercury surface? Assume Boyle's law, *i.e.*, pV = constant, for the air inside the bubble.

29. Two long parallel plates are placed vertically in a vessel of water. The distance between the plates is 1.0 mm. What is the difference in level of the water between the plates and outside of the plates?

30. A hydrometer consists of a spherical bulb and a cylindrical stem of cross section 0.4 cm.^{2}. The total volume of bulb and stem is 13.2 cm.^{3}. When immersed in water, it floats with the stem vertical, and 8 cm. of the stem is above the surface. In alcohol 1 cm. of the stem is above the surface. Calculate the density of the alcohol.

31. A spherical soap bubble is blown so that its radius increases at the constant rate of 1 cm./sec. Calculate the rate of increase of surface energy of the bubble when its radius is 2 cm. $\alpha = 26$ dynes/cm. for the soap film.

32. A tube of circular cross section and radius 0.14 cm. is weighted at one end and floats vertically in water, heavy end down. The mass of the tube is 0.20 gram. If water wets the tube and the angle of contact is zero, how far below the surface is the bottom end of the tube? $\alpha = 72$ dynes/cm. for water.

CHAPTER XIV

FLUID DYNAMICS

The study of fluid dynamics or of hydrodynamics comprises the study of the laws of motion of fluids. In this chapter we shall restrict ourselves to the case of incompressible fluids. Our results, however, are also approximately valid for the flow of gases, such as air, provided the velocities are not too high. If a volume change of 1 part in 100 may be considered negligible, it turns out that for the purposes at hand we may consider air as an incompressible fluid up to velocities of about 50 meters/sec.

A liquid in motion presents a complicated state of affairs, since a complete description of its motion would demand a knowledge of the motion of each of the molecules of which it is composed. Such a detailed picture is, of course, hopelessly involved, since the molecules possess a random heat motion even when the liquid is at rest, and superimposed on this random motion we have the velocities which in their totality make up the observable velocity of the liquid. Hence we adopt the continuous picture of a liquid and neglect entirely the random heat motion, a procedure which is quite justifiable since the latter averages to zero in an infinitesimal volume element of the liquid. The motion of a continuous medium is completely described if we describe the motion of each volume element of the medium, *i.e.*, we pick a volume element of the fluid and specify its velocity (direction and magnitude) at each point of its path and also specify the time it reaches each point of its path. Even this mode of procedure is very complicated and we shall, in our applications, confine ourselves to motions of physical and engineering interest which are describable in a simpler manner.

Hydrodynamic phenomena are intricate enough so that very often they contradict our common sense and can only be understood by a careful application of Newton's laws of motion. In the case of frictionless ideal fluids, the energy principle often allows a solution of a flow problem of which the details may be very involved. A simple example may help to illustrate this

235

point.   Consider the flow of a liquid out of a small hole in the bottom of a tank of uniform large cross section A, in which the liquid stands at height h.   In time Δt the level sinks an amount Δh, so that we lose a mass $A\rho\Delta h$ of liquid from the tank; otherwise no change takes place in the tank.   The end result is the same as if this amount of liquid had fallen through a height h.   The loss of potential energy of this amount of liquid is

$$-\Delta V = A\rho g h \cdot \Delta h$$

and since we have assumed no friction this must be equal to the gain of kinetic energy of this amount of liquid.   If v is the velocity of efflux, we have

$$\Delta K.E. = A\rho\Delta h\frac{v^2}{2}$$

Here we have neglected the kinetic energy gained by the liquid remaining in the tank, a procedure which will be justified in a later section.   We have

$$\Delta K.E. = -\Delta V$$

so that

$$v^2 = 2gh$$

or

$$v = \sqrt{2gh} \tag{1}$$

a result known as Torricelli's theorem.

One-dimensional problems concerning the flow of water are called *problems of hydraulics*, in contradistinction to hydrodynamics which deals with the flow of any fluid in three dimensions.

87. Stationary Flow.—We start our discussion of hydrodynamics with a consideration of the simplest kind of flow, known as *stationary* or *steady* flow, *in which the velocity at a given point P of space does not change with time.*   Let us imagine that we take a snapshot of the moving fluid.   At every point P of space we can draw a vector v representing the direction and magnitude of the velocity of the fluid particle which is situated at P when the picture is taken.   We shall, in general, find different velocities at different points of the picture.   The totality of these velocity vectors describes the state of motion uniquely at one instant of time.   The condition of stationary flow is that a later snapshot of the fluid reveals the same velocity vectors at each point P of space. Of course, the fluid particle which was at point P in the first snapshot is found at another point Q in the second picture and a new particle has moved into the position at P.

At any point P of space, then, the particle at that point possesses the same vector velocity no matter at what instant of time we look at it. If we pick out such a particle (by coloring it red, for example) and follow it in its motion, it is found to move from P to Q along a definite path (Fig. 77). Every succeeding particle coming to P then follows the same path to Q and takes on the same set of velocity values v_1, v_2, $v_3 \cdot \cdot \cdot$ for steady flow. Thus the fluid streams as if it were enclosed in a number of little tubes. These little tubes are called *tubes of flow* and the lines which indicate the path of a particle are called *lines of flow* or *streamlines*. These lines of flow give the direction of the velocity of flow at every point of space. They are analogous to lines of force which give the direction of the intensity of a field of force

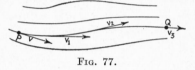

Fig. 77.

at every point. A tube of flow is made up of a bundle of similar lines of flow. *The liquid can never flow from one line of flow to another*, as this would contradict the definition of line of flow. Thus the idea of tubes of flow may be taken quite literally and we may think of these tubes as made of real matter, as liquid which is in a tube never gets out.

If we describe the motion of the liquid in one tube of flow, we then may obtain the description of the liquid flow as a whole by repeating this description for all the tubes of flow present. In the special case in which the motion in each tube of flow is identical with that in every other tube (this also means that the tubes of flow are all parallel to each other), we may consider the liquid as flowing in one large tube. This view is widely adopted by hydraulic engineers in the study of liquids streaming in pipes, and, if the flow characteristics are different in different tubes, they take averages and still consider but one large tube. This procedure, of course, can be at the best only a rough approximation.

88. Equation of Continuity.—Not every conceivable streamline picture represents a possible fluid motion, since we must require that no liquid disappear, *i.e.*, we must have conservation of the mass of liquid under consideration. Since each tube of flow contains its own particles of fluid, this condition must hold not only for the whole liquid but also for every individual tube of flow. Such a tube of flow may change its size as we move along it, and there may be different pressures at different points in it. We must consider two cross sections of the tube, A_1 and A_2 (Fig. 78). The mass of fluid which flows through the surface A_1 in time dt is

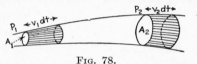

FIG. 78.

$$dm = \rho A_1 v_1 dt$$

where v_1 is the velocity at the point P_1. Similarly the mass of fluid flowing in time dt across A_2 is the liquid contained in the cylinder of volume $A_2 v_2 dt$ and is

$$dm = \rho A_2 v_2 dt$$

If there are no sources or sinks and if the liquid is incompressible, all the liquid entering across A_1 must leave across A_2. Hence

$$\rho A_1 v_1 dt = \rho A_2 v_2 dt$$

or

$$A_1 v_1 = A_2 v_2 \qquad (2)$$

i.e., the velocities in a given tube of flow must vary inversely as the cross sections of the tube.

In the case of liquid flowing in a pipe of cross section A where we treat the pipe as one big tube of flow, we have for the discharge rate of the tube

$$Q = Av \qquad (3)$$

where v is the common velocity of the liquid at the cross section A, and Q has the dimensions of l^3/t and is expressed in cubic feet per second, cubic centimeters per second, or any equivalent measure. Even in cases where there are different velocities in different tubes of flow, engineers frequently use Eq. (3), where v then represents the *average* velocity of the liquid in the pipe.

Equation (2) known as the *equation of continuity* holds in this form only for incompressible fluids. For compressible fluids it must be extended to take into account the fact that varying masses of liquid may be squeezed into a given volume because of the variable density of the fluid.

89. Bernoulli's Principle.—The application of Newton's second law of motion to the particles of a liquid in a tube of flow leads to an equation called *Bernoulli's equation* after its discoverer, Daniel Bernoulli (1738). In the steady state the velocity and pressure at a given point of space do not change with time. If the pressure varies from point to point of a tube of flow, this variation of pressure with position results in a force acting on the particles of liquid in the tube which accelerates them. Besides this force there are also the body forces acting on the liquid, but, as in the last chapter, we shall restrict our attention to gravity as the only body force acting. We shall set up Newton's second law by calculating expressions for the force per unit mass due to (1) the change of pressure along the tube of flow and (2) the weight of the liquid. Let us call the distance measured along a tube of flow from an arbitrary origin s, and consider a volume element of the liquid at a point P of the tube where the cross section is A (Fig. 79). To obtain the force per unit mass along the tube of flow due to changing pressure, we note that the resultant force due to the pressure on the two end faces of the particle is

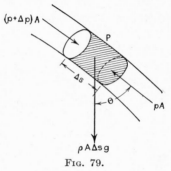

Fig. 79.

$$pA - (p + \Delta p)A = -\Delta pA$$

The mass of this volume of liquid is $\rho A \Delta s$, so that the pressure force per unit mass along the tube is

$$-\frac{\Delta pA}{\Delta sA\rho} = -\frac{1}{\rho}\frac{\Delta p}{\Delta s}$$

and, as $\Delta s \to 0$, this expression becomes

$$-\frac{1}{\rho}\frac{dp}{ds} \qquad (4)$$

The weight of the liquid in the volume element is

$$-\rho A g \Delta s$$

and, dividing by the mass, we find $-g$ as the body force per unit mass. The component of this force parallel to the tube of flow is $-g \cos \theta$, if θ is the angle between the direction of the tube and the vertical. Thus Newton's second law may be written in the form

$$-\frac{1}{\rho}\frac{dp}{ds} - g \cos \theta = \frac{dv}{dt} \tag{5}$$

if v is the speed of the liquid particle at the point P. To integrate this equation we place

$$\frac{dv}{dt} = \frac{dv}{ds} \cdot \frac{ds}{dt} = v\frac{dv}{ds}$$

so that Eq. (5) becomes

$$-\frac{1}{\rho}\frac{dp}{ds} - g \cos \theta = v\frac{dv}{ds}$$

or, rewritten,

$$\frac{1}{\rho}dp + g \cos \theta\, ds + vdv = 0$$

Now $ds \cos \theta$ is just the vertical component of the displacement ds which we shall denote by dh. Thus we may write

$$\frac{1}{\rho}dp + g\, dh + v\, dv = 0$$

If we now integrate this equation remembering that ρ is constant, there follows

$$\frac{p}{\rho} + gh + \frac{v^2}{2} = \text{constant} \tag{6}$$

This is Bernoulli's equation. It expresses the conservation of energy as applied to the liquid in a tube of flow. The first term represents the potential energy per unit mass of the liquid due to the pressure, the second term is the potential energy per unit mass of the liquid in the earth's gravitational field, and the last term on the left side of the equation is the kinetic energy per unit mass of the liquid. The sum of the potential and kinetic energy per unit mass has the same value at different points of the same tube of flow.

For the purposes of many applications, it is convenient to write Eq. (6) in the form

$$\frac{1}{\rho}p_1 + gh_1 + \frac{v_1^2}{2} = \frac{1}{\rho}p_2 + gh_2 + \frac{v_2^2}{2} \tag{7a}$$

where the subscripts 1 and 2 refer to two different points in the tube of flow.

If the flow occurs in a horizontal plane, $h_1 = h_2$, and we have

$$\frac{1}{\rho}p_1 + \frac{v_1^2}{2} = \frac{1}{\rho}p_2 + \frac{v_2^2}{2} \qquad (7b)$$

This tells us that the pressure is higher where the velocity is lower. For a liquid at rest, we have p equal to the hydrostatic pressure. Consequently, the pressure of a liquid in motion (the dynamic pressure) is always lower than that in the same liquid at rest.

90. Applications of Bernoulli's Principle.—The Bernoulli equation is one of the most important in the hydrodynamics of ideal liquids. We shall give several applications.

a. Stationary Flow of a Free Liquid Surface.—On the free surface of a liquid we have constant pressure, and hence the Bernoulli equation takes the form

$$\frac{v^2}{2} + gh = \text{constant}$$

If, at a height h_1, the velocity v_1 is zero, we have for the velocity at any other height h_2 (below h_1)

$$v = \sqrt{2g(h_1 - h_2)} = \sqrt{2gh}$$

This equation holds for streamlines which start on a free surface and later are again found on a free surface, such as in the case of flow from a tank where a streamline starts from the liquid surface and later appears in the free jet which emerges from the opening. This is identical with Eq. (1).

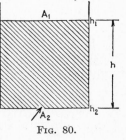

Fig. 80.

Let us calculate a more exact expression for the velocity of efflux taking into account the velocity of the top surface of the liquid. If the velocity in a tube of flow at height h_1 is v_1, then we have for v, the velocity in the same tube at h_2 (Fig. 80),

$$\frac{v^2}{2} + gh_2 = \frac{v_1^2}{2} + gh_1$$

or

$$v^2 - v_1^2 = 2g(h_1 - h_2) = 2gh$$

which may be written

$$v^2 = \frac{2gh}{1 - \frac{v_1^2}{v^2}} \tag{8}$$

To calculate the ratio of v_1/v, we shall consider the flow as one big tube of flow whose area at h_1 is A_1 and at h_2 is A_2. The equation of continuity gives

$$\frac{v_1}{v} = \frac{A_2}{A_1}$$

so that

$$v = \sqrt{2gh} \cdot \sqrt{\frac{1}{1 - \left(\frac{A_2}{A_1}\right)^2}} \tag{9}$$

If the hole is very small compared with the area of the surface, we have approximately

$$v = \sqrt{2gh}\left[1 + \left(\frac{A_2}{A_1}\right)^2\right]^{\frac{1}{2}} = \sqrt{2gh}\left[1 + \frac{1}{2}\left(\frac{A_2}{A_1}\right)^2\right] \tag{10}$$

If $A_2/A_1 << 1$, we may entirely neglect the term $(A_2/A_1)^2$ and thus refind the Torricelli theorem. In actual cases the state of affairs is more complicated than here pictured as all the tubes of flow starting at h_1 do not continue into the stream at h_2, but many are broken up at the edge of the hole and numerous eddies are formed so that Eq. (10) is not applicable without modification. An approximate method of modification is to consider the hole at the bottom of smaller effective area than its geometrical area and to introduce an empirical coefficient of contraction.

b. The flow of a fluid from inside a vessel under the action of a constant inner pressure may be handled as follows:

In a horizontal streamline, we have

$$\frac{1}{\rho}p + \frac{v^2}{2} = \text{constant}$$

If the fluid, *e.g.*, a gas, is at rest inside the vessel, then

$$\frac{1}{\rho}p_1 = \frac{1}{\rho}p_0 + \frac{v^2}{2}$$

where p_1 is the pressure inside the vessel, and p_0 the pressure outside. Hence

$$v = \sqrt{\frac{2}{\rho}(p_1 - p_0)} \tag{11}$$

If the cross section of the emerging jet is A, the mass of fluid emerging per second is $\rho A v$ and the loss of momentum per second is

$$\rho A v^2 = 2(p_1 - p_0)A$$

This rate of change of momentum is equal to the total force driving the fluid from the container. By the third law there is of course an equal and opposite force exerted back on the container by the outstreaming fluid.

    c. Streaming Around an Obstacle; Pitot Tube.—If an obstacle is placed in a liquid flowing with constant velocity v_0, the liquid comes to rest just before the obstacle and the streaming is divided into two branches, one on each side

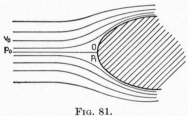

Fig. 81.

of the obstacle. The original streamline pattern which consisted of parallel straight lines is deformed as shown in Fig. 81.

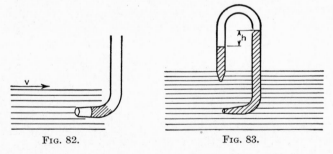

Fig. 82.   Fig. 83.

    At the point O, the velocity is zero and we have the hydrostatic pressure

$$p_1 = p_0 + \frac{\rho v_0^2}{2}$$

if p_0 is the pressure in that part of the flowing liquid where the streamlines are straight. We may use the above relation to measure the velocity of the flowing liquid. If we insert a curved glass tube, as shown in Fig. 82, the pressure p_1 is transmitted through the stationary liquid in the tube and may be measured in the ordinary way. The pressure p_0 may be measured by inserting a straight tube transverse to the flow lines. Thus we may connect these tubes together as shown in Fig. 83 to form what is known as a *Pitot tube*. The pressure difference in the tubes is given by

$$p_1 - p_0 = \rho g h$$

so that the velocity of the liquid is

$$v = \sqrt{\frac{2}{\rho}(\rho g h)} = \sqrt{2gh}$$

If we wished to measure the velocity of a streaming gas, we would merely invert the device shown above and pour some liquid in it. The difference of level of the liquid being h and its density ρ', the velocity of the gas would then be given by

$$v = \sqrt{\frac{2}{\rho}(\rho' g h)}$$

where ρ is the density of the flowing gas.

It is of course assumed in the preceding discussion that the tubes inserted are so small that the disturbance of the lines of flow caused by their presence may be neglected, except in the immediate vicinity of the tubes.

91. Qualitative Examples. *a. Attraction of a Disk.*—Suppose we connect a disk QQ to a hollow cylindrical tube as shown, so that we may blow air through the tube, and place a solid disk PP in contact with the disk QQ (Fig. 84). If we do not blow through the tube, the disk PP will fall away from QQ as expected. If we blow through the tube, we might expect PP to be forced away from QQ faster than if we do not blow. Actually the disk QQ seems to attract PP, and the harder we blow, the greater this attraction. This phenomenon is understandable with the help of Bernoulli's equation. When we blow, an air stream is set in motion between the disks with a velocity v. In this stream the pressure is less than atmospheric, and, since there is atmos-

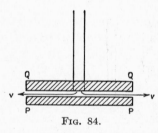

Fig. 84.

pheric pressure below the disk PP, there is a resultant force upward on PP,

$$F = (p_0 - p)A = \rho\frac{v^2 A}{2}$$

where A is the area of the disk and v the average velocity of the air flowing between PP and QQ. The greater the velocity v, the larger this upward force, so that it is easy to produce an upward force larger than the weight of the disk, with the surprising result that the disk PP "sticks" to the fixed disk QQ.

A similar experiment may be carried out by hanging up two spheres so that their surfaces are almost in contact. If we then blow between the spheres, they come together since the pressure in the region between them is less then atmospheric and is atmospheric elsewhere. This gives rise to a resultant force pushing the spheres together.

b. Celluloid Ball in an Air Blast.—If we place a celluloid ball, such as a ping-pong ball, in an air blast, it is observed that the ball stays within the blast of air even though the blast make an angle with the vertical. Since the pressure inside the air blast is less than the static atmospheric pressure outside the moving air, it is clear that there is a resultant force so directed as to push the ball always toward the center of the blast where the pressure is lowest.

92. Viscosity; Coefficient of Viscosity.—Thus far we have been considering ideal fluids, *i.e.*, those for which no work is done in a change of shape of the fluid. Actually, no fluid is perfectly ideal, although many liquids and gases approximate this condition very closely. Some liquids, such as glycerine and heavy oil, depart widely from this ideal condition and are known as *viscous* liquids. The viscosity of a liquid is a name for the internal friction of the liquid. We can arrive at an understanding of this internal friction by considering a simple experiment. Suppose we place a layer of viscous liquid, such as glycerine, on a glass plate and then place a similar glass plate on top of this liquid. If we now pull the top plate horizontally with a constant force F, it is found that the top plate attains a constant velocity v (Fig. 85). Furthermore the liquid clings to the plates, so that the layer of liquid clinging to the top plate moves with a velocity v and the layer of liquid clinging to the bottom plate remains at rest. The velocities of intermediate sheets of liquid are proportional to their vertical distances from the bottom plate.   Suppose the thickness of the liquid layer is a and the area of each glass plate is A.

The friction force is equal and opposite to the applied force since there is no acceleration.   The impressed force F is proportional to v and to A and is inversely proportional to the thickness of the liquid layer.   Thus we may write

$$F = \eta A \frac{v}{a} \qquad (12)$$

where η is the proportionality factor and is called the *coefficient of viscosity* of the liquid.   It has the dimensions

$$[\eta] = \frac{[F]t}{l^2} = \frac{m}{lt}$$

and is usually expressed in dyne-sec./cm.^{2} = gram/cm.-sec.

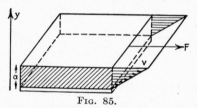

FIG. 85.

More generally, if we consider $a \to 0$, we have

$$F = \eta A \frac{dv}{dy} \qquad (13)$$

where y is measured perpendicularly to the direction of motion. This type of flow is called *laminar* flow since the liquid sheets (laminae) flow over each other.   The work done by the viscous force appears as heat energy and raises the temperature of the liquid.   The coefficient of viscosity is strongly dependent on temperature and decreases with increasing temperature.   For water we have the following values in dyne-sec./cm.^{2}:

η	T
0.018	0°C.
0.010	20°C.
0.003	98°C.

Glycerine has a viscosity coefficient of about 11 dyne-sec./cm.^{2} at room temperature, *i.e.*, about 1,000 times as great as water.

93. Laminar Flow in Cylindrical Pipes; Poiseuille's Law.—We now consider laminar flow in cylindrical pipes.   In this case we think of the sheets of liquid as cylindrical tubes sliding over one another.   Such flow takes place for sufficiently viscous liquids in small pipes.   We shall give more exact criteria at the end of the chapter.

Consider a length l of a horizontal cylindrical pipe of radius R (Fig. 86). The pressure at $x = 0$ is p_1, and the pressure at $x = l$ is p_2. Let us calculate the viscous force exerted on a laminar sheet of radius y. The area of the sheet (cylindrical surface) is $2\pi y \cdot l$, and hence the viscous force is

$$F_v = \eta 2\pi l y \frac{dv}{dy}$$

The resultant force due to the pressure on the liquid contained inside this cylinder of radius y is (see Fig. 86)

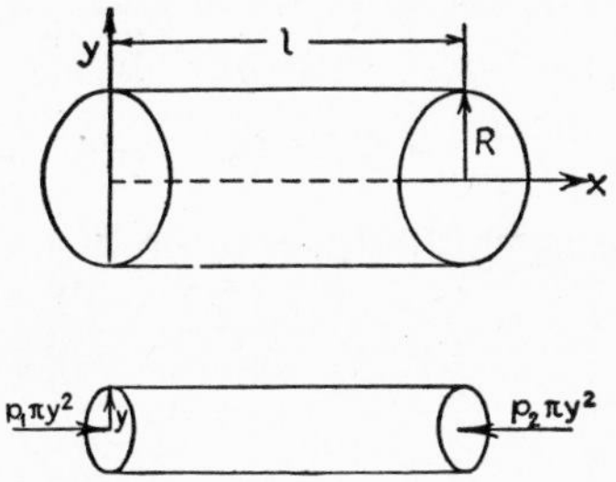

$$p_1 \pi y^2 - p_2 \pi y^2 = \pi y^2 (p_1 - p_2)$$

For equilibrium, we have

$$\pi y^2 (p_1 - p_2) + \eta 2\pi l y \frac{dv}{dy} = 0$$

whence

$$\frac{dv}{dy} = -\frac{1}{2\eta} \cdot \frac{p_1 - p_2}{l} \cdot y \qquad (14)$$

Fig. 86.

an equation which gives us the rate of change of velocity along a radius of the pipe. $(p_1 - p_2)/l$ is the pressure drop per unit length along the pipe.

To find v as a function of y, we integrate Eq. (14) and obtain

$$v = -\frac{1}{4\eta} \cdot \frac{p_1 - p_2}{l} \cdot y^2 + c \qquad (15)$$

and we determine c by the condition that the liquid clings to the inner surface of the pipe, *i.e.*, $v = 0$ for $y = R$.

Thus

$$c = \frac{1}{4\eta} \cdot \frac{p_1 - p_2}{l} \cdot R^2 \qquad (16)$$

Inserting the value of c found in Eq. (16) into Eq. (15), we obtain

$$v = \frac{1}{4\eta} \cdot \frac{p_1 - p_2}{l} \cdot (R^2 - y^2) \qquad (17)$$

If we plot the velocity of a tube of the liquid as a function of the radius of the tube y, we obtain a picture of the velocity distribution perpendicular to the direction of flow. Thus we have a parabolic distribution of velocity across the pipe as shown in Fig. 87.

To get an expression for the discharge rate of such a tube, we consider a cylindrical tube of liquid of radius y and thickness dy (Fig. 88). The cross section of such a tube is $2\pi y dy$, and the discharge rate of this tube is

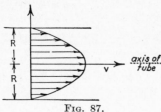

FIG. 87.

$$dQ = v \cdot 2\pi y dy$$

where v is the velocity at the radius y.

Inserting its value from Eq. (17) we have

$$dQ = \frac{\pi}{2\eta} \cdot \frac{p_1 - p_2}{l} \cdot (R^2 - y^2) y dy$$

and the total discharge rate of all the tubes making up the liquid in the pipe is

$$Q = \frac{\pi}{2\eta} \cdot \frac{p_1 - p_2}{l} \int_0^R (R^2 - y^2) y dy \quad (18)$$

The value of the integral is

$$\int_0^R R^2 y dy - \int_0^R y^3 dy = \frac{R^4}{2} - \frac{R^4}{4} = \frac{R^4}{4}$$

so that Eq. (18) becomes

$$Q = \frac{\pi R^4}{8\eta} \cdot \frac{p_1 - p_2}{l} \quad (19)$$

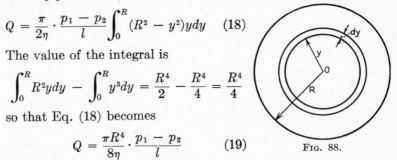

FIG. 88.

This law is known as Poiseuille's law and provides an excellent means for experimentally determining η for various liquids. The discharge rate is most easily controlled by choosing a tube of proper radius R.

94. Stokes's Law.—If a sphere is dragged with constant velocity through a viscous liquid slowly enough so that the motion of the liquid relative to the sphere is laminar, the force applied measures the viscous force of the liquid on the sphere. The exact calculation of this force requires mathematical methods beyond the scope of this book, but we can investigate the form of the law from dimensional considerations. The friction force depends on the viscosity coefficient η, on the velocity of the sphere v, and on the radius of the sphere R.

$$F = f(v, \eta, R)$$

Now the dimensions of these quantities are:

$$[v] = lt^{-1}$$
$$[\eta] = ml^{-1}t^{-1}$$
$$[R] = l$$
$$[F] = mlt^{-2}$$

Thus we see that the function f must be $k\eta vR$ where k is a dimensionless constant. Exact calculation reveals the value of this constant as 6π, so that

$$F = 6\pi\eta vR \qquad (20)$$

a law known as Stokes's law after its discoverer. For spheres falling under the action of gravity, we have for F,

$$F = \tfrac{4}{3}\pi R^3(\rho - \rho_0)g$$

where ρ is the density of the sphere and ρ_0 that of the fluid in which it falls. Inserting this in Eq. (20), we find

$$6\pi\eta vR = \tfrac{4}{3}\pi R^3(\rho - \rho_0)g$$

or

$$v = \frac{2}{9\eta}R^2(\rho - \rho_0)g \qquad (21)$$

showing that larger spheres fall faster than smaller spheres of the same material in a viscous medium.

95. Pressure Changes Perpendicular to the Streamlines. In deriving Bernoulli's equation we considered only the component of acceleration along a streamline and the components of the forces in this direction.

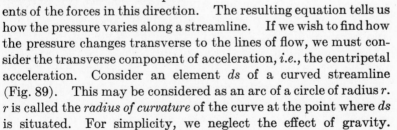

Fig. 89.

The resulting equation tells us how the pressure varies along a streamline. If we wish to find how the pressure changes transverse to the lines of flow, we must consider the transverse component of acceleration, *i.e.*, the centripetal acceleration. Consider an element ds of a curved streamline (Fig. 89). This may be considered as an arc of a circle of radius r. r is called the *radius of curvature* of the curve at the point where ds is situated. For simplicity, we neglect the effect of gravity.

Consider a volume element as shown of base ΔA and height dr (Fig. 89). The resultant force on this element is

$$p\Delta A - (p + dp)\Delta A = -\Delta A \cdot dp$$

This must be equal to

$$ma_r = -\frac{mv^2}{r}$$

so that

$$-\Delta A \cdot dp = -\Delta A \cdot dr\rho\frac{v^2}{r}$$

or

$$\frac{dp}{dr} = \rho\frac{v^2}{r} \tag{22}$$

so that the pressure increases as we go from the concave to the convex side of a streamline, and it increases by an amount $\rho\frac{v^2}{r}$ per unit distance perpendicular to the streamline. In particular, if the streamlines are straight lines, $r = \infty$ and we find $dp/dr = 0$, so that there are no pressure differences normal to these streamlines.

Equation (22) allows us to understand why the boundary surface between a moving and stationary fluid (the so-called *vortex sheet*) is unstable. Consider a uniformly streaming fluid in contact with a fluid at rest. The pressure at the boundary must be the same just above the bounding surface as just below it, so that there is a sudden jump in the velocity at the boundary.

Suppose a minute change occurs at the boundary which causes a small bend in the streamline there. In order to have a steady state with this curved line, it would be necessary to have a larger pressure on the convex side than on the concave side. Moreover, if the original state is to be reobtained, this excess pressure must be even larger than that necessary to maintain the curved flow. These differences of pressure do not exist, however, at the boundary surface, nor are they caused by such a bend, so that any such disturbance once started grows indefinitely, or more exactly, grows until an eddy forms. Thus we have the formation of eddies at the boundary, and, if the original velocity v is large enough, we may completely destroy the steady character of the motion and produce a turbulent motion *to which our formulas must not be applied.*

96. Turbulent Motion; Pressure Resistance; Reynolds Number.*—If we pull a sphere through a liquid, the motion of the liquid maintains for small velocities a steady character (laminar flow). The resistance of the liquid to the motion is given by Stokes's law [Eq. (20)]. We notice that when a certain critical velocity v_c is exceeded (v_c depends on the liquid and on the shape of the body), the motion of the liquid changes its character entirely and becomes turbulent—eddies and whirls are formed. Vortices are formed in *back* of the sphere. A similar departure from stationary flow occurs for pipes when the liquid velocity exceeds a certain critical value. The appearance of turbulent flow is characterized by a change in the force opposing the motion of the body, giving rise to the so-called *pressure resistance* as contrasted with the viscosity resistance. This is due to the formation of vortices in back of the sphere. In the case of stationary flow, the streamline picture is symmetrical about the

sphere, and hence the pressure distribution is also symmetrical so that there is no resultant force on the sphere due to pressure. In the case of vortex motion this symmetry is destroyed, and the pressure in front is greater than that behind the sphere (Fig. 90). This

Fig. 90.

is of course in addition to the viscous drag which is always present but is very much smaller than the pressure resistance.

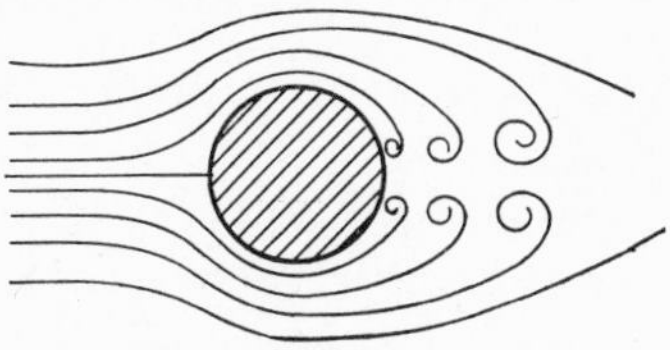

The force due to pressure resistance exerted on a body depends on the cross section of the body perpendicular to the direction of motion, on the density of the liquid since the work done goes into kinetic energy of the vortices and eventually into heat, and on the velocity

$$F = f(v, \rho, A)$$

where A is the largest cross section perpendicular to the direction of motion. Dimensionally

$$[v] = lt^{-1}$$
$$[\rho] = ml^{-3}$$
$$[A] = l^2$$
$$[F] = mlt^{-2}$$

* The considerations in this section are rough approximations, and, although important in practice, they should be considered as qualitative results in comparison with Bernoulli's equation and Poiseuille's law.

so that we obtain

$$F = k\rho v^2 A \tag{23}$$

where k is a dimensionless constant depending on the shape of the body. As examples, we give the values of k for a few cross sections (Fig. 91). It should be noticed that for turbulent motion the resistance to the motion is proportional to v^2, whereas for laminar flow it is directly proportional to v.

If we now inquire as to when turbulent motion sets in, we must consider the factors on which the critical velocity depends. In the case of cylindrical tubes for which we have already considered laminar flow in detail, the critical velocity* may depend on the viscosity of the fluid, on its density and on the diameter of the tube d. Hence

$$v_c = f(\eta,\ \rho,\ d)$$

Dimensionally

$$[\eta] = ml^{-1}t^{-1}$$
$$[\rho] = ml^{-3}$$
$$[d] = l$$
$$[v_c] = lt^{-1}$$

so that

$$v_c = R\frac{\eta}{\rho d} \tag{24}$$

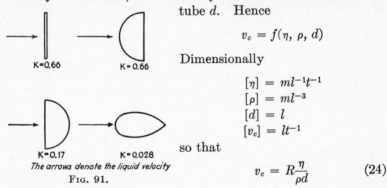

K=0.66   K= 0.66

K=0.17   K= 0.028

The arrows denote the liquid velocity

Fig. 91.

where R is a dimensionless number called *Reynolds number* and does not depend on the liquid. For cylindrical pipes $R \cong 1,000$. As an example of the above, consider the flow of water in a pipe of 10 cm. diameter. The critical velocity is

$$v_c = 1,000 \times \frac{\eta}{\rho d} \cong 1,000 \times \frac{10^{-2}}{1 \times 10} = 1 \text{ cm./sec.}$$

whereas for glycerine in the same tube,

$$v_c = 1,000 \times \frac{\eta}{\rho d} \cong 1,000 \times \frac{10}{10 \times 1.3} = 760 \text{ cm./sec.}$$

so that the flow of glycerine is almost certain in practice to be laminar whereas that of water will be turbulent in most practical cases.

* This critical velocity is not uniquely defined, since in laminar flow the velocity varies across a section of the tube. Roughly we may think of this critical velocity as the average velocity in the tube.

97. Some Laws of Vortex Motion.—Vortex motion plays such a large part in the theoretical and experimental study of hydrodynamics that we shall summarize a few of its most important characteristics *for ideal fluids.* Our knowledge of these laws is largely due to von Helmholtz.

1. Vortices occur when the individual particles (*i.e.*, volume elements) possess angular momentum.

2. A rotating particle can never rotate alone, but the neighboring particles partake of the rotation, and the axes of rotation form closed vortex lines or curves. Vortex lines always form closed curves or end on the sides of the vessel or in the free surface of the liquid.

3. A vortex ring always consists of the same liquid. No energy is transferred to another part of the liquid.

4. The vortex strength of a ring is constant, *i.e.*, the vortex carries its energy with it in its motion through the remaining liquid.

These laws may be illustrated to a large extent by the help of smoke rings. We have given the above laws in order to offer the student at least a passing acquaintance with some of the more important aspects of vortex motion.

Problems

1. Starting from the definition of work, prove that the work done per unit mass (*e.g.*, a gram) of an incompressible liquid by the force due to changing pressure, when it moves from a region where the pressure is p_0 to a region where the pressure is p, is given by

$$W = -\frac{1}{\rho}(p - p_0)$$

where ρ is the density of the liquid.

If the liquid is compressible, the density ρ depends on the pressure. In this case show that

$$W = -\int_{p_0}^{p}\frac{dp}{\rho}$$

2. Using the result of Prob. 1, derive Bernoulli's equation by a direct application of the law of conservation of mechanical energy.

3. Water flows out of a small hole of radius 2 in. in the bottom of a cylindrical vessel 1 ft. in radius. Calculate the velocity of efflux when the height of the liquid is 2 ft. in the vessel. What percentage error is made by neglecting the velocity of the top surface of the liquid?

4. Water stands in a vessel of rectangular cross section 20 by 30 cm. to a height of 50 cm. If it flows out of a hole in the bottom of cross section 2 cm.², calculate the time necessary for the vessel to become empty.

5. Water flows horizontally out of a tank through a hole in its side ¼ in. in diameter. The tank stands on the edge of a table 4 ft. high and the pressure inside the tank is maintained at 8 lb./in.² (gage pressure). How far from the edge of the table does the stream hit the floor? How fast is it then going? Calculate the vertical component of the force exerted by the stream on the floor.

6. A horizontal pipe of 6.00 in.² cross section tapers to 2.00 in.². If sea water is flowing at the rate of 180.0 ft./min. in the large pipe where a pressure gage reads 10.50 lb./in.², what will the gage pressure be in the adjoining part of the small pipe? The barometer reads 30.0 in. What assumptions have you made about the properties of the water and the nature of the flow? What is the discharge rate?

7. Water flows through a horizontal pipe of cross-sectional area 1.44 in.². At one section the cross-sectional area is 0.72 in.². The difference in pressure between this section and a section where the pipe has its larger diameter is 5.0×10^{-3} lb./in.². How many cubic feet of water flow out of the pipe in 1 min.?

8. At a point on a pipe line which is 10.0 ft. lower than the surface of the water in a reservoir the pressure is found to be 4.20 lb./in.² greater than atmospheric pressure. What would be the pressure at another point at the same level, if the diameter of the pipe at the second point is half that at the first point? What would be the velocity of the water at each point? Assume streamline flow.

9. A U-tube containing mercury is connected in a vertical position to a horizontal pipe in which water is flowing. The legs of the U-tube enter the tube at points where the pipe diameters are 4 and 8 cm., respectively. The difference of level of the mercury in the legs is observed to be 4.1 cm. Calculate the velocity of the liquid at each point. (This device is known as a *Venturi meter*.)

10. A Pitot tube is mounted on the wing of an airplane to measure the velocity of the plane relative to the air. The tube contains alcohol and shows a difference of level of 4.8 in. Calculate the velocity of the plane relative to the air in miles per hour. Take the density of air as 1.3×10^{-3} times the density of water.

11. A circular stream of water flows vertically from a circular hole in the bottom of a tank, open at the top. The initial velocity of the water as it emerges is 700 cm./sec. If the stream remains circular, how far will it have fallen before its diameter has decreased to half of its initial diameter? What depth of water in the tank is needed to give this initial velocity?

12. Water flowing in a horizontal pipe discharges at the rate of 0.12 ft.³/sec. At a point in the pipe where the cross section is 0.01 ft.², the absolute pressure is 18 lb./in.². What must be the cross section of a constriction in the pipe such that the pressure there is reduced to 15 lb./in.²?

13. A horizontal pipe of cross section 8 sq. in. has a constriction of cross section 2 sq. in. Water flows in streamline flow in the pipe with a velocity of 3 ft./sec. in the large pipe. Calculate the velocity of the liquid in the constriction and the difference of pressure between a point in the constriction and a point in the large pipe. How many cubic feet of water will flow per minute out of the large pipe?

14. A fire engine pumps 10,000 lb. of water per minute from a lake and ejects it from a nozzle 17 ft. above the lake surface with a velocity of 32 ft./sec. What horse-power output must the engine have, neglecting friction losses?

15. A pipe, carrying water, broadens from a cross section of 10 cm.² to an area of 30 cm.². The difference in pressure between the two parts is 100 dynes/cm.². What is the total flow of water through the pipe?

16. Water of density 2 slugs/ft.³ flows steadily in a pipe line of constant cross section and is supplied by a tank. At a point 4.5 ft. below the level in the tank the pressure in the flowing stream is found to be 1 lb./in.² above atmospheric pressure.

a. What is the velocity of the water at the above point?

b. If the pipe rises to a point 9 ft. above the level of the water in the tank, what are the velocity and pressure at the latter point? (Assume streamline flow.)

17. A horizontal glass tube consists of three sections, *A*, *B*, and *C*, in series, each of constant cross section. Water flows through the tube discharging into the air at the open end of *C*. Each of the sections *A* and *B* has a small hole in the wall. It is found that water is ejected from the hole in *A*, whereas air bubbles appear in the water at the hole in *B*. Explain this. Which section of the tube has the largest diameter and which the smallest?

18. Salt water (64 lb./cu. ft.) in a large enclosed tank is to be driven out through a pipe with an efflux velocity of 4 ft./sec. What gage pressure of air must be established inside the tank to accomplish this result if the open end of the pipe is 2 ft. above the level of the liquid in the tank? Neglect viscosity effects.

19. Water flows steadily from a horizontal tube of cross section 5 cm.^{2} into two horizontal tubes of cross sections 4 and 3 cm.^{2}. The velocity of flow in the 5-cm.^{2} tube is 100 cm./sec. and in the 3-cm.^{2} tube it is 60 cm./sec.

a. Calculate the velocity of flow in the 4-cm.^{2} tube.

b. What is the difference of pressure between the two smaller tubes?

c. Which tube has the lowest pressure?

20. A submarine elevator fin has a volume of 20 cu. ft., an area of top surface (and also of bottom surface) of 50 sq. ft. The mean density of the fin is two times that of water. In a test tank, water was run past the fin so that the velocity along the upper surface, v_1, was 13 ft./sec. and that along the lower surface, v_2, was 12 ft./sec. Calculate the vertical component of the force required to hold the fin stationary (assume the top and bottom surfaces to be effectively horizontal). What is this force when the water is stationary with respect to the fin?

21. Water is siphoned out of a tank by a pipe of 0.5 in.^{2} uniform cross section. The top point of the pipe is 4 ft. above the water surface in the tank, and the open end is 2 ft. below the water surface. Assuming steady flow, calculate the pressure at the highest point of the pipe. What is the discharge rate?

22. A viscous liquid flows in laminar flow under the action of gravity between two vertical parallel plates of large area. If the plates are separated by a distance $2a$, show that the velocity of the liquid at a distance x from a plane halfway between the plates is given by

$$v = \frac{\rho g}{2\eta}(a^2 - x^2)$$

where ρ is the density of the liquid and η the coefficient of viscosity.

(HINT: Consider a slab of liquid of width w, height h, and thickness $2x$, where x is the distance from the plane halfway between the plates to one of the faces wh.)

23. A viscous liquid flows in laminar flow out of a vertical cylindrical pipe under the action of gravity alone. Calculate the distribution of velocity across the pipe.   Derive a formula for the discharge rate.   Calculate the discharge rate for glycerine in a vertical tube 2 cm. in diameter.

24. The following experiment was performed to determine the coefficient of viscosity of a heavy lubricating oil.   A tank of the oil at 20°C. and maintained at a constant gage pressure of 380.0 cm. of mercury was connected to one end of a glass capillary tube 2.00 mm. in diameter and exactly 1 meter long.   The other end was open to the atmosphere and delivered 30.39 cm.[3] of the oil in exactly 2 min.   The barometer read 76.0 cm.   Compute the coefficient of viscosity of the oil.

25. Calculate the steady velocities with which raindrops of radii 0.001 and 0.05 mm. fall.   (Look up the viscosity coefficient and the density of air.)

26. A glass sphere of radius 3 mm. is dropped from rest inside a vessel of glycerine.   Write the differential equation of the motion of the sphere. Integrate this equation to find the velocity as a function of the time.   Show that, as the time increases, the velocity approaches a limiting value given by Stokes's law.

CHAPTER XV

STATIC ELASTICITY

We now turn to the discussion of elastic solids, and in this chapter we shall study problems of equilibrium of such bodies from the standpoint of the continuous theory of matter, and we shall consider bodies at rest. We say that an elastic body is deformed when the mass points (volume elements) of which the body is composed are displaced *with respect to each other*. If all the mass points undergo the same displacements, we have translation of the body as a whole and, since this does *not* represent a deformation, we omit such displacements from our consideration. Similarly a rotation of the body as a whole leaves the distance between every pair of mass points unaltered and hence does *not* constitute an elastic deformation. A body is held in equilibrium in a deformed state by the application of external forces and torques, and these must add up to zero according to Newton's first law of motion. If the external forces are removed, the body will return to its original state, a condition which we assume fulfilled in all the cases we shall discuss. From an atomic standpoint we can understand the phenomenon of elasticity in a qualitative manner as follows: Suppose we picture a solid as composed of atoms (or molecules) in definite positions acting on each other with forces depending on their separation, such as are exerted by springs. If we try to compress a body we move the atoms closer together, and the compression of the springs gives rise to a repulsive force which just balances the external force. If we try to stretch the body, the springs become stretched as the atoms move apart and pull the atoms back to their original positions. Of course the law of force is, in general, more complicated than that of a stretched or compressed spring, but for the solids, such as metals where the deformations are small, springs provide a very good approximation.

98. Stresses.—In the study of the statics of rigid bodies we have seen that the internal forces which hold the component parts of the body at fixed distances from each other played no part in the final equations of equilibrium. This fact, which is an immediate consequence of Newton's third law, is still valid for non-rigid elastic solids, as the reader may easily ascertain by referring to the arguments of Chap. IX. Thus the relations between the external forces and torques which were derived for rigid bodies must hold equally well for elastic solids.

In the case of elastic bodies, however, we must concern ourselves with the internal forces, since they play an important part in determining the changes of size and shape which elastic bodies undergo when subjected to the action of external forces. Our problem, then, is to apply Newton's laws of motion to each volume element of which the body is composed in addition to the body as a whole. Thus we must adopt some method of specification of the internal forces which act on an arbitrary particle or volume element.

As we have done in the study of hydrostatics, we divide these forces into two types: body forces and surface forces. The body forces are defined in Sec. 80; the surface forces which are transmitted across the surfaces bounding the volume element under consideration no longer have the simple property of acting at right angles to the surface of the volume element being studied, as they did in the case of hydrostatics. For the sake of simplicity we shall disregard the effects of body forces and consider only the surface forces.

Surface forces are described in terms of components of *stress*— a set of quantities specifying the force per unit area acting on any surface of a volume element of the body under consideration. Thus the idea of stress is a generalization of the idea of pressure which we have utilized in our study of the motion and equilibrium of fluids.

Suppose we consider an element of area ΔA of the surface bounding a volume element of the body. To specify completely the state of affairs at this element of area, we must know

a. The magnitude and direction of the force acting on the area.

b. The size of the area ΔA and its orientation in space, the latter being uniquely determined if the direction of a line perpendicular to the area is given.

Let n be a vector of unit length drawn normal to ΔA in a direction outward from the volume element (Fig. 92). If the surface force acting on the volume element across ΔA is F (Fig. 92a), we can resolve this force into two components, a component F_n perpendicular to ΔA (Fig. 92b) and a component F_t tangent to ΔA (Fig. 92c).

We now define the normal stress component on ΔA as

$$S_n = \frac{F_n}{\Delta A} \tag{1}$$

This component of stress has the dimensions of pressure, *i.e.*, force per unit area. In fact, pressure is a normal stress. We shall adopt the convention of calling S_n positive if the force F_n acting on the volume is an outward pull, corresponding to

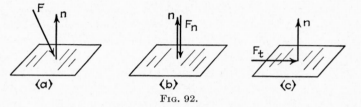

<（a）> <（b）> <（c）>

Fig. 92.

tension. Thus the normal stress on any surface element in an ideal fluid is given by

$$S_n = -p \tag{1a}$$

In Fig. 92b S_n corresponds to a compression and is negative.

The tangential component of the force acting on ΔA gives rise to the so-called *tangential* or *shearing* component of stress S_t, defined by

$$S_t = \frac{F_t}{\Delta A} \tag{2}$$

These shearing stresses are zero in ideal fluids and a concise definition of an ideal fluid is that it is a fluid in which shearing stresses cannot be set up. In the case of viscous liquids, however, we have met an example of shearing stress. In Sec. 93, where we considered the laminar flow of a liquid in horizontal sheets, we might have written Eq. (13) as

$$S_t = \frac{F}{A} = \eta\frac{dv}{dy} \tag{3}$$

since the viscous force acts horizontally and the normal to A is vertical.

Thus far we have concerned ourselves only with the forces acting on a specified element of area ΔA located at a given point

P inside an elastic body. The components of stress for this surface have been defined. Suppose, however, we consider an element of area at the same point P which is oriented differently from the first. In general the stress components for this second area will be different from those on the first. To specify completely the state of stress at a point, it is necessary to have sufficient information to be able to calculate the stress components for any surface whatsoever at the point under consideration. The information which must be obtained can be summarized as follows: At the point P we construct three elements of area whose normals are mutually perpendicular, as shown in the accompanying figure (Fig. 93). The directions of the normals

FIG. 93.

are labeled x, y, and z; as shown, x and y lie in the plane of the page, and z points out at the reader at right angles to the page.

If the stress components are known for these three surface elements, then it is possible to calculate from these the stress components for any other elementary surface at the point under consideration. We shall omit any detail of such a calculation but wish to emphasize the fact that the components of stress for *three* mutually orthogonal surfaces must be given to determine completely the state of stress at any point. This complication does not exist for ideal liquids, since not only are there no shearing stresses but also the normal stress is the same $(-p)$ for any surface at a given point (independence of pressure forces on the orientation of the surface).

To calculate the components of stress inside an elastic body when it is held in equilibrium by external forces, it is necessary to proceed as follows:

1. Apply Newton's laws of motion to an arbitrary volume element within the body. The sum of the forces and torques acting on this element must be zero for equilibrium. This leads to a set of relations among the stress components.

2. The above equations must be solved, and the solutions must have the property that, when we choose our volume element at

the surface of the body, they yield the value of the external force acting on the body at that point.

It would be beyond the scope of this book to set up the equations mentioned above in their general form, but we shall consider the stress distributions for two simple cases in detail.

99. Stresses (*Continued*). *a. Simple Compression or Tension.*—Suppose we consider a uniform rod of length l and cross section A, to which equal and opposite forces are applied uniformly over, and normal to, the end faces. If the forces push inward on the bar, we have the case of simple compression, and if they pull outward, we speak of simple tension. The qualitative effect of a compression of the above type is to shorten the bar and to increase its cross section slightly with corresponding changes for tension. In the following we shall assume that the change in cross-sectional area is so small that it can be neglected as far as the stress calculation is concerned. This is always true in practice.

$$S_n = -p = \frac{F}{A} \text{ on end face}$$

The bar is shown in the accompanying figure (Fig. 94). The external forces are shown, and the stress on the end faces is normal

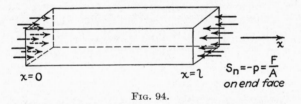

$$x=0 \qquad x=l \qquad S_n = -p = \frac{F}{A} \text{ on end face}$$

Fig. 94.

and equal to F/A everywhere on these faces. The tangential component of stress is zero on these faces. We may denote the three fundamental surfaces by x, y, z, corresponding to their respective normals. The stress distribution inside the bar is as follows: On every x-surface (parallel to the end face) there is a uniform normal stress equal to F/A, the value on the end face, and no tangential stress. On every y- or z-surface the normal and tangential stress is zero. Hence we have the simple case of only one component of stress (for the three fundamental surfaces under consideration) different from zero, and this stress is constant, independent of position inside the bar. It is evident that this stress distribution yields the correct values for the stresses on the external faces, since the end faces (which are x-surfaces) have exactly the uniform normal stress F/A, whereas the lateral surfaces (which are y- and z-surfaces) have zero stress since there are no external forces acting on them. We have to prove that the above stress distribution satisfies the equilibrium laws for an arbitrary volume element. Consider

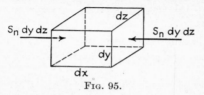

FIG. 95.

an arbitrarily chosen parallelepiped of sides dx, dy, and dz, at some point inside the bar (Fig. 95). The forces acting on it are shown. Since the only x-components of the forces are those on the end faces, we must have S_n equal on both end surfaces. The y- and z-components of the forces on all surfaces are zero, and hence the laws of equilibrium are satisfied.

It must be emphasized again that the above stress components refer to three surfaces whose normals are x, y, and z, respectively. It is not correct, for example, to state that there are no shearing stresses in this type of deformation. This statement is only

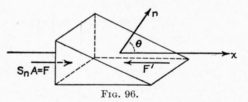

FIG. 96.

true for the three surfaces under consideration. Let us calculate the normal and tangential components of stress on a plane surface whose normal makes an angle θ with the x-axis (Fig. 96). Consider a wedge-shaped volume, as shown in the accompanying figure. The only forces acting on it act on the left-hand face and on the slant face, as shown. The forces acting on the other surfaces are zero since they are y- and z-surfaces. For equilibrium we must have

$$S_n A = F' \tag{4}$$

and we now must resolve F' into two components, one normal to the slant face and one tangent to it. These components are

$$F_n = F' \cos \theta = S_n A \cos \theta$$

and

$$F_t = F' \sin \theta = S_n A \sin \theta \tag{5}$$

The normal and tangential components of stress on the slant face are by definition

$$\left.\begin{array}{l} S_n' = \dfrac{F_n}{A'} = S_n \cos\theta \, \dfrac{A}{A'} \\[2mm] S_t' = \dfrac{F_t}{A'} = S_n \sin\theta \, \dfrac{A}{A'} \end{array}\right\} \tag{6}$$

where A' is the area of the slant face. Since $A = A' \cos\theta$, these can be written

$$\begin{array}{l} S_n' = S_n \cos^2\theta \\[1mm] S_t' = S_n \sin\theta \cos\theta \end{array} \tag{7}$$

where S_n is equal to F/A, F the external force and A the cross section of the bar.

From these equations, we see that there are both normal and tangential stresses on any slant face in the bar. The maximum value of S_n' occurs for $\theta = 0$, when $S_{n_{\max}}' = S_n$, as we should expect since this corresponds to an x-surface. The maximum value of the shearing stress occurs for $\theta = 45°$, and for this slant surface $S_{t_{\max}}' = S_n/2$. The value of the normal stress on the 45° surface is seen to be equal to $S_n/2$ also.

b. Simple Shear.—This case is defined most simply by considering a solid slab of cross section A and thickness d. Equal and opposite forces are applied uniformly over and tangential to the two faces of the slab. When this is done, we speak of the slab being put into simple shear. The qualitative effect of a simple shear is to displace one face parallel to the other. In Fig. 97 are shown the

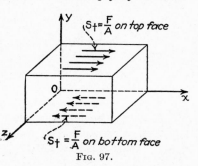

FIG. 97.

external forces, and the stress on the faces is tangential and equal to F/A everywhere on these faces. The normal component of stress is zero everywhere on these faces, and all components of stress are zero on all the other faces of the slab.

The stress distribution inside the slab is as follows: On every y-surface (parallel to the faces on which the external forces are applied) there is a uniform tangential or shearing stress equal to F/A and no normal stress. On every x- or z-surface both the normal and tangential stresses vanish. Hence we have once again the simple case of only one component of stress (for the fundamental surfaces under consideration) different from zero, and this component is constant, independent of position inside the slab. It is clear that this stress distribution yields the correct values F/A on the top and bottom faces of the slab and zero on the other external faces.

When we come to examine the conditions for equilibrium of the slab, we run into a slight complication. The conditions for translation are clearly satisfied, but the condition that the sum of the moments of the forces vanish is *not* satisfied. From this we must conclude that a single stress component cannot exist alone for the case under consideration but that we must apply equal and opposite forces to the external x-faces to preserve equilibrium. This leads to relations between the various shearing components of stress which must exist in general, but since we shall not have occasion to utilize them, we shall pass over this point. There is a deformation, simple torsion, to which we shall return later for which the simple analysis which we have given will hold exactly, and in this case it will turn out that we are not troubled by any such complication as we have met here.

Finally, we must emphasize again that the stress components of which we have been talking refer *only* to the three fundamental surfaces whose normals are x, y, and z. On any other surface there will exist, in general, both normal and tangential stress components which may be readily computed.

In practice the two simple cases discussed above seldom occur alone, but they are fundamental because any stress distribution, no matter how complicated, may be compounded out of elementary tensions or compressions and shears.

100. Strain.—Thus far we have concerned ourselves solely with the specification of the forces acting on an elastic body, and now we must turn to the method of description of the deformations which occur under the action of external forces. Since a body is deformed only if the particles of which a body is composed are displaced relatively with respect to each other, we introduce a set of quantities which measure these relative displacements and which are called *strains*. We shall postpone the general definitions of strains to the next section and confine our attention to the cases of simple tension and of simple shear.

a. Simple Tension or Compression.—We first consider the deformation occurring when a bar of original length l_0, width and breadth d_0, is subjected to simple tension or compression. In Fig. 98 the full-line figure represents the bar before deformation, and the dotted-line figure shows the bar after deformation. The length of the deformed bar is l_1, and its width and breadth are d_1.

The original length l_0 is changed to l_1, and we define

$$\epsilon_l = \frac{l_1 - l_0}{l_0} = \frac{\Delta l}{l_0} \qquad (8)$$

as the longitudinal component of strain, or, for brevity, the *longitudinal* strain. It is the fractional change of length (the change of length per unit original length) and is dimensionless; ϵ_l is positive for tension and negative for compression.

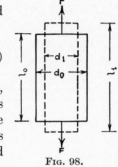

FIG. 98.

The original cross-section dimension d_0 is changed to d_1, and we define

$$\epsilon_t = \frac{d_1 - d_0}{d_0} = \frac{\Delta d}{d_0} \qquad (9)$$

as the *transverse* component of strain. For most materials it is found experimentally that the ratio of transverse to longitudinal strain is negative and practically constant. This constant is called *"Poisson's ratio"* and is denoted by σ.

$$\sigma = -\frac{\epsilon_t}{\epsilon_l} \qquad (10)$$

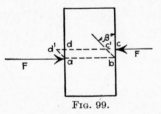

FIG. 99.

For practically all materials σ lies between $\frac{1}{4}$ and $\frac{1}{2}$.

b. Simple Shear.—Once again we consider a bar and produce the deformation by applying equal and opposite forces, almost along the same straight line, perpendicular to the length of the bar. The effect of these forces is to displace the cross section *cd* relative to the section *ab* into the position *c'd'* (Fig. 99). This deformation can be specified by giving the changes in angles between straight lines. Thus we define the *shearing* strain γ as

$$\gamma = \tan \beta = \frac{dd'}{ad} \cong \beta \qquad (11)$$

In most cases of practical interest the strains are small so that β is a small angle and we may place $\tan \beta = \beta$.

The changes in volume for the above deformations are readily calculable in terms of the strain components which we have introduced.

Consider a portion of an elastic body, originally of cubical shape, subjected to simple tension.   Let us take a cube such that each

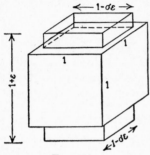

FIG. 100.

side is of unit length.   After deformation we have a parallelepiped of length $1 + \epsilon$ (Fig. 100) (ϵ = longitudinal strain) and of width = thickness $= 1 - \sigma\epsilon$.   Hence the volume after deformation is

$$V_1 = (1 + \epsilon)(1 - \sigma\epsilon)\,(1 - \sigma\epsilon)$$
$$= 1 + \epsilon - 2\sigma\epsilon + \cdots$$

where the dots denote terms involving ϵ^2 which we neglect since ϵ is very small compared with unity.

Before deformation the volume was $V_0 = 1$, so that the change in volume per unit volume (called the *volume dilation*) is

$$\delta = \frac{V_1 - V_0}{V_0} = \frac{\epsilon(1 - 2\sigma)}{1} = \epsilon(1 - 2\sigma) \tag{12}$$

Experiment shows that a body under tension always suffers an increase in volume $\delta_T > 0$ and for compression the volume decreases $\delta_c < 0$, so that

$$\sigma \leq \tfrac{1}{2} \tag{13}$$

When $\sigma = \tfrac{1}{2}$ we have the case of no volume change.

For the case of simple shear, the change in volume is zero and we have only a change of shape.   This may be seen from Fig. 101 where the dotted figure represents the cube after deformation.

101. The General Analysis of Strain.—In the case of an arbitrary deformation, we proceed to describe the state of strain as follows: We choose one of the mass points of the elastic body as our origin O and refer all the displacements of the other mass points to the position of this mass point.   At O we construct a set of three axes, mutually orthogonal, which we call the x-, y-, and z-axes.   The position of a point of the body P with respect to O is fixed by giving the three coordinates x, y, and z of the point P.   Consider the volume element (or mass point) at P before deformation.   After deformation the position of the mass point which was at P is P' (still with respect to the mass point which was at O before deformation) (Fig. 102).

The point P has undergone a vector displacement $\vec{s}$ with respect to O, and the components of $\vec{s}$ we shall call a, b, and c, respectively. If we specify the vector $\vec{s}$ for every point of the body, we have a complete description of

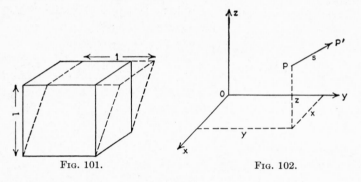

FIG. 101.   FIG. 102.

the deformation state. In general, $\vec{s}$ will be different for different points P and hence is a function of x, y, z, *i.e.*,

$$\vec{s} = f(x,\ y,\ z)$$

To say that a vector is a function of position (*i.e.*, depends on position) means that each of its components is a function of the coordinates. Thus

$$a = f_1(x,\ y,\ z)$$
$$b = f_2(x,\ y,\ z)$$
$$c = f_3(x,\ y,\ z)$$

We define the *strain* in general as the set of quantities which specify the rate of change of the displacement of a point in the body with respect to the coordinates, *i.e.*, we specify how much the displacement vector changes as we go from one point to another in the body. If all points move the same amount, all these rates of change are zero and this is the case of translation of the body, in which case there is no deformation or strain.

Thus we have the quantities da/dx, da/dy, da/dz, db/dx, db/dy, etc., specifying the strain at a point. In these derivatives we differentiate with respect to only *one* coordinate, keeping the others fixed. The three derivatives da/dx, db/dy, dc/dz are the three longitudinal-strain components. The first, for example, tells us how fast the x-component of the displacement vector changes in the x-direction. The remaining six derivatives determine the shearing strains. It turns out that there are only three independent shearing strains, corresponding to the changes of the right angles between the x- and y-axes, y- and z-axes, and z- and x-axes.

We can illustrate this best in the case of a simple tension (a pure dilation) in which each displacement component is proportional to the corresponding coordinate. In this case the corresponding strain component is constant. Thus, for simple tension,

$$a = kx$$

since the horizontal component of the displacement of each point is proportional to its x-coordinate. Thus every point on the end face at $x = l$ is displaced an amount Δl to the right, whereas every point on the face at $x = 0$ is not displaced at all in a *horizontal* direction (Fig. 103). Obviously, then, a does not depend on y (or z) since it is the same for all points in any vertical section through the rod. Thus we may write

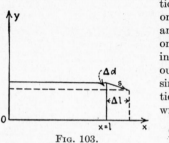

Fig. 103.

$$\frac{da}{dx} = k = \frac{a}{x} = \frac{\Delta l}{l} = \epsilon_l; \qquad \frac{da}{dy} = \frac{da}{dz} = 0$$

and we refind our elementary definition of longitudinal strain.

Similarly, for the y-coordinate

$$b = k_1 y$$

the y-component of the displacement of a point is proportional to its y-coordinate only. Thus every point in the base at $y = 0$ undergoes no displacement in a vertical direction and every point in the top face moves down a distance Δd. We may then write

$$\frac{db}{dy} = k_1 = \frac{b}{y} = -\frac{\Delta d}{d} = \epsilon_t; \qquad \frac{db}{dx} = \frac{db}{dz} = 0$$

For the z-coordinate everything is the same as for the y-coordinate, so that

$$\frac{dc}{dz} = k_1 = \frac{c}{z} = -\frac{\Delta d}{d} = \epsilon_t; \qquad \frac{dc}{dx} = \frac{dc}{dy} = 0$$

(The z-axis is perpendicular to the plane of the page.)

102. Stress-strain Relations; Hooke's Law.—Thus far our attention has been given to a description of the deformation state of an elastic body and a description of the state of stress of an elastic body. We now must inquire into the relation between stress and strain. The answer must be taken from experiment and is known as *Hooke's law*. It states that *the stress components are linear functions of all the strain components*. It is important to remember that *each* stress component depends on *all* the strains and *vice versa*. Perhaps we may add that, if w is a linear function of x, y, and z, this means that w is related to x, y, and z by an equation of the form

$$w = ax + by + cz$$

where a, b, and c are constants.

In the case of homogeneous isotropic bodies the number of proportionality constants which appear in Hooke's law are only *two* and are called the *elastic constants* of the material of which the body is composed. We can illustrate best in the case of simple tension or compression. Here we have

$$\epsilon_l = \frac{1}{E}S_n \tag{14}$$

where S_n is the constant stress and E is known as *Young's modulus* or the *stretch modulus* of the elastic body. Equation (14) may also be written

$$\frac{F}{A} \cdot \frac{l}{\Delta l} = E \tag{15}$$

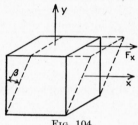

Fig. 104.

E has the dimensions of stress. As we have pointed out, *all* the other components of stress are zero. It does not follow, however, that the other components of strain are zero, since each component of strain depends on *all* the stress components. In fact for pure tension there are no shearing strains, but there are two transverse components of strain, which we denote by ϵ_{ty} and ϵ_{tz}. These transverse components are

$$\epsilon_{ty} = -\sigma\epsilon_l = -\frac{\sigma}{E}S_n$$

and

$$\epsilon_{tz} = -\sigma\epsilon_l = -\frac{\sigma}{E}S_n \tag{16}$$

where σ is Poisson's ratio. The negative sign indicates a transverse contraction if there is an extension in the x-direction. The two constants E and σ completely determine the behavior of an isotropic homogeneous elastic body. For the case of pure shear, and x-force acting on a surface whose normal points in the y-direction Hooke's law becomes (Fig. 104);

$$\gamma = \tan \beta = \frac{1}{\mu}S_t \tag{14}$$

μ is known as the *shearing modulus* or *torsion modulus*. It can be calculated from σ and E, and the relation can be shown to be

$$\mu = \frac{E}{2(1 + \sigma)} \tag{17}$$

103. Hooke's Law for Principal Axes.—It can be shown mathematically that any elastic deformation can be built up as the sum of three simple tensions or compressions along three mutually perpendicular axes. These three axes are known as the *principal axes of strain.* Similarly the state of stress may be represented by three normal stresses due to tension or compression along three mutually perpendicular axes known as the *principal axes of stress.* For the case of isotropic bodies these two sets of axes coincide. The geometrical meaning of these axes may be seen as follows: If we consider the points of an undeformed elastic body which lie on the surface of a very small sphere, these points will lie on the surface of an ellipsoid after deformation. The axes of this ellipsoid are the principal axes of stress and strain. It may be easier for the student to consider a two-dimensional elastic body such as a sheet of rubber. Suppose we draw a small circle on this sheet. If the rubber is then stretched, the circle becomes an ellipse and the long and short axes of this ellipse are the principal axes at the point where the circle is located.

Let us call the principal axes 1, 2, and 3. A simple pull along the 1-axis means that we have only one component of normal stress S_1 and three components of strain ϵ_1', ϵ_2' and ϵ_3'. These are related by the equations

$$\epsilon_1' = \frac{1}{E}S_1, \qquad \epsilon_2' = -\frac{\sigma}{E}S_1, \qquad \epsilon_3' = -\frac{\sigma}{E}S_1$$

Similarly, for the other two axes,

$$\epsilon_1'' = -\frac{\sigma}{E}S_2, \qquad \epsilon_2'' = \frac{1}{E}S_2, \qquad \epsilon_3'' = -\frac{\sigma}{E}S_2$$

and

$$\epsilon_1''' = -\frac{\sigma}{E}S_3, \qquad \epsilon_2''' = -\frac{\sigma}{E}S_3, \qquad \epsilon_3''' = \frac{1}{E}S_3$$

The resulting strain due to all three simple tensions or compressions S_1, S_2, and S_3 is obtained by simply adding the strain separately produced by each simple tension. Thus we have for the resultant components of strain:

$$\epsilon_1 = \frac{1}{E}(S_1 - \sigma S_2 - \sigma S_3)$$

$$\epsilon_2 = \frac{1}{E}(-\sigma S_1 + S_2 - \sigma S_3)$$

$$\epsilon_3 = \frac{1}{E}(-\sigma S_1 - \sigma S_2 + S_3)$$

This is the general expression for Hooke's law applied to isotropic bodies when we choose *the principal axes as the coordinate axes.*

104. Compressibility; Compression Modulus.—In Sec. 100 we have shown that the change in volume per unit volume of a body subjected to simple tension or compression in one direction is

$$\left(\frac{\Delta V}{V}\right)_{TorC} = (1 - 2\sigma)\epsilon_l \qquad (18)$$

Suppose we have a body subject to uniform normal forces all over its surface. We can accomplish this by immersing it in a fluid, in which case the normal stresses are equal to the hydrostatic pressure. For simplicity let us consider a cube whose faces each have the area A, and let the hydrostatic pressure be increased from p to $p + \Delta p$ (Fig. 105). The surface forces on each pair of faces give rise to a volume dilation given by Eq. (18), and, since there are three pairs of faces, the total volume dilation is three times that for compression in one dimension. Thus, using Hooke's law, Eq. (18) becomes

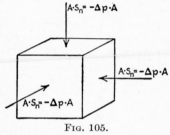

Fig. 105.

$$\delta_{TorC} = \frac{1 - 2\sigma}{E} S_n = -\frac{1 - 2\sigma}{E} \Delta p$$

and, multiplying by three, there follows

$$\delta = \frac{\Delta V}{V} = -\frac{3(1 - 2\sigma)}{E} \Delta p \tag{19}$$

The compressibility of a substance (solid, liquid or gas) is defined by

$$\kappa = -\frac{1}{V} \frac{dV}{dp} \tag{20}$$

so that for elastic solids

$$\kappa = \frac{3(1 - 2\sigma)}{E} \tag{21}$$

This expression has a meaning only for solids since Poisson's ratio σ is meaningless for a fluid.

The reciprocal of the compressibility is called the *bulk modulus* B and is

$$B = \frac{1}{\kappa} = \frac{E}{3(1 - 2\sigma)} \tag{22}$$

Equation (20) defining the compressibility is sometimes written in terms of the density ρ of the substance. Since

$$V = \frac{M}{\rho}, \qquad dV = -\frac{M}{\rho^2} d\rho, \qquad \text{and} \qquad \frac{dV}{V} = -\frac{d\rho}{\rho}$$

the compressibility becomes

$$\kappa = \frac{1}{\rho}\frac{d\rho}{dp} \tag{23}$$

105. Simple Torsion.—As our last application we consider the case of simple torsion of a vertical cylindrical rod of radius R and length L.

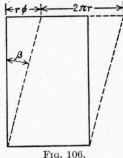

Fig. 106.

Consider the rod held fixed at the bottom and a torque τ applied to the upper end about the long axis of the cylinder. The upper face twists through an angle θ, the bottom face stays fixed, and intermediate sections twist through angles proportional to their heights above the bottom face. Consider a section at the height l and suppose it twists through an angle φ. Then

$$\varphi = kl$$

and since, when $l = L$,

$$\varphi = \theta$$

we have

$$k = \frac{\theta}{L}$$

so that

$$\varphi = \frac{\theta}{L}l \tag{24}$$

Now let us consider a cylindrical shell of radius $r < R$ and of height l, thickness dr. Imagine this shell to be split up the side and unrolled flat on a plane. We then get a rectangle of height l and width $2\pi r$ (Fig. 106). After twisting (shown dotted), the upper side is moved to the right a distance $r\varphi$, *i.e.*, each point on the upper face moves a distance $r\varphi$.

Here we have a case of simple shear, and the shearing strain is $\tan \beta = r\varphi/l$, which, upon using Eq. (24), becomes

$$\gamma = \tan \beta = r\frac{\theta}{L} \tag{25}$$

and does not depend on the height of the shell, only on its radius.

Now consider the force acting on the top face of a shell of thickness dr, radius r, and height l (Fig. 107). This force is uniformly distributed over the area $2\pi r\,dr$ and gives rise to the shearing strain calculated in the last paragraph. Since this force acts everywhere at right angles to the radius drawn to the point at which the force is applied, the torque of this force taken about the axis of the cylinder is

$$d\tau = r \cdot S_t \cdot 2\pi r \, dr \tag{26}$$

where S_t is the shearing stress on the shell.

By Hooke's law we have, using Eq. (25),

$$S_t = \mu\epsilon_t = \frac{\mu\theta}{L}r \tag{27}$$

so that Eq. (26) becomes

$$d\tau = \frac{2\pi\mu\theta}{L}r^3 dr \tag{28}$$

Note that this expression does not depend on the height of the cylindrical shell. To get the total torque on any cross section of the solid cylinder, we must integrate Eq. (28) over all shells from $r = 0$ to $r = R$. Thus there follows

$$\tau = \frac{2\pi\mu\theta}{L}\int_0^R r^3 dr = \frac{\pi\mu\theta}{2L}R^4 \tag{29}$$

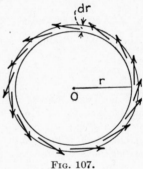

Fig. 107.

This is, of course, equal in magnitude to the externally applied torque. This equation allows a simple experimental determination of μ. The torque necessary to twist this rod through an angle θ is then

$$\tau = k'\theta$$

with

$$k' = \frac{\pi\mu R^4}{2L}$$

If a disk of moment of inertia I is suspended from the rod (I is taken about the long axis of the rod), we have already shown that it performs angular harmonic motion with the period

$$T = 2\pi\sqrt{\frac{I}{k'}} = 2\pi\sqrt{\frac{2IL}{\pi\mu R^4}} \tag{30}$$

so that

$$\mu = \frac{8\pi IL}{T^2 R^4} \tag{31}$$

All quantities on the right-hand side can be experimentally determined so that we can determine μ.

We see from the above that a wire of small radius gives a longer period of vibration than a rod of the same material and length. The dependence on length is not so marked since $T \sim \sqrt{L}$ and $T \sim 1/R^2$.

To recapitulate, we have applied Hooke's law to only two simple cases, simple tension and simple torsion, in which examples the calculations are relatively simple. The general problem involves mathematical technique beyond the scope of this book but starts from the same fundamental equations.

Problems

1. A cubical block is subjected to simple tension in one direction perpendicular to one face. Show that the fractional decrease in area of the cross section is given by $2\sigma\epsilon$, where σ is Poisson's ratio and ϵ the longitudinal strain.

2. A steel rod 1 by 1 by 10 in. is stretched by a force applied at the end B, the end A being clamped so that the central point of the 1- by 1-in. face at A remains fixed. If the rod is given a longitudinal strain of 0.0020, find the magnitude and direction of the vector displacement of a point at the center of one of the 1- by 10-in. faces.

3. If a cubical block of a solid is compressed in one dimension until it has shortened by 1 per cent of its original length, by how many per cent would its volume decrease if Poisson's ratio were $\frac{1}{2}$? $\frac{1}{4}$? 0?

4. A steel rod 2 ft. long and 0.06 in.² in cross section is *rigidly* clamped at both ends. The center of this rod is moved toward one end a distance of 0.0001 in., stretching one-half of the rod and compressing the other. Calculate the work done in carrying out this deformation.

5. A 100-lb. weight is hung by a steel wire 50 ft. long of cross section 0.01 in.².

a. Calculate the stretch of the wire.

b. If the wire is further stretched vertically and released, how many vibrations per second will the 100-lb. weight make?

6. A 10-lb. weight hangs on a vertical steel wire 2 ft. long and of 0.0020 in.² cross section. Hanging from the bottom of this weight is a similar steel wire which supports another 10-lb. weight. Find the vertical displacement of a point half-way along the lower wire.

7. Fifty feet of copper wire and 50 ft. of steel wire are fastened end to end, and the whole length of 100 ft. is stretched 0.50 in., each half stretching 0.25 in. Find the ratio of the diameters of the two wires.

8. If allowed to shorten without developing tension, a steel bar will shorten 20 parts in 10,000 when cooled from 200° to 0°C.

a. What force would be necessary to keep a steel rod 1 in. in diameter from shortening when cooled from 200° to 0°C.?

b. What would the stress in the rod be when the temperature is 0°C.?

9. A hollow glass sphere of 500 cm.³ content is filled with water. If a bullet of volume 1.0 cm.³ is fired through this sphere, calculate the pressure on the inner surface of the sphere when the bullet is inside it, assuming that no water has escaped from the sphere. What would be the effect on your answer if you considered the escaping water?

10. Show that the work done in producing an increase in length Δl of a wire of length l and cross-sectional area A is $\dfrac{EA}{l}\dfrac{(\Delta l)^2}{2}$.

11. A copper wire ($E = 16 \times 10^6$ lb./in.², $\sigma = 0.34$) and a steel wire ($E = 30 \times 10^6$ lb./in.², $\sigma = 0.28$), each 1 ft. long and 0.01 in.² in area when unstretched, are welded together end to end. The combined wire supports a 400-lb. weight. What is the elongation of the combined wire? What are the per cent changes in cross-sectional areas under tension?

12. A bar of copper of length 2 ft. is welded end to end with a bar of steel of length 15 in. The cross section of each bar is 0.1 in.². The compound bar is stretched in simple tension by forces applied uniformly to its ends, each force of magnitude 1,000 lb.

a. Calculate the longitudinal component of stress in each bar.

b. Calculate the increase of length of each bar.

13. A steel wire 5 ft. long, diameter 0.1 in., is fastened end to end with 10 ft. of copper wire of the same diameter. The double wire is hung vertically with the free end of the steel wire fixed and a weight is hung on the other end. The bottom point of the double wire is observed to descend a distance of 0.25 in. What is the increase of length of each section of the wire?

14. A steel block, 5 ft. long and 2 by 1 ft. in cross section, is placed in a testing machine and compressed by a force of 500 tons applied perpendicularly to the 2- by 1-ft. face. Find:

a. The stress in the block.

b. The change in length of the block.

c. The fractional change in volume.

15. A rigid bar 3 ft. long is supported in a horizontal position by a steel wire at one end and a copper wire at the other. Each wire is 5 ft. long and 0.005 in.² in cross section. A downward force of 450 lb. is applied to the bar at such a point that both wires stretch the same amount. Find:

a. The tension in each wire.

b. The position of the point of application of the 450-lb. force. Neglect the weight of the 3-ft. bar.

16. An elevator, with its load, weighs 1 ton, and it is supported by a single steel cable.

a. Find the cross-sectional area of the cable, if the tensile stress in it is not to exceed 5,000 lb./in.² with the elevator at rest.

b. The elevator is descending at 50 ft./sec. Find the shortest distance in which it can be stopped if the stress in the cable is not to exceed 10,000 lb./in.².

c. If the length of the cable in part *b* is 500 ft., how much is the cable stretched while the elevator is being stopped, compared with its length under no load?

17. By eliminating dp between the equation $\dfrac{dp}{dy} = \rho g$ and $\kappa = \dfrac{1}{\rho}\dfrac{d\rho}{dp}$, obtain the differential equation for ρ as a function of the depth y below the surface of the water. Show that the integrated form of this equation is $\rho = \dfrac{\rho_0}{1 - \kappa\rho_0 g y}$.

Set up the integral from which the variation of pressure with depth can be found.

18. A steel wire 1 mile long and 2 in. in diameter hangs vertically in a mine shaft. How much longer is the wire in this position than when horizontal with no load applied? Neglect changes in linear density due to changes in cross section.

19. Plot a curve of the potential energy of a bar under tension and compression as a function of its strain, showing that the curve is a parabola. (This curve holds for only small displacements where Hooke's law holds.)

20. Construct a curve which you think would represent a qualitatively correct plot of potential energy vs. strain of a rod in pure tension for all values of the strain from zero to the point where the rod breaks.

21. A 32-lb. weight supported at the end of a metal wire of unstretched length 2 ft. is whirled in a vertical circle with a constant angular velocity of 2 r.p.s. The cross section of the wire is 0.01 in.^{2}. Calculate the elongation of the wire when the weight is at the lowest point of its path. Young's modulus for the metal is 35×10^6 lb./in.^{2}

22. For processes in which the density of a gas is proportional to its pressure, show that the compressibility is equal to the reciprocal of the pressure.

23. What is the difference between the buoyant force on a metal block of volume 1 ft.^{3}, at the surface of the ocean, and at a depth such that the pressure is 200 atm. greater than at the surface? Assume the metal to be incompressible. One cubic foot of sea water weighs 64 lb. at a pressure of 1 atm. The compressibility of water is 50×10^{-6} per atmosphere.

24. A block of steel would increase its volume by 330 parts per million when heated from 20 to 30°C. at constant pressure. What increase of pressure would be necessary to keep the block from expanding when its temperature is thus raised?

The compressibility of steel is 4.4×10^{-8} in.^{2}/lb.

25. A steel wire 10 ft. long, of diameter 0.2 in., is stretched by a force of 100 lb. and then twisted about its long axis by a torque of 5 lb.-in. Calculate the work done in producing the above combined deformation.

26. A copper rod 40 cm. long and 1.0 cm. in diameter has torques of 50 kg.-cm. applied in opposite directions about its long axis at its two ends. How many degrees will one end face be turned relative to the other?

27. *a.* What is the shearing strain of a thin hollow cylindrical shell 0.01 cm. thick at the surface of the rod of Prob. 26. Strictly speaking, is the strain constant throughout this thin shell? If not, by how many per cent does it vary?

b. Answer the same questions for a 0.01-cm. thick shell 0.25 cm. from the axis.

28. What is the shearing stress on the two shells of Prob. 27?

29. One end of a 1-in. diameter rod 2 ft. long is clamped, and the other end is twisted through an angle of 3° (about the long axis of the rod). Find the displacement, in degrees and in inches, of a point in the rod 18 in. from the clamped end and $\frac{1}{4}$ in. from the axis.

30. A cylindrical copper disk 12 cm. in diameter and 1.0 cm. thick is suspended at its center on a steel wire 1.00 mm. in diameter and 1.0 meter long, the axis of the disk coinciding with the axis of the wire. Calculate the period of this system when oscillating as a torsion pendulum. Density of copper = 8.9 grams/cm.[3].

31. Let the disk and the wire of Prob. 30 both be made half as thick. How does this change the period of the pendulum?

32. A certain length of steel wire has been stretched by a known force and its elongation noted, and has also been used as a support of a torsion pendulum, thus finding that Young's modulus for this steel is 29.4×10^6 lb./in.[2] and the shearing modulus is 11.7×10^6 lb./in.[2]. When a wire of the same diameter and length is made up of a new alloy steel, it is found that this wire is stretched only 91.5 per cent as much by the same force, and that the period, when used in the same apparatus as a torsion pendulum, is only 96.5 per cent as great as for the first wire. Find Young's modulus and Poisson's ratio for the alloy steel.

33. A hollow steel rod has an outer diameter of 1 in. and an inner diameter of $\frac{7}{8}$ in. Calculate the torsional constant for a section 3 ft. long. What would be the diameter of a solid rod having the same torsional constant? What is the saving in material by making the rod hollow?

34. The drive shaft of an automobile rotates at 3,000 r.p.m. and transmits 10 hp. from the engine to the rear wheels. What is the value of the torque acting on the shaft? Through what angle is one end of the shaft twisted with respect to the other if the shaft is 1 in. in radius, is 5 ft. long, and has a torsion modulus of $12^3 \times 10^6$ lb./sq. ft.?

35. Calculate the torque in dyne-cm. necessary to hold a hollow cylinder of inside radius 2 cm. and thickness 1 mm. twisted through an angle of 1°. The length of the hollow cylinder is 1 meter, and the shear modulus of the metal is 6×10^{11} dynes/cm.[2].

36. Suppose a solid rod of radius 1 cm. is melted and recast into a thin shell of the same length and of inner radius 10 cm. Find the ratio of the stiffness coefficient of the thin shell to that of the solid rod, assuming that the elastic properties are not changed.

CHAPTER XVI

DYNAMICS OF ELASTICITY; ACOUSTICS

The elasticity of bodies allows the transmission of energy through them since every part of an elastic body exerts forces on its surroundings. Thus, if one part of an elastic body is set in motion, it sets the neighboring parts in motion, these latter in turn set their neighbors in motion, and so on. Thus we have the energy expended in setting the first part in motion transmitted from point to point of the body. For simplicity, let us restrict ourselves for the present to a consideration of deformations which are transmitted in one direction only (*e.g.*, in the x-direction). These deformations are transmitted with a characteristic velocity V. Such a propagation of deformations is called *wave* propagation and we speak of the whole process as *wave motion*.

We must distinguish between two kinds of waves: (1) those in which the deformation takes place in the direction of propagation, and (2) those for which the deformation is at right angles to the direction of propagation. The former are called *longitudinal* waves, and the latter *transverse* waves. In the transverse waves, the deformations which are transmitted are shearing deformations and in longitudinal waves they are compressions or tensions. In a solid both types of waves may exist. They travel with different velocities and the velocity of the longitudinal waves is always greater than that of the transverse waves. Since no shearing deformations can be set up in liquids or gases (at least in ideal fluids), only compressional, longitudinal waves are possible. In air these waves are recognized by us as sound so that the subject of acoustics has to do largely with a study of longitudinal wave motion. We shall first discuss transverse waves on a stretched string since they are easiest to visualize.

106. The Wave Equation.—Let us consider a long string stretched in the x-direction on which a transverse wave is traveling. At some instant of time $t = 0$ the shape of the string may be represented by

$$y = f(x), \qquad t = 0 \tag{1}$$

where y is the sideways displacement of the string and x the distance measured along the string. The shape of the string may be, for example, of the form shown in Fig. 108. It is an experimental fact that this disturbance or pulse travels along the string without changing in form. At a time t later we find the whole figure displaced to the right (if the wave travels to the right) by an amount $x = Vt$, where V is the wave velocity. Now let us construct a new coordinate system with its origin at O' (Fig. 109), *i.e.*, at the point $x = Vt$. Let us further denote by x' the distance of a point P measured from O'. x, of course,

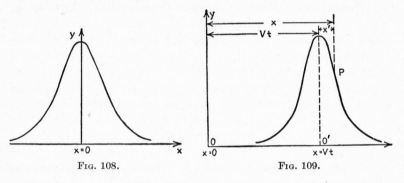

FIG. 108.   FIG. 109.

measures the horizontal distance from O to P. From the figure it is clear that

$$x = x' + Vt$$

or

$$x' = x - Vt$$

$$\tag{2}$$

With respect to the new moving axes we have exactly the same picture at time t as we had with respect to the old axes at $t = 0$. Therefore at time t we can write, in place of Eq. (1),

$$y = f(x'), \qquad t = t \tag{3}$$

and putting in the value of x' from Eq. (2), we find

$$y = f(x - Vt) \tag{4}$$

This is the general equation representing a wave of any shape traveling to the right.

In interpreting this equation we note that for any fixed value of the time t the equation gives y as a function of x. This defines a curve, and this curve represents the actual shape of the string at the instant of time under consideration. Furthermore, if we focus our attention on one point of the string, *i.e.*, a fixed value of x, as we might do by placing a screen in front of the string with a narrow vertical slit at this point, Eq. (4) gives y as a function of the time t. This is the equation of motion of the piece of string visible through the slit and describes how the position of this particle changes with time.

The argument presented above would hold equally well for longitudinal waves. Suppose we consider a long straight tube of air whose axis is taken as the x-axis and consider how a pressure change travels in this tube. We then are led by exactly the same reasoning to an equation of the same form as Eq. (4) which gives the pressure variations with time at all points of the tube.

107. Periodic and Simple Harmonic Waves; Superposition.— In the preceding section we have discussed a general equation representing a traveling wave. We now shall turn to a more detailed investigation of periodic waves. In particular let us consider periodic pressure changes in air which are recognized by our auditory nerves as musical sounds. Non-periodic pressure changes are heard as noise. Although we shall carry through the discussion for pressure waves in an air column, it must be emphasized at the start that precisely the same considerations hold for periodic transverse waves on a stretched string, or for the displacements of the air particles in sound waves, which are longitudinal.

It will be necessary to consider only simple harmonic waves, *i.e.*, sinusoidal waves. We must pause for a moment to see why this does not constitute a restriction on our general problem. It can be shown mathematically that it is possible to represent any periodic function as a sum of sine and cosine functions, where the lowest frequency in the sum gives the same period as the function itself and the remaining terms have frequencies which are integral multiples of the lowest. This means that, if the periodic function is $f(t)$,

$$f(t) = A_0 + A_1 \sin \omega t + A_2 \sin 2\omega t + A_3 \sin 3\omega t$$
$$+ \cdots + B_1 \cos \omega t + B_2 \cos 2\omega t + \cdots$$

This is known as *Fourier's theorem* and there are definite rules for finding the A's and B's if $f(t)$ is given. Sinusoidal pressure variations are recognized as pure tones. The use of Fourier's theorem in applications to physical problems is made possible by an important principle, known as the *principle of superposition*.

For simplicity, we present the principle for the case of sound waves. Suppose we have a number of sources of sound located at the same point, each giving rise by itself to a definite sound wave. If all these sources act simultaneously, the resultant wave emitted can be calculated by adding the contributions due to the separate sources, considering each to be independent of the presence of the others. Applying Fourier's theorem and the principle of superposition to the case of periodic waves, we see that, if we can analyze a problem for a pure tone, *i.e.*, a sine wave, we then can build up the solution of any problem by adding the solutions obtained for a number of sine waves. Conversely, it is possible to represent a relatively complicated wave motion by a sum of simpler motions (sine waves) and to treat each simple motion as if it existed alone. The general solution to any problem is then obtained by adding the solutions found for the simple component motions.

Suppose in a long straight tube at $x = 0$ we have a sinusoidal variation of pressure given by *

$$p = a \sin 2\pi nt, \qquad x = 0 \tag{5}$$

where a is the amplitude, *i.e.*, the maximum value of the pressure. We obtain the equation of a pressure wave by noting that the state of affairs at $x = 0$ occurs at the position x at a time Δt sec. later, where $\Delta t = x/V$.

If we had a watch running Δt sec. behind the one used in measuring t in Eq. (5) and call its reading t', then $t' = t - \Delta t$. With this watch one would record exactly the same variations at x as one did with the first watch at $x = 0$, so that

$$p = a \sin 2\pi nt', \qquad x = x$$

Now since $t' = t - \Delta t = t - x/V$, we have

$$p = a \sin 2\pi n\left(t - \frac{x}{V}\right) \tag{6}$$

This is the equation of a sinusoidal pressure wave traveling to the right with a velocity V.

There are *two* sinusoidal variations in this wave.

1. At any time t_0, p varies sinusoidally with x: At a time later, $t_0 + t_1$, the whole curve is displaced to the right by an amount

---

* In this equation p represents the gauge pressure, *i.e.*, the difference between absolute and atmospheric pressures.

$\Delta x = Vt_1$, so that we get the curves as in Fig. 110, *i.e.*, the crest a takes positions a, a', and a'' at successive instants of time and thus travels to the right with a velocity V. The three curves represent "snapshots" of the pressure wave at times t_0, $t_0 + t_1$, and $t_0 + t_2$. Thus we are led to the idea of a "traveling" wave.

2. At any fixed point of the tube, let us say $x = x_0$, p varies sinusoidally with the time (Fig. 111).

The wave length of the wave, denoted by λ, is defined as the distance between two similar points of the wave, *e.g.*, between

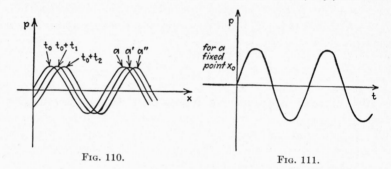

Fig. 110.   Fig. 111.

two neighboring crests. According to Eq. (6) at time t and position x, the pressure is

$$p = a \sin 2\pi n \left(t - \frac{x}{V} \right)$$

and this same value of p is found again when the angle increases by 2π radians, since

$$\sin \alpha = \sin (\alpha + 2\pi)$$

Hence an increase of λ in x corresponds to an increase of 2π in the angle, and we have

$$2\pi n \left(t - \frac{x}{V} \right) = 2\pi n \left(t - \frac{x + \lambda}{V} \right) + 2\pi$$

or

$$0 = -\frac{2\pi n \lambda}{V} + 2\pi$$

so that

$$\lambda = \frac{V}{n} \tag{7}$$

giving the relation between wave velocity, frequency, and wave length. Since $n = 1/T$, where T is the time of one vibration (the period), we have

$$\lambda = VT \tag{8}$$

and hence we can write our equation for the traveling wave as

$$p = a \sin 2\pi \left(\frac{t}{T} - \frac{x}{\lambda} \right) \tag{9}$$

The velocity of sound waves in air at room temperature is very nearly 1,100 ft./sec., so that a tuning fork vibrating with a frequency of 1,000 per second generates a sound wave of wave length

$$\lambda = \frac{V}{n} = \frac{1,100}{1,000} = 1.1 \text{ ft.}$$

108. Velocity of Transverse Waves on a String.—In the last two sections we have treated the kinematical description of traveling waves, and we must now concern ourselves with the dynamics of wave motion. Let us consider the problem of transverse waves on a stretched string.

We shall assume that the initial tension in the string when it is straight is large enough so that we may neglect the changes in tension due to the bending of the string, and we shall neglect the effect of the earth pull. Let the tension in the straight string be T_0, the length of the string L, and its mass M. We now consider a small length dx of the string. When the string is straight, this piece of the string is pulled on each end by equal and opposite forces T_0 so that it is in equilibrium. During the motion the string will form some sort of continuous curve at a given instant of time. In this position the pulls on the ends of the piece of string will be equal in magnitude but not quite opposite in direction, so that there is a resultant force not zero acting on this piece of the string. The y-component of this force, which is due to the curvature of the string, must be equal to the mass of the element on which it acts times the y-component of acceleration of this portion of the string. We shall adopt the procedure of calculating the force per unit length of the string, and then placing this equal to the mass per unit length times the acceleration of the string at the point where this force acts. Consider the piece of the string lying between

x and $x + dx$ (Fig. 112). The y-component of the resultant force on this piece is

$$dF_y = T_0 \sin \theta_2 - T_0 \sin \theta_1 \cong T_0 (\tan \theta_2 - \tan \theta_1)$$

Here we have replaced the sine by the tangent, which is allowable if we consider only small vibrations since, then, the angles θ are small. Now $(\tan \theta_2 - \tan \theta_1)$ is the change in $\tan \theta$ as we go from the point x to the point $x + dx$, and hence is $d(\tan \theta)$, so that

$$dF_y = T_0 \, d (\tan \theta) \qquad (10)$$

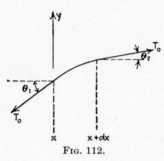

Fig. 112.

Since for small displacements the length of our piece of the string is nearly dx, the y-component force per unit length is

$$\frac{dF_y}{dx} = T_0 \frac{d}{dx} (\tan \theta) = T_0 \frac{d^2y}{dx^2} \quad (11)$$

From this equation we see that the force per unit length causing the vibration depends on the rate of change of the slope of the string since $\tan \theta$ represents the slope of the curve (dy/dx) at the point under consideration.

Newton's second law of motion requires that this be equal to the mass per unit length, which we denote by $\mu = M/L$, times the y-component of acceleration of the point at which the force acts. Thus for this case the second law becomes

$$T_0 \frac{d^2y}{dx^2} = \mu \frac{d^2y}{dt^2} \qquad (12)$$

Equation (12) is known as the *differential equation of wave motion*, or, more briefly, the wave equation since its solutions turn out to represent waves. We shall not derive these solutions but shall content ourselves with showing that Eq. (12) is satisfied by the expressions we have obtained to represent wave motion. Consider a traveling sinusoidal wave of the form given by Eq. (6),

$$y = A \sin 2\pi n\left(t - \frac{x}{V}\right) \qquad (13)$$

If we differentiate twice with respect to x, we find

$$\frac{d^2y}{dx^2} = -\frac{4\pi^2n^2}{V^2}A \sin 2\pi n\left(t - \frac{x}{V}\right) \qquad (14)$$

and differentiating Eq. (13) twice with respect to t, there follows

$$\frac{d^2y}{dt^2} = -4\pi^2n^2A \sin 2\pi n\left(t - \frac{x}{V}\right) \tag{15}$$

If we now substitute expressions (14) and (15) into Eq. (12), we find Newton's second law satisfied if

$$\frac{T_0}{V^2} = \mu$$

or

$$V = \sqrt{\frac{T_0}{\mu}} \tag{16}$$

which fixes the velocity of the transverse waves on a stretched string in terms of the tension and mass per unit length of the string.

109. Velocity of Acoustic (Longitudinal) Waves.—Let us apply the procedure of the last section in calculating the velocity of longitudinal waves. A longitud- inal sinusoidal wave in a rod of cross section A will be considered. If a wave is traveling in the x-direc- tion along the rod, then for a piece of the rod of length Δx we shall have at a definite instant of time a

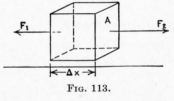

Fig. 113.

force F_1 acting on the face at x and a force F_2 acting on the face at $x + \Delta x$ (Fig. 113). For equilibrium these forces are equal, but, when there is acceleration of the particles as there is in a wave motion, the forces will be different at the two faces. If S_n is the longitudinal-stress component, then the resultant force is

$$-F_1 + F_2 = \Delta S_n \cdot A$$

where ΔS_n is the difference between the stresses at the two surfaces. Thus for this case the force per unit length of the rod is

$$\frac{\Delta S_n}{\Delta x} \cdot A$$

or, if $\Delta x \to 0$,

$$\frac{dS_n}{dx} \cdot A \tag{17}$$

In order to proceed we must remind ourselves of the relation between the normal stress S_n and the particle displacement w

for simple tension or compression. This relation is given by Hooke's law, so that $S_n = E\epsilon_l$ at every point of the rod, where E is Young's modulus. Since the stress changes from point to point, so does the strain ϵ_l. At any point of the rod the longitudinal strain is given by the rate of change of w with x at that point. Thus $\epsilon_l = dw/dx$, and hence

$$S_n = E\frac{dw}{dx} \tag{18}$$

If we insert this value of S_n in the expression (17) we find, for the force per unit length,

$$AE\frac{d^2w}{dx^2} \tag{19}$$

This must equal the mass per unit length times the acceleration. If ρ is the density, the mass per unit length is ρA, and this, times the acceleration, is

$$\rho A\frac{d^2w}{dt^2} \tag{20}$$

Thus the second law of motion yields

$$E\frac{d^2w}{dx^2} = \rho\frac{d^2w}{dt^2} \tag{21}$$

This equation for the longitudinal displacement w is just like Eq. (12) of the previous section for the transverse displacement y in the case of the stretched string. We can find the velocity of the longitudinal waves by the same method as employed in the last section. In a traveling sine wave each particle oscillates back and forth in simple harmonic motion about an equilibrium position. In particular the particle at x has a displacement w along the x-axis given by

$$w = W \sin 2\pi n\left(t - \frac{x}{V}\right) \tag{22}$$

where W is the amplitude of the motion. Performing the differentiations as before and substituting in Eq. (21), one finds readily

$$\frac{E}{V^2} = \rho$$

or

$$V = \sqrt{\frac{E}{\rho}} \tag{23}$$

as the expression for the velocity of a compressional wave in a bar.

If we wish to find the velocity of such a wave in a liquid or gas, we proceed as above using $-p$ instead of S_n. Then expression (17) for the force per unit length in the direction of the wave becomes

$$-A\frac{dp}{dx} \tag{24}$$

We now may not use Hooke's law but must revert to the definition of compressibility. In so doing it must be remembered that the pressure p denotes the excess over static pressure in the fluid. Thus, since

$$\kappa = -\frac{1}{p}\frac{\Delta v}{v} \qquad (v = \text{volume})$$

we may write

$$p = -\frac{1}{\kappa}\frac{\Delta v}{v} = -\frac{1}{\kappa}\frac{A\Delta w}{A\Delta x}$$

since Δw is the amount by which Δx changes during the compression. Thus we find that

$$p = -\frac{1}{\kappa}\frac{dw}{dx}$$

and the force per unit length becomes

$$\frac{A}{\kappa}\frac{d^2w}{dx^2} \tag{25}$$

Comparing this with the similar expression (19) for the rod, we see that the only change has been to replace E by $1/\kappa$. The rest of the argument is identical with the foregoing discussion so that we need not repeat the details. Thus we find

$$V = \sqrt{\frac{1}{\kappa\rho}} \tag{26}$$

as the expression for the velocity of sound waves in a gas or liquid.

Before concluding this discussion it will be worth while to investigate the variations of pressure in such a wave. We obtain this by equating expression (24), giving the force per unit length along the wave, to the mass per unit length times the acceleration. This gives

$$\frac{dp}{dx} = \rho 4\pi^2 n^2 W \sin 2\pi n\left(t - \frac{x}{V}\right)$$

and, integrating with respect to x, there follows

$$p = -\rho 2\pi n V W \cos 2\pi n\left(t - \frac{x}{V}\right)$$

or

$$p = a \cos 2\pi n\left(t - \frac{x}{V}\right) \qquad (27)$$

where a denotes the maximum pressure in the wave and is related to the amplitude of oscillation of the air particles W by

$$a = -2\pi n V \rho W \qquad (28)$$

The essential result is that we have a sinusoidal pressure wave along with the wave representing the motion of the individual particles of the fluid.

110. Standing Waves.—In finite bodies traveling waves are reflected from the boundaries of the bodies and give rise to waves traveling in the opposite direction which add to the original waves according to the principle of superposition. Consider a column of air in which we have a traveling wave

$$p_1 = a \sin 2\pi n\left(t - \frac{x}{V}\right)$$

and suppose that the reflected wave has the same amplitude (complete reflection at the end of the column) so that it is a similar wave traveling to the left:

$$p_2 = a \sin 2\pi n\left(t + \frac{x}{V}\right)$$

The total pressure is then

$$p = p_1 + p_2 = a\left[\sin 2\pi n\left(t - \frac{x}{V}\right) + \sin 2\pi n\left(t + \frac{x}{V}\right)\right]$$

and since we have the trigonometric relation

$$\sin \alpha + \sin \beta = 2 \sin \frac{\alpha + \beta}{2} \cos \frac{\alpha - \beta}{2}$$

we may write

$$p = 2a \sin 2\pi n t \cos 2\pi \frac{x}{\lambda} \qquad (29)$$

This is the equation of the so-called *standing* wave. It is called standing because there are certain points where p is *always* zero, *i.e.*, atmospheric pressure.

These are the positions in the tube given by

$$\cos \frac{2\pi x}{\lambda} = 0$$

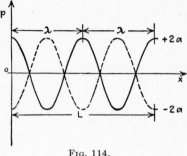

Fig. 114.

Now the cosine of an angle is zero if the angle is an odd multiple of $\pi/2$, so that the points of zero pressure, called the pressure *nodes*, occur at positions determined by

$$\frac{2\pi x}{\lambda} = k\frac{\pi}{2}, \qquad k = 1, 3, 5, 7, \cdots$$

or for values of x given by

$$x_k = k\frac{\lambda}{4}, \qquad k = 1, 3, 5, 7, \cdots \tag{30}$$

i.e., when x has the values

$$x = \frac{\lambda}{4}, \frac{3\lambda}{4}, \frac{5\lambda}{4}, \cdots$$

At points halfway between nodes we have the pressure varying sinusoidally with the time between values $+2a$ and $-2a$, *i.e.*, at the points

$$x = 0, \frac{\lambda}{2}, \frac{2\lambda}{2}, \frac{3\lambda}{2}, \cdots$$

we have pressure maxima (Fig. 114). At any instant of time the pressure curve lies between the full and dotted curves.

The particle velocities u at different points of the tube are determined by*

$$\frac{du}{dt} = -\frac{1}{\rho}\frac{\partial p}{\partial x} = \frac{4\pi a}{\lambda\rho} \sin 2\pi nt \sin \frac{2\pi x}{\lambda}$$

whence

$$u = -\frac{2a}{V\rho} \cos 2\pi nt \sin \frac{2\pi x}{\lambda}$$

* This equation is obtained by equating the force per unit length (24) to the mass per unit length (ρA) times the acceleration $\dfrac{du}{dt}$

Thus the velocities of the individual particles form standing waves of the same type as the standing pressure wave.   However, since the sine and cosine terms are interchanged, we see that velocity nodes occur where the pressure maxima occur and pressure nodes appear where the velocity reaches its greatest value.   This we can schematically represent as follows:

Pressure node ⟵———⟶ velocity maximum
Velocity node ⟵———⟶ pressure maximum

In all musical instruments the sound is produced by standing waves.

111. Phase Changes in Reflection; Organ Pipes.—In the last section we have seen that the superposition of a traveling and a reflected wave gives rise to a standing wave.   We shall now consider the process of reflection of a wave more closely, still confining ourselves to the case of total reflection; *i.e.*, no wave motion is set up in the neighboring bodies.   Suppose we have an air column in which we have a traveling pressure wave traveling toward an end which is closed.   The resultant velocity of each air particle at this boundary must be zero at all times as no particle can get out of the tube and hence there is a velocity node at the closed end.   This can occur only if at every instant of time the amplitudes of the direct and reflected velocity waves add up to zero, *i.e.*, the amplitudes are equal and opposite and the crest of the direct wave coincides with the trough of the reflected wave. Thus we see that the reflected wave is out of phase with the direct wave by $\lambda/2$, if λ is the wave length.   The pressure wave must have a maximum where the velocity of the particles is always zero as we have shown in the previous section, so that there is a pressure maximum at the closed end of the tube.   This means that the reflected pressure wave is in phase with the direct pressure wave so that the total pressure at the end is always twice the pressure in each wave at that point.

At an open end we have just the opposite situation since the pressure is constant at this end and equal to atmospheric pressure. Since we measure pressures with respect to atmospheric pressure, we have a *pressure node* and a *velocity maximum* at an open end. For transverse waves we have very much the same behavior. For example, a transverse wave on a string has a displacement node at a fixed end, so that the reflected wave is half a wave length out of phase with the oncoming wave.

In the case of an organ pipe we have the typical case of a musical instrument in which there are standing waves. The tube alone is responsible for the production and determination of the tone. The mouthpiece acts only as a means of exciting the vibrations, which are standing waves in the tube. The pitch of the emitted note can be calculated from the length of the pipe alone. The mouthpiece end of an organ pipe is always open, so that we always have a pressure node at the bottom. We then have two cases to discuss:

a. The open pipe, in which the top end is left open.

b. The closed pipe, in which the top end is closed.

a. The Open Organ Pipe.— In this case the only vibrations (or modes of vibration) which are possible are those which keep pressure nodes at both ends. These are sketched in

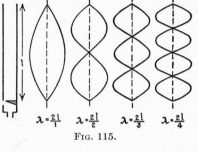

Fig. 115. These curves represent the variation of pressure along the tube for the first four modes of vibration. We could, of course, keep on extending this scheme, and in the kth mode of vibration

$$\lambda_k = \frac{2l}{k}$$

The frequencies of the sound waves corresponding to these wave lengths are called the *natural* or *proper* frequencies of the pipe and are given by

$$n_1 = 1 \cdot \frac{V}{2l}; \qquad n_2 = 2 \cdot \frac{V}{2l}; \qquad n_1 = 3 \cdot \frac{V}{2l}; \text{ etc.}$$

or, in general

$$n_k = k \cdot n_1 = k \cdot \frac{V}{2l}, \qquad k = 1, 2, 3, 4, \cdots \qquad (31)$$

if V represents the velocity of sound in the gas. Since the higher frequencies (overtones) are whole-number multiples of the fundamental frequency n_1, they form a harmonic series. The amplitudes of the various overtones which determine the quality of the emitted sound depend, among other things, on the geometrical shape of the pipe, especially on the ratio of cross-section dimension to length.

b. The Closed Organ Pipe.—For pipes closed at the top, we have a velocity node and a *pressure maximum* at the top and a pressure node at the bottom. The possible vibrations are then quite different from those of an open pipe; several modes of vibration are sketched in Fig. 116. The corresponding frequencies are

$$n_1 = 1 \cdot \frac{V}{4l}; \qquad n_2 = 3 \cdot \frac{V}{4l}; \qquad n_3 = 5 \cdot \frac{V}{4l}; \text{ etc.}$$

so that, in general,

$$n_k = (2k - 1)n_1 = (2k - 1)\frac{V}{4l}, \qquad k = 1, 2, 3, \cdots \quad (32)$$

Here all the even harmonics are missing, and the lowest frequency (the fundamental) is one-half the fundamental frequency of the same length open pipe.

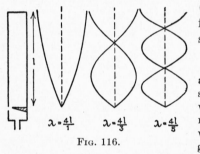

$$\lambda = \frac{4l}{1} \qquad \lambda = \frac{4l}{3} \qquad \lambda = \frac{4l}{5}$$

Fig. 116.

112. Reflection and Transmission at a Boundary.—In the preceding section we discussed the reflection of waves, assuming that we had total reflection. Now we shall investigate what happens at a boundary when we get only partial reflection and partial transmission of the waves. Consider two strings of different densities and the same cross section

$$\overline{\qquad\qquad\qquad\quad | \qquad\qquad\qquad}$$
$$1 \qquad x = 0 \qquad 2$$

joined together at $x = 0$ and subjected to the same tension. Let the velocity of a transverse wave be V_1 in the left-hand string and V_2 in the right-hand string. Now, if a wave travels along string 1 to the right and hits the boundary $x = 0$, some of this wave will be transmitted in the second string and some will be reflected.

For the incident wave in string 1 we write

$$y_i = A \sin 2\pi n\left(t - \frac{x}{V_1}\right) \tag{33a}$$

For the reflected wave in string 1 we write

$$y_r = B \sin 2\pi n\left(t + \frac{x}{V_1}\right) \tag{33b}$$

since it travels to the left.

For the transmitted wave in string 2 we write

$$y_t = C \sin 2\pi n\left(t - \frac{x}{V_2}\right) \tag{33c}$$

Now at the boundary the displacement in string 1 must equal the displacement in string 2 if the string does not break there so that we have

$$\text{at } x = 0, \qquad y_i + y_r = y_t \tag{34}$$

Furthermore, the slope of the string at $x = 0$ must be the same in string 1 as in string 2. To see this consider Eq. (10) applied to a piece dx including the point $x = 0$. The expression (10) is equal to the mass per unit length, times dx, times the acceleration. As $dx \to 0$, Eq. (10) also approaches zero. Since T_0 is not zero, the change in tan θ must be zero at $x = 0$, and this is the same as saying that the slope must not change abruptly at $x = 0$. Thus we have,

$$\text{at } x = 0, \qquad \frac{\partial y_i}{\partial x} + \frac{\partial y_r}{\partial x} = \frac{\partial y_t}{\partial x} \tag{35}$$

Equations (34) and (35) are known as the boundary conditions. From Eqs. (33a, b, c) we have:

$$\frac{\partial y_i}{\partial x} = -\frac{2\pi n A}{V_1} \cos 2\pi n\left(t - \frac{x}{V_1}\right)$$

$$\frac{\partial y_r}{\partial x} = \frac{2\pi n B}{V_1} \cos 2\pi n\left(t + \frac{x}{V_1}\right)$$

$$\frac{\partial y_t}{\partial x} = -\frac{2\pi n C}{V_2} \cos 2\pi n\left(t - \frac{x}{V_2}\right)$$

If we now substitute our expressions for y_i, y_r, and y_t in Eq. (34) and place $x = 0$ we find

$$A \sin 2\pi n t + B \sin 2\pi n t = C \sin 2\pi n t \tag{36}$$

and placing $x = 0$ in the derivatives of the y's and putting them in Eq. (35), we get

$$-\frac{2\pi n A}{V_1} \cos 2\pi n t + \frac{2\pi n B}{V_1} \cos 2\pi n t = -\frac{2\pi n C}{V_2} \cos 2\pi n t \tag{37}$$

If we divide Eq. (36) by $\sin 2\pi n t$ and Eq. (37) by $-2\pi n \cos 2\pi n t$, we find as the boundary conditions

$$\left.\begin{array}{l} A + B = C \\[2mm] A - B = \dfrac{V_1}{V_2}C \end{array}\right\} \tag{38}$$

We now place $V_1/V_2 = K$; K is just like the index of refraction in optics, *i.e.*, the ratio of the velocities in the two bodies. Solving Eqs. (38) for B and C, we find

$$\left.\begin{array}{l} B = \dfrac{1 - K}{1 + K}A \\[3mm] C = \dfrac{2}{1 + K}A \end{array}\right\} \tag{39}$$

giving us the amplitude of the reflected and transmitted waves in terms of the amplitude of the incident wave. Now in case the second string has a much larger density than the first, $V_2 < < V_1$ and K becomes very great compared to 1. In this case we can neglect 1 compared to K and we find

$$B = -A$$

and C becomes very small, so we can neglect it. This is the case of total reflection, and we see that the reflected wave has the same amplitude but is 180° out of phase with the incident wave, as we have discussed in Sec. 111.

113. Forced Vibrations and Resonance.—The problem of forced vibrations of elastic bodies is very similar to that of forced vibrations of a single particle whose free vibrations are harmonic. We have discussed the latter problem in Sec. 44 of Chap. VII and refer the reader to that section. One of the important results was that the steady-state motion of a harmonic oscillator, when subject to the action of an external force which varies sinusoidally with time, is a harmonic motion of the same frequency as that of the exciting force and of amplitude depending very strongly on the difference between the frequencies of the exciting force and the natural frequency of the oscillator. The amplitude becomes extremely large when the two frequencies are about equal (in the absence of friction an infinite amplitude is predicted), and when there is but little friction, the relative response to frequencies other than the natural frequency is negligible. This phenomenon of resonance is displayed also by elastic bodies, such as the stretched wire or organ pipe.

We have seen that for given boundary conditions (string fastened at its ends; closed or open pipe) there exists a whole series of natural frequencies, infinite in number. If an external sinusoidally varying force is applied to such a body, the steady-state motion produced will be appreciable only if the frequency of the force is practically equal to one of the natural frequencies of the body. This phenomenon is utilized to demonstrate the natural modes of vibration of a stretched string. If one were to deform a stretched string and release it, the ensuing vibration would be, not simple harmonic corresponding to one of the possible modes, but a superposition of harmonic motions of the different possible natural frequencies and hence would be extremely complicated. On the other hand, by applying an external force of frequency equal to one of the natural frequencies, that mode alone is excited and one can demonstrate a natural mode of vibration of the string.

If the exciting force is not simple harmonic in time, one can always represent it according to Fourier's theorem by a sum of harmonic forces and the response will then occur at those frequencies which lie near to one or more of the Fourier component frequencies. This is demonstrated in the operation of an ordinary organ pipe. At the mouthpiece air is blown past a sharp edge; the flow becomes turbulent, eddies form more or less periodically, and the pressure varies accordingly. The exciting force is certainly not sinusoidal, but the pipe responds only to that Fourier component of frequency equal to its own natural frequency. The harder one blows the faster the air moves, and the eddies form more rapidly with a consequent increase in the amplitudes of the higher frequency components of the exciting force. Thus there is a good chance of exciting the overtones of the pipe, whereas at low velocities only the fundamental occurs with an appreciable intensity.

The phenomenon of resonance plays a large part in the action of the ear. Roughly, we can think of the ear containing some 20,000 chords, each with its own natural frequency. The oscillations of these chords excite the auditory nerve and give rise to the sensation of hearing. The minimum energy necessary to excite one of these chords sufficiently so that it can be detected is about 10^{-11} erg, making the ear one of the most sensitive sense organs. The reason such a sensitive organ does not get injured when there are large noises lies in the fact that the sensation of loudness is not at all proportional to the intensity of sound striking the ear. In fact, if we plot sensation of loudness against the intensity of sound we obtain something like the curve in Fig. 117. This curve has the form

$$S = k \log \frac{I}{I_0}$$

114. Addition of Oscillations; Interference; Beats.

We now turn our attention to the question of addition of oscillations, *e.g.*, the addition of two sound waves at a given point of space.

We have already emphasized in our discussion of the principle of superposition that the amplitudes add.

If *the waves have the same frequency and wave length*, we have two limiting cases:

a. The Crests of the Waves Coincide.   In this case the waves reinforce each other, and the resultant amplitude is twice that of one wave, if they are each of equal amplitude.   More generally, the resultant amplitude is the sum of the two amplitudes.

b. The Crests of One Wave Coincide with the Troughs of the Other.   In this case, for two equal waves the sum of the amplitude is always zero.   This effect is called *total interference*.   Thus we see that two sounds can produce silence!   If two waves travel in the same direction in the same tube, we get total interference at all points where the phase difference is $\lambda/2$.

In all other cases we get partial interference and the resultant amplitude lies between zero and the sum of the two amplitudes.

If *the waves have different frequencies and wave lengths*, we can write for the pressure in each wave at a point P, if they are in phase at $t = 0$,

$$p_1 = a \sin 2\pi n_1 t$$
$$p_2 = a \sin 2\pi n_2 t$$

so that the resultant pressure is

$$p = p_1 + p_2 = a(\sin 2\pi n_1 t + \sin 2\pi n_2 t)$$

or

$$p = 2a \sin 2\pi\left(\frac{n_1 + n_2}{2}\right)t \cdot \cos 2\pi\left(\frac{n_1 - n_2}{2}\right)t \qquad (40)$$

An interesting case occurs when $n_1 - n_2$ is small compared with n_1 and n_2.   In this case we hear *beats*.   If we write

$$\delta = \frac{n_1 - n_2}{2} \qquad \text{and} \qquad \frac{n_1 + n_2}{2} = n \cong n_1 \cong n_2$$

we obtain

$$p = 2a \cos 2\pi\delta t \sin 2\pi n t \qquad (41)$$

Now $\cos 2\pi\delta t$ varies very slowly compared to $\sin 2\pi n t$, *i.e.*, there are a large number of oscillations of the frequency n during the time it takes the cosine to go through one period, so that we can think of the resultant pressure as a sine wave of slowly varying amplitude.   The ear hears this slow periodic variation of amplitude as beats, and the number of beats per second equals the number of maxima and minima of cos $2\pi\delta t$ per second (Fig. 118).

115. Doppler Effect.—The pitch of a pure note is determined by its frequency, *i.e.*, by the number of waves (each of length λ) which strike the ear per second. The pitch of a note changes if the observer moves with respect to a fixed source of sound, or if the source moves with respect to a fixed observer. By *fixed*, we mean at rest with respect to the air, which is the elastic medium transmitting the sound waves. There are two cases.

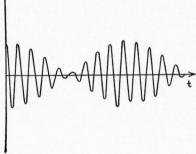

CASE I. *Moving Observer, Fixed Source.*—Suppose an observer O is moving toward a fixed source of sound S with a velocity v. The source is to consist of a tuning fork, let us say, with frequency n. It emits waves of wave length $\lambda = V/n$. In time Δt, $n\Delta t$ waves pass a *fixed* observer's ear. During this time the

Fig. 118.

moving observer moves a distance $v\Delta t$ toward the source. In this distance there are $v\Delta t/\lambda$ waves, so that the total number of waves passing his ear in time Δt are

$$n\Delta t + \frac{v\Delta t}{\lambda} = \left(n + \frac{v}{\lambda}\right)\Delta t$$

This number divided by Δt gives the apparent frequency n' heard by the observer, so that

$$n' = n + \frac{v}{\lambda} = n\left(1 + \frac{v}{V}\right)$$

If the observer moves away from the source we must replace v by $-v$, so that in general, for case I,

$$n' = n\left(1 \pm \frac{v}{V}\right) \tag{42}$$

Thus the pitch of a note apparently increases as an observer approaches the fixed source and decreases as he moves away from it.

CASE II. *Fixed Observer, Moving Source.*—Suppose the source is moving toward the observer with a velocity v. The source of frequency n emits $n\Delta t$ waves in Δt sec. Were the source at rest these waves would spread over a distance $V\Delta t$, but because of the motion of the source they are crowded into a distance $(V - v)\Delta t$. Thus the waves from a moving source have a wave length

$$\lambda' = \frac{V - v}{n}$$

The fixed observer hears waves of wave length λ' moving with a velocity V with respect to him, so he hears the frequency

$$n' = \frac{V}{\lambda'} = n\frac{V}{V - v} = \frac{n}{1 - \dfrac{v}{V}}$$

If the source is moving away from the observer, we must replace v by $-v$ so that we have in general, for case II,

$$n' = \frac{n}{1 \mp \dfrac{v}{V}} \tag{43}$$

Thus we see that the qualitative effect is the same in both cases; the quantitative change in frequency, however, depends on the motion of source and observer, *not with respect to each other* but with respect to the elastic medium which transmits the waves.

In the case that $v/V < \, < 1$, Eqs. (42) and (43) become practically identical, since

$$\frac{1}{1 \mp \dfrac{v}{V}} = \left(1 \mp \frac{v}{V}\right)^{-1} = 1 \pm \frac{v}{V} + \left(\frac{v}{V}\right)^2 \pm \cdots$$

Neglecting terms in $(v/V)^2$ and higher powers, we have

$$\frac{1}{1 \mp \dfrac{v}{V}} = 1 \pm \frac{v}{V}$$

agreeing with the corresponding expression in Eq. (42).

116. Proper Frequencies; Proper Functions in General.—We have already seen in the study of the vibrating string and the organ pipe that, with given boundary conditions (end conditions), only certain frequencies of free oscillations are possible. In the cases we have discussed these frequencies are whole-number multiples of the lowest allowed frequency. These frequencies are called the *proper frequencies* of the system. In general we find that all elastic bodies possess a definite set of proper frequencies for given boundary conditions, but in general these frequencies have *not* the simple characteristic that the ratio of one of them to the fundamental is a whole number. For example, a stretched membrane possesses natural frequencies which do *not* form a harmonic series, although some of them may stand in the ratio of whole numbers. Similarly, a vibrating rod has a non-harmonic set of natural or proper frequencies. Hence these bodies would not be suitable for musical instruments. In all these cases we have standing waves, and certain regions of the bodies stay at rest all the time. These nodes are curves in the case of two-dimensional bodies such as membranes (nodal lines), and for three-dimensional bodies (elastic solids) they form nodal surfaces.

Furthermore, for the case of a vibrating string we find as the equations describing standing waves relations of the type

$$y = 2a \sin 2\pi nt \sin \frac{2\pi x}{\lambda} \qquad \text{or} \qquad y = 2a \sin 2\pi nt \cos \frac{2\pi x}{\lambda}$$

the former holding for strings held fixed at both ends. The picture of the string at any instant of time is fixed by the equation

$$y = C \sin \frac{2\pi x}{\lambda} = C \sin \frac{k\pi x}{L} \ (t = \text{constant})$$

where C is a constant, L the length of the string, and k is a whole number specifying the harmonic (mode of vibration). This function $\sin \frac{2\pi x}{\lambda} \left(\text{or} \cos \frac{2\pi x}{\lambda} \right)$ fixes the position of the nodes, and is called the *proper function* of the string. Similarly, the nodes of any vibrating elastic bodies are fixed by certain functions of position which are called the proper functions of the problem. In general these functions are *not* sinusoidal functions but are functions which vanish for certain values of the coordinates. The determination of these functions and the corresponding values of the proper frequencies form an exceedingly important part of modern atomic theory.

Problems

1. Using the same type of argument as presented in Sec. 106, show that $f(x + Vt)$ represents a wave traveling to the left along the x-axis with a velocity V.

2. Calculate the velocity of a sound wave in a bar of steel and in a bar of copper.

3. A sound wave is sent out just under the surface of the water in an ocean. If the ocean is 2 miles deep at this point, calculate the time elapsed before the wave reflected from the bottom is heard at the surface. This provides a convenient way of measuring ocean depths.

4. Two sinusoidal sound waves have wave lengths of 2 and 4 in. respectively. The phase relations are such that they each change from minus to plus at the same point. If the amplitudes are in the ratio 1:3, plot the resultant wave, and each wave separately.

5. Plot the two waves of Prob. 4 and their resultant for the case in which the 2-in. wave has its maximum at the point where the 4-in. wave crosses the axis from minus to plus.

6. Two tones of frequencies 375 and 400 vibrations per second, respectively, are overtones of the same fundamental frequency. What is the largest frequency possible for this fundamental, and which overtones of this frequency do the above two vibrations represent?

7. The pressure in a traveling sound wave is given by

$$p = 10 \sin 200\pi\left(t - \frac{x}{1,100}\right) \text{ dynes/cm.}^2$$

where t is in seconds and x in feet.

   a. Find the wave length of the wave.

   b. Plot the pressure as a function of x at the following instants of time: $t = 0$, $t = \frac{1}{400}$ sec., $t = \frac{1}{200}$ sec., $t = \frac{3}{400}$ sec., and $t = \frac{1}{100}$ sec. Draw these plots with one set of axes.

8. The equation of a traveling transverse wave in a certain cord is given by

$$y = 20 \sin \pi(2.50t - 0.01x)$$

where x and y are in centimeters and t is in seconds.

   a. What are the values of the amplitude, wave length, frequency, and velocity of the wave?

   b. What is the maximum transverse velocity of a point on the cord?

9. Pure soft iron and steel have practically the same density, but Young's modulus for steel is about twice that for pure iron. Sound waves are traveling along an iron and a steel rod, as given by the equations:

$$p_1 = 12 \times 10^5 \sin 1,000 \left(t - \frac{x}{5,100}\right) \text{ dynes/cm.}^2$$

$$p_2 = 2 \times 10^5 \sin 1,100 \left(t - \frac{x}{3,600}\right) \text{ dynes/cm.}^2$$

(x in meters, t in seconds). Which of these waves is in iron? What are its speed, frequency, and amplitude? Give one value of x (distance from origin) at which the pressure produced by the wave is zero at the instant $t = 0.10$ sec. Are there other points along the rod at which the pressure is zero at this instant?

10. A wire is stretched between two supports with a force such that its length is increased by 1 part in 10,000. The velocity of longitudinal waves in the stretched wire is 5,000 ft./sec.   Find the velocity of transverse waves.

11. A steel wire 10 ft. long and 0.01 in.^{2} in cross section is put into tension and observed to increase its length by 1 part in 2,000.

   a. Calculate the velocity of a transverse wave on this stretched wire.

   b. Calculate the velocity of a longitudinal wave in this wire.

   c. Prove that the ratio of the velocity of a longitudinal wave to that of a transverse wave in a stretched wire is the square root of the ratio of Young's modulus to the longitudinal stress.

12. Two sinusoidal waves give rise to pressure variations at a given point of space according to the equations:

$$p_1 = a \sin 2\pi n t$$
$$p_2 = a \sin \left(2\pi n t - \frac{2\pi}{3} \right)$$

Calculate the amplitude of the resultant wave at this point of space.

13. A piece of steel wire originally 49.5 cm. long is stretched so that its ends can be fastened to two rigid supports 50 cm. apart. What is the fundamental frequency of transverse vibration of the stretched wire? (Density of steel = 8 grams/cm.^{3}; Young's modulus = 2×10^{12} dynes/cm.^{2}.)

14. An open organ pipe has a fundamental frequency of 275 vibrations per second.

A closed pipe is found to have its first overtone equal in frequency to the first overtone of the open pipe.

How long is each pipe?   (The velocity of sound in air is 1,100 ft./sec.)

15. A column of air in a tube 85 cm. long, closed at one end and open at the other, is set into vibration at its fundamental frequency by means of resonance with a tightly stretched wire placed near the open end. The wire is 25 cm. long, held at both ends, has a total mass of 10 grams, and oscillates in its fundamental mode of vibration.

   a. At what frequency does the air column vibrate?

   b. What is the tension in the wire?

16. The fundamental and first overtones of an organ pipe are 200 and 600 vibrations per second. Take the velocity of sound as 1,100 ft./sec.

   a. Is the pipe open or closed?

   b. What is its length?

   c. Draw the standing pressure waves corresponding to the above two frequencies.

17. A copper wire of cross section 0.11 cm.^{2} and length 2 meters is subjected to a tension of 10^6 dynes. Calculate the velocity of transverse waves on this wire. If the ends are held fixed, what are the lowest two frequencies with which this wire may vibrate? The density of copper is 9 grams/cm.^{3}.

18. A steel wire 0.0126 cm.^{2} in cross section and 10 cm. long is stretched until its fundamental note is the same frequency as that of an organ pipe 55 cm. long, closed at one end. What tension must be applied to the wire? The velocity of sound in air may be taken as 330 meters/sec., the density of steel as 7.8 grams/cm.^{3}

19. A traveling wave $p_1 = A \sin 2\pi n \left(t - \dfrac{x}{V} \right)$ and a reflected wave $p_2 = -A \sin 2\pi n \left(t + \dfrac{x}{V} \right)$ combine to form a standing wave. Derive the equation for the standing wave, and calculate the position of the pressure nodes.

20. An electrically driven tuning fork is mounted 2.0 cm. above the open end of a vertical, cylindrical tube 4.0 cm. in diameter. The lower end of the tube is closed by a movable piston so that the effective length of the tube can be varied. Resonance (decided increase in the volume of the sound) occurred first at a tube length of 25.0 cm. Resonance occurred again at 75.0 cm. and also at 125.0 cm. If the temperature of the laboratory was 25°C. and the barometer read 76.0 cm., compute the frequency of the tuning fork.

21. Air waves travel in a tube 2 meters long with the normal velocity of sound at room temperature. Calculate the two lowest frequencies of the standing waves in the tube when

a. The tube is open at both ends.

b. The tube is open at one end and closed at the other.

22. Calculate the frequencies of Prob. 21, if the tube is filled with hydrogen instead of air, assuming the compressibility of hydrogen is the same as that of air (same pressure and temperature).

23. The fundamental vibration of an open organ pipe 1 meter long filled with air has the same frequency as the first overtone of a closed pipe filled with hydrogen. How long is the closed pipe?

24.
$$y_1 = A \sin 2\pi\left(\frac{x}{\lambda} - \frac{t}{P}\right), \qquad P = 10 \text{ sec.} \qquad (1)$$

$$y_2 = A \sin 2\pi\left(\frac{x}{\lambda} + \frac{t}{P} + \frac{1}{2}\right), \qquad \lambda = 8 \text{ cm.} \qquad (2)$$

Equation (1) represents the equation of a wave incident from the left on a boundary at $x = 0$. Equation (2) represents a reflected wave traveling toward the left. Find the resultant displacement at points $x = 0, -1, -2, -3, -4$ cm. at $t = 0, 1, 2, 3, 5$ sec.

Solve graphically and analytically.

25. A copper wire 2 mm.^{2} in cross section is subject to a tension equal to the weight of a 5-kg. body.

a. Calculate the velocity of a transverse wave on this wire.

b. Calculate the velocity of a longitudinal wave on this wire.

26. A steel wire 1 mm. in radius is stretched with a tension T between two supports. At the same instant a longitudinal and a transverse wave are started at one end. When the longitudinal wave has reached the other end, the transverse wave has gone $\frac{1}{100}$ of the length of the wire. Find the tension in the wire.

27. An aluminum wire 2 mm. in diameter is joined at one end to a steel wire of 1 cm. diameter and the whole is stretched with a uniform tension T. If a sinusoidal transverse wave of amplitude 5 mm. travels along the aluminum wire and strikes the junction, calculate the amplitude of the transmitted and reflected waves. Calculate these amplitudes when the initial traveling wave is in the steel.

28. The water level in a vertical glass tube 1 meter long can be adjusted to any position in the tube. If a tuning fork of frequency 500 per second is held over the open end of the tube, where must the water level be to produce resonance? At how many points will resonance occur?

29. The maximum tensile stress under which steel remains elastic is 7.02×10^9 dynes/cm.^{2}. Its density is 7.8 grams/cm.^{3}. What is the highest fundamental frequency of transverse vibration which can be obtained with a stretched steel wire 50 cm. long? Give the corresponding values of the next three overtones and the positions of the nodes of the motion.

30. A tightly stretched wire of length L held fixed at both ends vibrates in its first overtone and the transverse displacement of the wire in inches is given by

$$y = 0.5 \sin \frac{2\pi x}{L} \cos 100\pi t$$

where t is in seconds and x and L are in feet.

   a. Calculate the transverse acceleration of a point of the wire one-quarter the length L from one end for $t = \frac{1}{100}$ sec.

   b. If the wire weighs 0.015 lb./ft., what is the transverse force on an element of the wire 0.001 ft. long at the above point, at time $t = \frac{1}{100}$ sec.?

31a. The fundamental frequency of a string 2 meters long and weighing 1,500 grams is 2 vibrations per second. What is the tension in the string?

   b. A tuning fork of frequency 360 vibrations per second causes resonance when held over the open end of a tube which is closed at the other end. The same tube also resonates to a fork having a frequency of 600 vibrations per second. If the velocity of sound in air is 336 meters/sec., what is the least possible length of the tube? What other frequencies will also produce resonance?

32. A steel wire 10 ft. long weighs $\frac{1}{9}$ lb. and is stretched taut with a tension of 20 lb. One end of the wire is held fixed, and the other end is driven in simple harmonic motion with an amplitude of $\frac{1}{10}$ in. and a frequency of 40 vibrations per second.

   a. What is the velocity of transverse waves on this wire?

   b. What is the wave length of the waves?

   c. Find the position of the nodes on the wire.

   d. What is the amplitude of the standing waves set up on the wire?

33. A section of steel wire 1 mm. in diameter subject to a tension equal to the weight of 5 kg. resonates to a frequency of 60 per second. Calculate the smallest possible length of this wire.

34. Solve Prob. 33 for a steel wire of twice the diameter, subject to twice the tension.

35. At a given point of space, two sound waves give rise to pressure variations:

$$p_1 = a \sin 2\pi n t$$
$$p_2 = a \sin (2\pi n t + \delta)$$

Make a plot of p_1, p_2 and the resultant pressure as a function of t for the following values of δ,

$$\delta = 0, \quad \frac{\pi}{4}, \quad \frac{\pi}{2}.$$

36. Two tuning forks of frequencies 500 per second and 501 per second are set in vibration. Calculate the number of beats heard per second.

37. An observer in an automobile traveling with a speed of 60 miles/hr. approaches a stationary whistle. Calculate the percentage change in the frequency heard by the observer from the frequency at rest.

38. Calculate the fractional change in pitch of an automobile horn observed by a pedestrian when the automobile travels away from him with a speed of 60 miles/hr.

39. Two express trains traveling with speeds of 70 and 50 miles/hr., respectively, approach each other. If the whistle is blown on the faster train, calculate the fractional change in frequency observed by the engineer on the other train.

40. A tuning fork of frequency 500 vibrations per second is rotated in a horizontal circle of radius 1 ft. with an angular velocity of 20 radians/sec. Calculate the highest and lowest frequencies heard by an observer at rest. The velocity of sound in air is 1,100 ft./sec.

CHAPTER XVII

TEMPERATURE AND THERMOMETRY

We now proceed to a study of a group of subjects which are usually classified under the heading of heat, and we shall see that it is advantageous to make close connection in this study with our previous work in mechanics. Of course our primary concepts of heat and warmth are direct outgrowths of our sense perceptions, as are all other primary concepts in physics. Starting with these simple perceptions physics undertakes to lay down proper measures to describe these experiences quantitatively. In so doing it has turned out that many of our experiences in connection with heat phenomena can be correlated and understood with the help of mechanical principles, and hence we shall make no attempt to split off the following work from our previous study but shall look upon it as a continuation and extension of this study. We must start, however, by describing some of our fundamental experiences in connection with heat phenomena and by introducing new concepts to describe them.

117. Thermal Equilibrium; Concepts of Quantity of Heat and of Temperature.—Let us consider a number of material bodies, some of which may feel "hot" to our touch, others "cold," and place such a system of bodies in a closed room free from external influences. In general, changes will occur, but eventually these bodies will settle down to a quiet state in which no more observable changes occur. They will, according to our sensation of warmth, all seem equally "hot" or cold. This quiet state is called a state of *thermal equilibrium*, and we shall assume that all bodies left to themselves reach such a state. Of course the time necessary to reach this state may and will be widely different for different initial states and different bodies, but this fact need not concern us here.

This idea of thermal equilibrium is essential as a starting point in building a set of laws to describe the thermal behavior of matter. Furthermore we must introduce two more concepts, both of which are direct consequences of our everyday experience.

305

They are the concept of *quantity of heat* and the *concept of temperature*. In accordance with our general scheme of procedure, we shall first qualitatively discuss these concepts and later lay down methods of measuring these quantities.

a. Concept of Quantity of Heat.—Suppose we produce a change in a body *A* by rubbing or by holding it near a flame so that it feels hotter to our touch than a similar body *B* which we have left untouched. We then place the body *A* in contact with the body *B* and wait until they reach thermal equilibrium. Then, if we touch *B*, we notice that it is hotter to our touch than before it was placed in contact with *A*, and we conclude that something has been transferred from *A* to *B*. This something we call *heat*, and we say that heat has been transferred from *A* to *B*. The important point is that, by merely placing body *B* in contact with body *A*, a change is produced in *B* similar to that which we originally produced in *A*.

b. Concept of Temperature.—The simplest idea of temperature is the idea of "hotness," and we distinguish in a primitive way between different degrees of hotness by our sense of touch. This sense of touch, like all human sensations, is too vague to serve as a means of measurement in physics, so that we must set up a quantitative measure of temperature. Our first step is to define a qualitative scale which will give more precision to the experiences described above than our own sensations. In doing so we proceed as follows: When two bodies *A* and *B* are in thermal equilibrium, the temperature of body *A* is equal to that of body *B*. Furthermore, when heat flows from body *A* to body *B* when they are placed in contact, we say that the temperature of body *A* is higher than that of body *B*. In building up quantitative scales of temperature, we must not contradict the above definitions.

118. The Measurement of Temperature.—There are certain physical properties of substances which change with temperature. Any of these properties may be used to set up a quantitative scale of temperature. The choice of the property and the scale of temperature are both entirely arbitrary. One of the most universal properties of matter which changes with temperature is the volume occupied by a substance, and we say that all bodies expand or contract when their temperature is changed. This property of expansion is extensively used in temperature-measuring devices, *i.e.*, in thermometers. We must, however, remember that other properties, such as electrical resistance or thermoelectric force, also are utilized for temperature measurements. We shall confine our attention in this chapter to expansion as a measure of temperature. In doing so, we must recall that the volume of bodies can be changed by mechanical forces, *e.g.*, by pressure, and it becomes necessary to specify the mechanical forces acting on the substances to be used as thermometers. For example, in gases the pressure plays just as important a part as the temperature in fixing the volume. The expansion of solids, liquids, and gases has been used as means of measuring temperature, and as examples we may mention metal thermometers, the well-known mercury-in-glass thermometers, and the gas thermometer. Strictly speaking, the latter two depend in their action on the difference in expansion of the liquid (or gas) and the container.

In our study we shall utilize principally the Centigrade (Celsius) scale of temperature as fixed by a standard mercury-in-glass thermometer. The freezing and boiling points of water are called 0° and 100°, respectively, at atmospheric pressure (76 cm. of mercury). The size of the unit temperature interval is fixed as follows: Suppose we place a mercury-in-glass thermometer in melting ice and make a scratch on the glass corresponding to the top of the mercury column. Then repeat the procedure in boiling water, making another scratch. We now divide the interval of *length* between these two scratches into 100 divisions and the distance between two neighboring scratches corresponds to a 1°C. temperature interval, *as defined by this thermometer*. The scale of temperature thus defined is called the "mercury-in-glass" scale and a standard procedure has been adopted in constructing thermometers to read temperature on this scale. Apart from the use of mercury in glass there are *two* arbitrary points about this scale: (1) the choice of the unit temperature interval and (2) the choice of the zero of temperature.

At this point we might mention two other scales of temperature. The Fahrenheit scale is a scale in which the unit temperature interval is $\frac{1}{180}$ the temperature difference between melting ice and boiling water at atmospheric pressure, and in which the temperature of melting ice is fixed as +32°. This temperature scale is widely used among engineers in English-speaking countries. The Réaumur temperature scale has a unit temperature interval of $\frac{1}{80}$ the difference of temperature between melting ice and boiling water, and its zero coincides with that of the Centigrade scale.

119. Expansion of Gases; Absolute-temperature Scale.—We start our analysis with the expansion of gases where the effect of temperature on the volume is largest. The volume of a body, as we have already stated, depends not only on the temperature but also on the pressure. (We shall only consider uniform normal

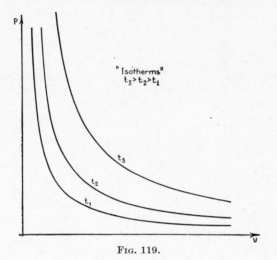

Fig. 119.

stresses. Shearing stress, of course, produces no change in volume.) Thus we may write

$$V = F(p, t)$$
or if we imagine the equation solved for p,
$$p = f(V, t)$$
$$\left.\right\} \quad (1)$$

In Eqs. (1), p denotes the pressure, V the volume, and t the temperature of the body. Such an equation as either of Eqs. (1) is known as the *equation of state* of the body.

For gases at moderate pressures and not too low temperatures it is found experimentally that the product of the pressure and volume of any gas is constant, provided the temperature is held constant. Thus, for a gas such as hydrogen we may write

$$pV = C = g(t) \qquad (2)$$

The value of the constant C is different at different temperatures, and we have indicated this by equating it to a function of the temperature $g(t)$. Equation (2) is known as *Boyle's law*. The curves pV = constant are called the *isothermal curves*, or simply *isothermals*, of the gas. These are sketched in Fig. 119. For calculation purposes it is sometimes more convenient to write Eq. (2) in the form

$$p_1V_1 = p_2V_2 \tag{2a}$$

where p_1, V_1 denote a pressure and the corresponding volume and p_2, V_2 another pressure and corresponding volume of the same sample of gas at the same temperature.

Within the range of temperatures and pressures where Boyle's law holds, it is further found experimentally that the product pV

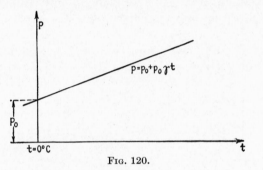

Fig. 120.

varies linearly with temperature as measured with a standard mercury-in-glass thermometer, *i.e.*, $g(t)$ is a linear function of t. Writing this as an equation, we have

$$pV = p_0V_0(1 + \gamma t) \tag{3}$$

Here t denotes Centigrade degrees, p_0 and V_0 denote the pressure and volume of the gas at 0°C., and γ is a constant whose numerical value has been measured as

$$\gamma = 0.00366 = \frac{1}{273.2} \; (°C.)^{-1}$$

Thus we may write

$$\frac{pV}{1 + \gamma t} = \text{constant}$$

The curves for which V is kept constant show how the pressure varies with temperature and are called *isochoric curves*, or simply *isochors*. These are straight lines, as shown in Fig. 120, determined by equations of the form

$$p = p_0 + p_0 \gamma t \qquad (4)$$

Equation (4) has been stated as an experimental fact determined with the help of a mercury thermometer. One can, however, equally logically postulate Eq. (4), and this defines the so-called gas scale of temperature, still retaining the two fixed points, 0° and 100°, as before. Then γ depends on the slope of the p vs. t lines and is given by

$$\gamma = \frac{p - p_0}{p_0 t}$$

With the help of a gas thermometer one could determine the length of the mercury column in glass as a function of temperature, and one would find very nearly that the length is a linear function of temperature (on the gas scale). We shall neglect completely the very slight differences existing between the mercury and various gas scales of temperature in the following discussion.

The constant γ is closely related to the coefficient of volume expansion β, which is defined by

$$\beta = \frac{1}{V}\left(\frac{dV}{dt}\right)_{p=\text{const.}} \qquad (5)$$

This is the fractional change in volume per degree and has the same dimensions as those of γ, viz., (degrees)$^{-1}$. For a gas at constant pressure, the volume changes with temperature according to the law

$$V = V_0(1 + \gamma t)$$

whence

$$\frac{dV}{dt} = \gamma V_0$$

Thus β becomes

$$\beta = \frac{1}{V}\left(\frac{dV}{dt}\right)_{p=\text{const.}} = \frac{\gamma V_0}{V} = \frac{\gamma V_0}{V_0(1 + \gamma t)} = \frac{\gamma}{1 + \gamma t} \qquad (6)$$

For temperatures small enough so that $\gamma t < < 1$, we may thus take $\beta = \gamma$.

We are now in a position to introduce a new and important scale of temperature called the *absolute scale*. More precisely, we shall introduce a new zero point called *absolute zero* and retain

the Centigrade unit.   The true absolute scale (Kelvin scale) has
practically the same unit as the Centigrade scale.   We define
the zero of the absolute scale as that temperature at which the
pressure of an ideal gas kept at constant volume would become
zero.   By an ideal gas we mean one which obeys the above laws
exactly.   Thus, if temperatures on the absolute scale are denoted

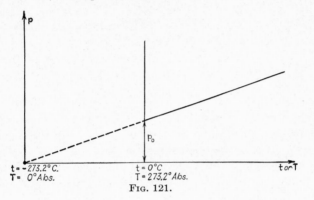

FIG. 121.

by T, the temperature $T = 0$ corresponds to the Centigrade
temperature

$$t = -\frac{1}{\gamma} = -273.2°\text{C}., \text{ (Fig. 121)}$$

and the relation between absolute and Centigrade temperatures is

$$T = t + 273.2 = t + \frac{1}{\gamma}$$

If we rewrite Eq. (3) in terms of absolute temperature, it
becomes

$$pV = p_0 V_0 (1 + \gamma t) = p_0 V_0 \gamma \left(t + \frac{1}{\gamma}\right) = p_0 V_0 \gamma T$$

or

$$\frac{pV}{T} = \text{constant} \qquad (7)$$

This exceedingly important and simple equation is the equation of
state of an ideal or perfect gas.   It is approximately obeyed by
real gases at high temperatures and low pressures.

The constant in Eq. (7) is proportional to the number of moles
(1 gram-molecular weight = 1 mole) of the gas under consideration.   The proportionality constant is *the same for all gases* and is

called the *universal gas constant*.   Denoting the number of moles by n and the gas constant by R, Eq. (7) becomes

$$pV = nRT \qquad (8)$$

This is another way of stating the well-known fact that the volume of 1 mole of *any* gas at 0°C. and 760 mm. Hg pressure is 22.4 liters.   We thus have:

1 atm. = 760 mm. Hg = 76 × 13.6 × 980 dynes/cm.²

$$\cong 10^6 \text{ dynes/cm.}^2$$

and hence the value of R is

$$R = \frac{pV}{nT} = \frac{10^6 \times 10^3 \times 22.4}{1 \times 273.2} = 8.31 \times 10^7 \text{ ergs/°Abs.}$$

This gas constant has the dimensions of work per degree Absolute and may be expressed in any units of work.   For example, one common procedure is to express the pressure in atmospheres and the volume in liters.   In this system of units, R becomes

$$R = \frac{1 \times 22.4}{1 \times 273.2} = 0.082 \text{ liter-atm./°Abs.}$$

It is suggested that the student use the gas law in the form of Eq. (8), calculating the number of moles by the relation

$$n = \frac{m}{M} \qquad (9)$$

where m is the mass of the gas in grams and M its molecular weight.

It is sometimes convenient to express results referred to 1 gram of the gas.   The volume of a substance per gram is called its *specific volume* (v_s), and is the reciprocal of the density of the substance.   If we wish to express Eq. (8) in terms of specific volume, we have, using Eq. (9),

$$pV = nRT = \frac{mRT}{M}$$

and, since $v_s = V/m$,
this becomes

$$pv_s = \frac{RT}{M} \qquad \text{or} \qquad p = \rho\frac{RT}{M} \qquad (10)$$

120. Expansion of Solids and Liquids.—In describing the thermal expansion of solids, it is usual to define a coefficient of *linear* expansion, referring to a change of length; this coefficient is defined as

$$\alpha = \frac{1}{l}\left(\frac{dl}{dt}\right)_{p=\text{const.}} \tag{11}$$

i.e., the fractional change in length per degree. For purposes of application use is made of the fact that the changes of length are small enough compared with the length under consideration, for most temperature ranges encountered in practice, for us to consider α as very nearly constant. Thus we may write, in place of Eq. (11),

$$\Delta l = \alpha_m l \Delta t$$

We use α_m to denote the mean value of α over the temperature range considered. The expanded length l' is

$$l' = l + \Delta l$$

so that

$$l' = l(1 + \alpha_m \Delta t) \tag{12}$$

The coefficient α has the dimensions of a reciprocal temperature and is of the order of magnitude of 10^{-5} per degree Centigrade for most substances. A noteworthy exception is found in fused quartz for which it is roughly 10^{-7} per degree Centigrade, or about 1 per cent of the usual value.

The coefficient of linear expansion α is closely related to the coefficient of volume expansion β defined in Eq. (5). For solids and liquids where the fractional change in volume is small compared with unity, we write, in place of Eq. (5),

$$\Delta V = \beta_m V \Delta t$$

or

$$V' = V(1 + \beta_m \Delta t) \tag{13}$$

The relations between α_m and β_m may be obtained by considering a cube of side l heated from t °C. to $(t + \Delta t)$ °C. at constant pressure, for example, in the atmosphere. The final volume is

$$V' = V(1 + \beta_m \Delta t) = l^3(1 + \beta_m \Delta t)$$

Each side increases its length from l to l' where, from Eq. (12),

$$l' = l(1 + \alpha_m \Delta t)$$

Since $V' = l'^3$, there follows

$$l^3(1 + \alpha_m \Delta t)^3 = l^3(1 + \beta_m \Delta t)$$

and, since $\alpha_m \Delta t < < 1$, we have very nearly

$$\beta_m = 3\alpha_m \tag{14}$$

Similarly we might consider the change of area of a body and define a coefficient of surface expansion. This can be easily shown to be equal to $2\alpha_m$ or $\frac{2}{3}\beta_m$.

121. Thermal Stresses.—It is possible to create comparatively large stresses by heating bodies and mechanically preventing them from expanding. Consider a bar of metal which is heated so that if unrestrained it would expand from a length l to a length $l + \Delta l$. Should we attempt to prevent this expansion it would be necessary to apply external forces large enough to compress this same bar an amount Δl. The longitudinal stress component would then be

$$S_n = E \frac{\Delta l}{l}$$

where E is Young's modulus for the metal. Since $\Delta l/l = \alpha \Delta t$, we thus would have a stress component

$$S_n = E\alpha \Delta t \tag{15}$$

Since $\alpha \cong 10^{-5}/°C.$ and $E = 30 \times 10^6$ lb./in.^{2} for steel, the stress set up in a steel bar which is prevented from expanding when its temperature is raised $100°C.$ is approximately

$$S_n = 10^{-5} \times 30 \times 10^6 \times 100 = 30{,}000 \text{ lb./in.}^2$$

Thus we see that even breaking stresses may easily be attained by such a method.

122. Examples.—The following examples may serve to illustrate the use of the above results:

1. A mercury column in glass is 1.000 meter long at $20°C.$ When the whole is heated to $30°C.$, the length of the mercury column becomes 1.00165 meters. If the coefficient of volume expansion of mercury is $1.81 \times 10^{-4}/°C.$, what is the coefficient of linear expansion of the glass?

Let A_0 be the cross section of the mercury column at $20°$ and A_1 that at $30°$. Then the final volume of mercury is

$$V' = l_1 A_1 = V_0(1 + \beta_{Hg} \Delta t) = l_0 A_0(1 + \beta_{Hg} \Delta t)$$

where l_0 and l_1 are the lengths of the column at $20°$ and $30°$, respectively.

Since the glass expands,

$$A_1 = A_0(1 + 2\alpha_{gl}\Delta t)$$

so that

$$l_1 A_0(1 + 2\alpha_{gl}\Delta t) = l_0 A_0(1 + \beta_{Hg}\Delta t)$$

whence

$$\frac{l_1}{l_0} = \frac{1 + \beta_{Hg}\Delta t}{1 + 2\alpha_{gl}\Delta t} \cong 1 + (\beta_{Hg} - 2\alpha_{gl}\Delta t)$$

since $2\alpha_{gl}\Delta t < < 1$.

From this follows

$$\frac{l_1 - l_0}{l_0} = \frac{\Delta l}{l_0} = (\beta_{Hg} - 2\alpha_{gl})\Delta t$$

and, solving for α_{gl},

$$\alpha_{gl} = \frac{\beta_{Hg}}{2} - \frac{1}{2}\frac{\Delta l}{l_0 \Delta t}$$
$$= \frac{1.81 \times 10^{-4} - 1.65 \times 10^{-4}}{2} = \frac{0.16 \times 10^{-4}}{2}$$
$$= 8 \times 10^{-6}/°C.$$

which is the required solution.

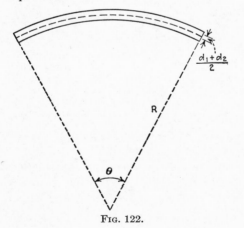

Fɪɢ. 122.

2. Two metal strips A and B each of length l at a temperature t_0 are riveted together so that their ends coincide. Let the thickness of the metal strip A be d_1, its coefficient of linear expansion be α_1, and the corresponding values for the strip B be

d_2 and α_2, with $\alpha_1 > \alpha_2$. When heated to a temperature $t_0 + \Delta t$, the top strip becomes longer than the bottom one, and hence the compound strip bends into the arc of a circle. The problem is to determine the radius of this circle.

The central line of each strip is subjected to neither tension nor compression, and hence each expands as if the whole strip were free.* Let l_1 be the expanded length of this central line of strip A, and l_2 that of strip B. As shown in Fig. 122, $\dfrac{d_1 + d_2}{2}$ is the separation of these central lines, and we have

$$l_2 = R\theta$$

$$l_1 = \left(R + \frac{d_1 + d_2}{2}\right)\theta$$

so that

$$\frac{l_1}{l_2} = 1 + \frac{d_1 + d_2}{2R} = \frac{1 + \alpha_1\Delta t}{1 + \alpha_2\Delta t} = 1 + (\alpha_1 - \alpha_2)\Delta t$$

or

$$\frac{d_1 + d_2}{2R} = (\alpha_1 - \alpha_2)\Delta t$$

whence

$$R = \frac{d_1 + d_2}{2(\alpha_1 - \alpha_2)\Delta t}$$

If $\alpha_1 = \alpha_2$, $R = \infty$ and hence the compound bar stays straight. If $d_1 = d_2 = d$, the above expression simplifies to

$$R = \frac{d}{(\alpha_1 - \alpha_2)\Delta t}$$

Problems

1. Make a graph plotting Centigrade temperatures as abscissas and the corresponding Fahrenheit temperatures as ordinates. What property of this graph gives the ratio of the size of unit-temperature difference of these temperature scales?

2. Set up a general equation expressing any temperature in degrees Centigrade in terms of temperature measured in degrees Fahrenheit. At what temperature would a Centigrade and Fahrenheit thermometer read alike?

3. Because of the presence of air in the space above the mercury, the height of the mercury column in a tube 85 cm. tall is 73 cm. when the height of a mercury column in a correct barometer is 75 cm. What would the latter read when the former reads 69 cm.?

---

* This is but a rough approximation. The line of zero stress must be determined by an application of Newton's laws.

4. At what depth below the surface of a lake would an air bubble have 1 per cent of the density of water? Assume that the air in the bubble obeys the perfect gas laws and the temperature is 4°C. The molecular weight of air may be taken as 28.8.

5. A barometer is made of a tube 90 cm. long and of cross section 1.5 cm.². The mercury stands in this tube to a height of 75 cm. when the room temperature is 27°C. A small amount of oxygen is introduced into the evacuated space above the mercury, and the column drops to a height of 70 cm. How many grams of oxygen were introduced?

6. A hollow cylindrical jar was lowered slowly to the bottom of a lake with its open end downward. The barometer read 30 in., the air temperature was 27°C., and the temperature at the bottom of the lake was 8°C. When raised to the top, a recording device showed that the water had risen 0.80 of the length of the jar. Calculate the depth of the lake. The density of mercury is 13.6 grams/cm.³.

7. A steel meter bar is to be calibrated within 0.001 mm. What is the maximum temperature change which may occur during the calibration and not affect this calibration? The coefficient of linear expansion of steel is $1.3 \times 10^{-5}/°C$.

8. A steel tape is correct at 60°F. When used at a temperature of 40°F. the distance between two points was measured as 221.32 ft. What is the true distance between the two points?

9. A brass ring has an inside diameter of 2.00 in. at a temperature of 60°F., and a steel shaft has a diameter of 2.02 in. at the same temperature. To what temperature must the ring be heated if the ring is to just slip over the shaft? The coefficient of linear expansion of brass is $1.9 \times 10^{-5}/°C$.

10. Two grams of nitrogen at 27°C. occupy a volume of 2 liters. What is the pressure of the gas?

If the pressure is doubled and the temperature raised to 127°C., calculate the final volume of the gas.

11. A bubble of air of 1 cm. radius is formed at the bottom of a lake 68 ft. deep where the temperature is 4°C. and rises slowly to the top where the temperature is 27°C. Calculate the radius of the bubble as it reaches the water surface. Neglect surface tension.

12. A steel wire 0.01 in. in diameter is fastened between clamps at the ends of a large brass bar. The tension in the wire is zero at 0°C. Find the tension when bar and wire are at 20°C.

13. A clock with a seconds pendulum (one vibration in 2 sec.) is correct at 25°C. The shaft of the pendulum is made of steel and its moment of inertia about the axis may be neglected compared to that of the bob.

a. What is the fractional change of length of the shaft when it is cooled to 15°C.?

b. How many seconds per day will the clock gain at 15°C.?

14. A steel piano wire 1 mm.² in cross section is clamped rigidly at its ends under a tension of 7.8×10^6 dynes at a temperature of 20°C. The lowest natural frequency (for transverse vibrations) of the wire is found to be 500 vibrations per second at this temperature. What is the length of the wire? What effect will cooling the wire have upon its natural frequency?

Calculate the lowest natural frequency of the wire when it has been cooled to 0°C. Assume that the wire is so clamped that its length does not change with change of temperature.

15. When laying rails for a railway, one must allow for thermal expansion. If 50-ft. rails are being laid in Death Valley at 40°F., what spacing should be allowed between the rails if a temperature of 130°F. is expected on hot days?

16. A steel ball will just slip through a brass ring at 20°C. If the steel ball is heated to 60°C., it is necessary to heat the brass ring to 45°C. before the ball will slip through. What is the coefficient of linear expansion for brass? What is the coefficient of volume expansion for brass?

17. A uniform steel rod 2.0 cm.² in cross section, and 30 cm. long at 20°C. is 0.165 cm. longer at 520°C. Calculate the coefficient of linear expansion for steel. If allowed to cool to 20°C., without contracting, calculate the longitudinal stress in the rod. Young's modulus $= 2 \times 10^{12}$ dynes/cm.².

18. The bulb of a mercury thermometer is a sphere of radius R, and the stem has a bore of radius r. Show that the distance between two scratches 1° apart is very nearly given by

$$d = \frac{4}{3}\frac{R^3}{r^2}(\beta_2 - \beta_1)$$

if β_2 and β_1 are the coefficients of volume expansion of mercury and glass, respectively.

19. A hollow steel sphere is filled with water at 20°C., and the whole is heated to 30°C. Neglecting the change of volume of the steel container due to the increased pressure but not due to the increased temperature, calculate the pressure of the water at 30°C. The compressibility of water is 49×10^{-6} per atmosphere, and the coefficient of cubical expansion of the water is $37 \times 10^{-5}/°C$.

20. A steel bar of length 80 cm. and cross section 2 cm.² is welded end to end with a copper bar of length 50 cm. and of the same section. The whole is heated to a temperature of 220°C. What is the least force that will prevent contraction if the double rod cools to 20°C.? What is the stress in each rod? Young's modulus for copper is 16×10^6 lb./in.² and for steel 30×10^6 lb./in.². The coefficient of linear expansion of copper is $17 \times 10^{-6}/°C$.

21. A closed glass vessel is partially filled with mercury and evacuated. Upon heating the whole the volume of the empty part remains constant. What fraction of the whole volume did the mercury originally occupy? The coefficients of cubical expansion of glass and mercury are 2.5×10^{-5} and 18×10^{-5} per degree Centigrade, respectively.

22. The interior volume of a hollow steel sphere is 1,000 cm.³. This volume is filled at a temperature of 20°C. with a liquid whose volume coefficient of expansion is 0.0014 per degree Centigrade, and the sphere is closed tightly.

a. By how many cubic centimeters would the volume of the liquid increase when heated to 100°C. if it were perfectly free to expand?

b. Assuming that the volume of the steel sphere does not change, compute the increase in pressure of the enclosed liquid when heated to 100°. The compressibility κ of the liquid is 90×10^{-6} per atmosphere.

23. A thin flexible rubber bag is partially inflated with 1 liter of air at 15°C. and atmospheric pressure and loaded with lead so that the total mass is 500 grams. If the bag is lowered to a depth z in a lake at 15°C. and then released, it will rise to the surface if $z < z_0$ but sink to the bottom if $z > z_0$. Find z_0. Neglect the volume of the lead and of the rubber.

CHAPTER XVIII

THE FIRST LAW OF THERMODYNAMICS

In this chapter we shall complete the task outlined in the preceding chapter, *viz.*, that of defining a measure of quantity of heat. In so doing, it becomes necessary to differentiate between two different but not entirely independent methods of procedure in developing physical laws to account for the observed facts. The first of these methods is that of thermodynamics in the study of thermal phenomena, and this may be considered as a special case of a more general method of attack which we shall label the *macroscopic method*. We use the word macroscopic here in the specific sense that a macroscopic system is one whose dimensions are large compared with atomic dimensions. The second method is that of the atomic theory, and we shall call this method the *atomic* or *microscopic method*. We must now explain in some detail what is to be understood under each of these headings.

123. The Macroscopic Method.—The starting point of the macroscopic method of attack is always some general physical principle. These principles are generalizations from experimentally observed facts and are the product of inductive reasoning. As an example of such a general law or principle we may call to mind Newton's law of universal gravitation. We have seen in Chap. XII how this general law was inferred from the empirical Kepler laws of planetary motion. The laws of thermodynamics which we shall develop are further examples of such general principles. The validity of these principles can only be insured by the success of the predictions which they make regarding actual experiments. The wider the range of experimental data explicable by the use of such a principle, the firmer becomes our belief in the validity of the principle.

In applying these general principles to specific problems, one usually starts by formulating the principle in a form appropriate to the case under consideration, and, from this, one derives results which can be tested by experiment. This, then, is a process of deductive reasoning. It may, of course, be necessary to make certain approximations in the course of such a solution, but this does not affect the general scheme of procedure. In the course of applying this method it may become necessary to introduce certain material constants describing the properties of matter. It is typical of the macroscopic method that such quantities are considered as quantities whose behavior must be determined by independent experiments, and hence this method can never yield any insight into the properties of matter. As an example, suppose we are concerned with a dynamical problem of a block sliding down an inclined plane. In the application of the general principles of mechanics we introduce a friction force. The determination of the law of friction and the value of the coefficient of friction to be used are found experimentally and are considered as empirical facts.

124. The Atomic Method.—The atomic method proceeds by constructing pictures or models of matter in terms of such basic constituents as atoms and molecules and then subjecting these models to the principles of mechanics and electrodynamics. According to these laws one can predict how the models will behave, and these predictions are then compared with experimental results. Successful models help us see the connections between various branches of physics and often lead to predictions not attainable by an application of the method of macroscopic physics. If a prediction is not verified by experiment, the difficulty may lie either with the model utilized or with the laws governing the behavior of these models. The rational procedure is to discard the model and construct a new one, and only if such attempts persistently fail does it become necessary to admit the invalidity of mechanical or electrodynamic principles as they are formulated for large bodies when applied to the realm of atomic phenomena. The latter situation has actually come to pass in physics and has resulted in the development of principles of quantum mechanics which when applied to bodies of dimensions large compared with atomic dimensions become identical with the principles of Newtonian mechanics. The results of thermodynamics always provide useful guidance in atomic studies, since the results of the latter must always be consistent with the requirements of the former.

To exemplify the general statements concerning the methods of physics, let us again consider the phenomenon of sliding friction.

Here we have a phenomenon resulting in the disappearance of mechanical energy and the evolution of a quantity of heat. From the macroscopic standpoint, this process is merely an experimental fact calling for the introduction of a dissipative force into the formulation of the problem. Similarly, in any process where mechanical energy disappears, dissipative forces are introduced and the question as to the nature of these forces does not arise; the dependence of these forces on various factors is left as a matter of empirical knowledge. On the other hand, atomic physics attempts to go further into the problem of the nature of friction forces and looks upon heat flow as a transfer of mechanical energy of molecules and atoms, this energy being in the form of kinetic and potential energy of a huge number of particles in random motion. The energy of this random motion is recognized by our sensory faculties as warmth. Thus, in this picture, if we include atoms and molecules in the mechanical system being studied, we need not talk at all of dissipation of energy. We do, however, recognize the fact that there is something fundamentally different about the mechanical energy of atoms and molecules which we perceive as heat from the mechanical energy of a stone in motion.

As another example, consider the melting of a solid. Thermodynamically, we realize that a certain amount of heat must be added per unit mass to the solid in order to change it to a liquid. Conversely when the liquid solidifies, a similar amount of heat is liberated. From the atomic standpoint, crystalline solids consist of atoms (or ions) held together by forces which hold them in equilibrium positions so that the whole solid is formed of a lattice structure of atoms. If we heat the solid, the atoms oscillate in simple harmonic motion about their equilibrium positions, the amplitudes and hence the energy of these motions increasing with increasing temperature. When the melting point is reached, we picture the amplitudes of the motion so large that equilibrium can no longer be maintained and the whole lattice collapses. The heat added during the melting process is the work necessary to remove the atoms from their equilibrium positions. In the liquid state, we still imagine attractive forces between the atoms, although these forces are much smaller than in the solid state. Heating the liquid causes evaporation which is due to the fact that some of the atoms gain enough kinetic energy to escape from the body of the liquid. The work done by these atoms against the attractive forces of the remaining atoms is the heat of vaporization. Finally, in the gaseous state, if we heat a gas kept at constant volume, the pressure increases. The molecular interpretation is that the molecules of the gas gain kinetic energy and hence momentum due to the heating process, and when they collide with the walls of the container they exert larger forces on it due to the increased rate of change of momentum. The average effect of these forces is identified with the observable pressure of a gas.

These qualitative examples may serve to indicate the general atomic picture of matter, and we shall attempt in the following to supplement our thermodynamic calculations with atomic ones.

125. The First Law of Thermodynamics.—We have already discussed the concept of quantity of heat, and there now remains the task of laying down a method of measuring this quantity. We find that, if a given body is heated by dissipating mechanical energy, the same total amount of work must be done on the body to raise the temperature of the body by a specified amount no matter how this process is accomplished. We are thus led to measure quantity of heat by the mechanical work necessary to produce it and hence *we identify heat as a form of energy*.

We are now prepared to formulate the first law of thermodynamics which expresses the general principle of conservation of energy, including heat energy. The general principle of conservation of energy states that in an isolated system in which any changes may occur (mechanical, electrical, thermal, chemical) the total energy of the system stays constant, and that this total energy can be changed only by doing work on the system by external means; and the increase in total energy of the system is just equal to the externally added work, which may be in the form of heat. In our formulation of this general principle we shall be concerned only with mechanical and thermal changes. In a conservative mechanical system the potential energy of the system depends on the configuration of the system and the kinetic energy on the speeds of the various particles which compose the system. The total mechanical energy stays constant. Thus we may think of the system in a definite energy state. If we now wish to generalize this picture to include thermal effects, we introduce a quantity known as the *internal energy* of a system which depends only on the state of the system, for example, on its mechanical state and temperature.*   If work is done by this system and heat is added to it, the increase in internal energy must just equal the heat added minus the work done by the system on its surroundings. Expressing this last statement analytically, we have

$$dE = dQ - dW \qquad (1)$$

where dE is the increase of internal energy of the system, dQ is the heat energy (measured in mechanical work units) added to the system, and dW is the work done by the system on its surroundings.

At first glance Eq. (1) seems to be merely an equation defining the internal energy of a system.   This, however, is not the whole story, since the internal energy depends *only* on the state of the system.   If the system is in a state 1 and is brought into a state 2, the increase of internal energy depends only on the initial and final states and not on the intermediate states which occur in this transition.   We may produce this change by adding heat and doing no external work, or by doing work on the system and not adding or subtracting heat, or by any combination of these two processes, but the increase of internal energy depends only on the initial and final states.   This reminds us of the definition of the potential energy of a mechanical system, in which exactly the same criterion held for the existence of this potential energy. Indeed, the concept of internal energy is the generalization of the mechanical idea of potential energy.   Thus the first law does more than define internal energy.   It states that, if a process is carried out in which a system is taken through a series of states ending in the same state in which it started (a so-called *cyclic process*), the change of internal energy is zero and hence the sum of the heat energy added and of the work done on the system is also zero.   This statement precludes the possibility of a perpetual-motion device, and the countless number of fruitless attempts to construct such a device provides a part of the experimental evidence justifying our belief in the validity of the first law.

In applying the first law, we shall restrict our attention to processes in which the work done is that due to an external pressure, *e.g.*, atmospheric pressure, acting on a system whose volume changes.   If the pressure is denoted by p, and the

* In general, the internal energy depends on other variables besides these.

system increases its volume by an amount dV, the work done by the system is

$$dW = +p\, dV$$

so that Eq. (1) becomes

$$dE = dQ - p\, dV \tag{2}$$

This is the form which we shall use in our subsequent applications. We must still refer to the units of energy and work to be used in Eq. (2). Of course, any consistent set of energy units, such as ergs or foot-pounds, may be used throughout. It has, however, been customary to define a new unit of energy which is used extensively in thermal problems. This unit is called the *gram calorie*, and it is defined as the energy required to raise the temperature of one gram of water one degree Centigrade, or, more precisely, from $14.5°$ to $15.5°C$. when the water is at atmospheric pressure. The ratio between this energy unit and the mechanical units must be determined by experiment. Thus we often read of the mechanical "equivalent" of heat, the numerical ratio of the energy unit usually employed in heat to a mechanical energy unit being meant. We have defined the joule by the relation

$$10^7 \text{ ergs} = 10^7 \text{ dyne-cm.} = 1 \text{ joule}$$

and it is found experimentally that

$$1 \text{ cal.} = 4.19 \text{ joules.}$$

Thus we may use either "thermal" or mechanical units of energy and convert our results from one set of units to the other. In English-speaking countries engineers often employ a thermal unit of energy known as the *British thermal unit* (B.t.u.). It is defined as the energy required to raise the temperature of one pound of water one degree Fahrenheit.

126. Heat Capacity; Specific Heat Capacity.—If heat is added to a body, the temperature of the latter will change in general and the size of this change for a given amount of heat added will depend on the body and also on the conditions to which the body is subjected while being heated. Thus, if we keep the volume V of a body constant while an amount of heat, dQ, is added and the temperature of the body changes by an amount dT, we define

$$C_v = \left(\frac{dQ}{dT}\right)_{V\,=\,\text{const.}} \tag{3}$$

as the heat capacity of the body at constant volume. The heat capacity per unit mass (a somewhat more convenient quantity) is similarly defined at constant volume by

$$c_v = \left(\frac{dq}{dT}\right)_{V=\text{const.}} = \frac{C_v}{m} \tag{3a}$$

and is called the specific heat capacity at constant volume. In the c.g.s. system the proper units are ergs per gram per degree Centigrade, although very frequently specific heat capacities are expressed in calories per gram per degree Centigrade.

Since we are restricting ourselves to changes where work is done only when a volume change occurs, it follows from the first law [Eq. (2)], since $dV = 0$, that

$$C_v = \left(\frac{dQ}{dT}\right)_v = \left(\frac{dE}{dT}\right)_v \tag{4}$$

so that the heat capacity of a body at constant volume is equal to the rate of increase of internal energy of the body with temperature.

Another important heat capacity is defined by the process of heating a body at constant pressure, *e.g.*, in the atmosphere. In this case the heat capacity at constant pressure is defined by the equation

$$C_p = \left(\frac{dQ}{dT}\right)_{p=\text{const.}} \tag{5}$$

with an equation similar to Eq. (3a) for the specific heat capacity at constant pressure. The two heat capacities C_p and C_v are practically equal for liquids and solids, but the difference between these quantities is important in the case of gases. This, of course, is due to the fact that the coefficient of expansion of liquids and solids is extremely small compared with that of gases.

It is usual to call specific heat capacity merely *specific heat*, but strictly speaking the specific heat of a body is equal to the dimensionless numerical ratio of the specific heat capacity of the body to that of water. Since the latter is one calorie per gram per degree Centigrade, specific heat and specific heat capacity are numerically equal when these latter are measured in calories per gram per degree Centigrade or British thermal units per lb.-degree Fahrenheit. We shall use the term *specific heat* to mean either quantity. There is no danger of confusion arising from this convention. Specific heats in general depend on temperature, and from the thermodynamic standpoint the temperature dependence as well as the values themselves must be experimentally determined.

127. The Water Calorimeter; Determination of Specific Heats. The simplest practical method for measuring a quantity of heat utilizes the so-called *water calorimeter*. This device consists of a container holding water, the temperature of which is measured by a thermometer. The quantity of heat to be measured is transferred to the water and the rise of temperature of the water noted. From this, the quantity of heat absorbed by the water may be immediately found. For example, if the heat of combustion of coal is to be measured, the coal is burned in a pressure-tight container which is immersed in the water of the calorimeter. If c_w and m_w denote the specific heat capacity and mass of the water in the calorimeter and c_c and m_c denote the corresponding quantities for the container, the rise of temperature Δt of water and container, due to the addition of a quantity of heat Q, is determined by

$$Q = (m_w c_w + m_c c_c)\Delta t \qquad (6)$$

if we neglect the heat lost to the surroundings and to the thermometer. In precise measurements the latter effects must be corrected for. The specific heats c_w and c_c are assumed constant over the temperature range Δt.

The mean values of the specific heats of metals may be determined by dropping a hot piece of the metal into the calorimeter and waiting until thermal equilibrium is attained. The system (water, container, and metal) neither gains nor loses an appreciable quantity of heat. Let c_m, m_m denote the specific heat capacity (assumed constant) and mass of the metal, t_m the initial temperature of the metal, t_0 the initial temperature of the water and container, and t the equilibrium temperature of the mixture. Since the total heat gained by the system is zero, the sum of the quantities of heat gained by each part of the system must add up to zero. Thus we have

$$(m_w c_w + m_c c_c)(t - t_0) + m_m c_m(t - t_m) = 0 \qquad (7)$$

Solving for c_m, we find

$$c_m = \frac{(m_w c_w + m_c c_c)(t - t_0)}{m_m(t_m - t)} \tag{7a}$$

or, if the final temperature t is desired, Eq. (7) yields

$$t = \frac{(m_w c_w + m_c c_c)t_0 + m_m c_m t_m}{m_w c_w + m_c c_c + m_m c_m} \tag{7b}$$

It must be emphasized that in the preceding discussion the specific heat capacities have been assumed constant. If the temperature dependence of c is known, the quantity of heat necessary to raise the temperature of a mass m from t_0 to t_1 is given by

$$Q = m\int_{t_0}^{t_1} c\, dt \tag{8}$$

a result which immediately follows by integration of the equation

$$\frac{dQ}{dt} = C = mc$$

which defines the specific heat c.

Problems

1. What power is necessary to raise the temperature of 10 kg. of water from 0° to 50°C. in 20 min.? Express the result in watts and in horse power.

2. In drilling a hole in a 2-lb. copper block, power is supplied at the rate of 0.5 hp. for 2 min. How much heat is generated? If 80 per cent of this heat generated warms the copper, calculate the rise in temperature of the copper. The specific heat capacity of copper is 0.09 cal./gram-°C.

3. A 2-gram lead bullet moving with a speed of 200 meters/sec. strikes and remains embedded in a 2-kg. wooden block used in a ballistic pendulum. Assuming that all the heat generated raises the temperature of the bullet, calculate the rise in temperature of the bullet. The specific heat capacity of lead is 0.03 cal./gram-°C.

4. A steam-boiler and electric-generator plant develops a constant electrical power output of 850 kw. and burns 10 tons of coal per day. The coal burned yields 14,000 B.t.u./lb. Calculate the over-all efficiency of the plant.

5. What is the least height from which a lead bullet must be dropped if its temperature is raised 100°C. when it collides inelastically with a non-conductor, if all the heat developed raises the temperature of the bullet.

6. One hundred grams of lead at a temperature of 200°C. is dropped into 300 grams of water contained in an aluminum vessel weighing 200 grams. The temperature of the water is initially 22°C. Calculate the final temperature of the mixture. The specific heat capacity of aluminum is 0.22 cal./gram-°C.

7. Forty pounds of water are contained in a vessel weighing 10 lb. A 5-lb. piece of metal of which the vessel is made, initially at a temperature of 380°F. is dropped into the water. If the final temperature of the water is 64°F. and its initial temperature is 60°F., calculate the specific heat capacity of the metal.

8. One hundred grams of lead at 100°C., 200 grams of iron at 120°C., and 50 grams of zinc at 200°C. are dropped into a copper vessel weighing 600 grams containing 250 grams of water initially at 20°C. Calculate the final temperature of the mixture. The specific heat capacity of iron is 0.11 cal./gram-°C.; of zinc 0.09 cal./gram-°C.; of lead 0.03 cal./gram-°C., and of copper 0.09 cal./gram-°C.

9. At very low temperatures the molal heat capacity of solids is given by the relation

$$C = 144\left(\frac{T}{\theta}\right)^3 \text{ cal./°Abs.}$$

where T is the Absolute temperature and θ a constant temperature characteristic of the solid. For diamond $\theta = 1840°$Abs. Calculate the heat energy necessary to heat 1 mole of diamond from 10° to 150°Abs.

10. The molal heat capacity of hydrogen at constant volume is found experimentally to be given by the equation

$$C_v = (4.51 + 0.0009T) \text{ cal./°Abs.}$$

where T is the Absolute temperature. One liter of hydrogen at atmospheric pressure and a temperature of 0°C. is heated at constant volume to a temperature of 1500°C. Calculate the increase of internal energy of the gas. What is the final pressure?

11. One thousand calories of heat are supplied to a system, while the system at the same time does 1,680 joules of external work. At the end of the process its internal energy has increased by 2,520 joules. Compute the value of the mechanical equivalent of heat from these data.

12. A cylinder containing 10 grams of gas is compressed from a volume of 500 cm.³ to a volume of 100 cm.³. During the compression process, 100 cal. of heat are removed from the gas, and at the end of the process the temperature of the gas has increased by 5°C. Compute the specific heat of the gas for this process.

CHAPTER XIX

HEAT CONDUCTION

Before applying the first law of thermodynamics to a study of actual phenomena, we must discuss the processes of heat transfer from one body to another. There are three processes of transferring heat from one point of a body to another point in the body, or in another body, namely, *radiation, convection,* and *conduction.* The process of radiation consists of the process of transfer of heat energy from one body to another even without the presence of an intervening material medium, such as the transfer of heat from the sun to the earth. An understanding and analysis of this process may be obtained only with the help of electrodynamic principles and hence lies beyond the scope of this book. The convection of heat consists of the motion of a hot body (or, more generally, of hot matter) from one point to another. This is a very efficient and controllable manner of accomplishing heat transfer and hence is of great practical importance. However, it offers us nothing new in principle. When the hot body arrives at its destination it must give up heat to another body, thus involving either radiation or conduction of heat. The process of heat conduction is very closely connected with our study of mechanics, and we shall examine this process more closely.

128. Steady Heat Flow.—From the standpoint of thermodynamics we recognize the fact that, when one part of a stationary body is heated, heat flows from the hotter to the cooler parts of the body. The amount of energy flowing across any small area ΔA per second, *i.e.,* the rate of heat flow, is experimentally found to be proportional to the rate of decrease of temperature with distance as we move across ΔA in a direction normal to it and is also proportional to ΔA, so that

$$H = -k\Delta A\frac{dT}{dx} \tag{1}$$

if x is the direction normal to ΔA. The proportional factor k is called the *coefficient of thermal conductivity,* and the negative

330

algebraic sign refers to $-dT/dx$, which is the rate of *decrease*, not increase, of T with x. H is called the *heat current*. Equation (1) is a fundamental equation in the theory of heat conduction.

From the standpoint of atomic theory we picture the atoms and molecules of a body colliding or interacting with their neighbors and exchanging mechanical energy. Thus in solids we get elastic waves, and these waves transmit heat energy within the body from one point to another. In gases we picture the atoms or molecules colliding with each other. In the hotter parts of the gas the molecules have a greater kinetic energy than in the cooler parts. If two similar molecules collide like mass points in an elastic collision, we know that they exchange velocities, so that the slower moving molecules get speeded up, and kinetic energy is transferred by this process.

We shall be concerned only with the case of the steady or stationary flow of heat. This is very similar to the case of the stationary flow of a fluid, and we have the condition that at any point of the body the temperature does not change with time although different points are at different temperatures. In this case the resulting heat flow is steady and obeys an equation of continuity. If no sources or sinks of heat are present, the heat current entering any volume element of the body must be equal to the heat current leaving this element.

Let us consider the linear flow of heat such as occurs along a rod when no heat is allowed to leak across the transverse surface. If the rod is of length l and *constant* cross section A, and we have the steady state, Eq. (1) becomes

$$H = -kA\frac{dT}{dx} \tag{2}$$

where now H is the constant heat current flowing in the whole rod. Let us take one end of the rod as an origin, and the x-axis

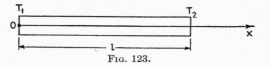

Fig. 123.

along the axis of the rod (Fig. 123). For small temperature differences we may treat k as a constant and Eq. (2) thus becomes

$$\frac{dT}{dx} = -\frac{H}{kA}$$

which when integrated yields

$$T = -\frac{H}{kA}x + \text{constant} \tag{3}$$

Suppose the end face at $x = 0$ is maintained at a temperature T_1, and the face at $x = l$ is maintained at a temperature T_2. Inserting the value $T = T_1$ when $x = 0$ in Eq. (3), we find that the constant has the value T_1. Thus Eq. (3) becomes

$$T = T_1 - \frac{H}{kA}x \tag{4}$$

which determines the temperature at any position x along the rod. The heat current in the rod is determined by placing $T = T_2$ when $x = l$ in Eq. (4). There follows

$$T_1 - T_2 = \frac{H}{kA}l$$

or

$$H = \frac{kA}{l}(T_1 - T_2) \tag{5}$$

Finally, if we insert this expression in Eq. (4), we find for the temperature at any point x,

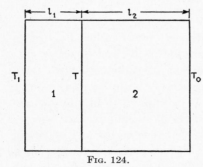

Fig. 124.

$$T = T_1 - \frac{T_1 - T_2}{l}x \tag{6}$$

129. Examples.—The following examples are given to illustrate the use of the above equations.

1. A compound wall is made of two slabs of different materials 1 and 2, each of area A, the first of thickness l_1, the second of thickness l_2 and with thermal conductivities k_1 and k_2, respectively. If the outer surfaces are maintained at temperatures T_1 and T_0 respectively ($T_1 > T_0$), what is the temperature of the common surface and what is the rate of heat flow across any cross section of the wall if we have a steady state?

Since we have a steady state the heat current is constant and equal in both slabs, and we may apply Eq. (5) first to slab 1 and then to slab 2. We then have (Fig. 124)

$$H = \frac{k_1 A}{l_1}(T_1 - T) = \frac{k_2 A}{l_2}(T - T_0) \qquad (7)$$

Denoting $k_1 A / l_1$ by y_1 and $k_2 A / l_2$ by y_2, we have

$$\frac{y_1}{y_2} = \frac{T - T_0}{T_1 - T}$$

and, solving for T,

$$T = \frac{T_1 y_1 + T_0 y_2}{y_1 + y_2}$$

or

$$T = \frac{T_1 \dfrac{k_1 A}{l_1} + T_0 \dfrac{k_2 A}{l_2}}{\dfrac{k_1 A}{l_1} + \dfrac{k_2 A}{l_2}} \qquad (8)$$

From Eq. (7) we have

$$T_1 - T = \frac{H}{k_1 A / l_1}$$

$$T - T_0 = \frac{H}{k_2 A / l_2}$$

Adding, we find

$$H\left(\frac{1}{k_1 A / l_1} + \frac{1}{k_2 A / l_2}\right) = T_1 - T_0 \qquad (9)$$

from which H may be found directly without solving for T.

2. A hollow sphere of inner radius R_1, outer radius R_2, has its inner surface maintained at a temperature T_1 and its outer surface at $T_2 (T_1 > T_2)$. The coefficient of thermal conductivity is k. Heat flows radially outward from the inner to the outer surface, and the flow is steady. It is required to find an expression for the heat current flowing across any spherical surface.

Since the flow is steady, the heat current across any spherical shell in the hollow sphere is the same as across any other shell (Fig. 125). Since the areas of different shells are different, we must revert to our fundamental Eq. (1), which we write in the form

$$H = -k\Delta A \frac{dT}{dr}$$

since any radius r is normal to the surface of the shell whose radius is r. Its area is $4\pi r^2$, and the above equation becomes

$$H = -k4\pi r^2 \frac{dT}{dr}$$

or rewritten

$$H\frac{dr}{r^2} = -4\pi k dT$$

Integrating this yields

$$-\frac{H}{r} = -4\pi kT + \text{constant}$$

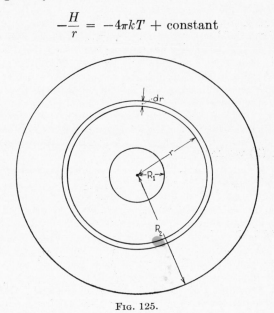

Fig. 125.

The constant is found by placing $r = R_1$ and $T = T_1$, so that

$$\text{Constant} = \frac{-H}{R_1} + 4\pi kT_1$$

Thus we may write

$$-H\left(\frac{1}{r} - \frac{1}{R_1}\right) = +4\pi k(T_1 - T)$$

To find H we place $r = R_2$ and $T = T_2$, yielding

$$H\left(\frac{1}{R_1} - \frac{1}{R_2}\right) = 4\pi k(T_1 - T_2)$$

or

$$H = 4\pi k(T_1 - T_2)\frac{R_1R_2}{R_2 - R_1}$$

which is the required result.

Problems

1. The coefficient of thermal conductivity of copper is 0.95 cal./sec.-cm.-°C. Calculate the number of B.t.u. per day which flow through a slab of copper 1 ft.² in area and 1 in. thick, when the opposite faces are maintained at a temperature difference of 1°F.

2. One end of a copper bar 18 cm. long and of cross section 4 cm.² is in a steam bath and the other end in a mixture of melting ice and water. The surface of the bar is thermally insulated so that no appreciable quantity of heat escapes through this surface. Calculate the heat current in the rod. What is the temperature at a point 4 cm. from the cold end of the bar?

3. A copper bar 15 cm. long and 6.0 cm.² in cross section has one end maintained at a temperature of 150°C. and the other end in contact with one end of an iron bar of equal cross section and 8.0 cm. long. The other end of the iron bar is maintained at a temperature of 20°C., and the sides of both bars are thermally insulated. Calculate the steady heat current in the rod and the temperature of the junction. The thermal conductivity of copper and iron are 0.95 and 0.16 cal./sec.-cm.-°C., respectively.

4. Heat flows radially out of a hollow sphere of inner radius 1 cm. and outer radius 10 cm., in steady flow. The thermal conductivity of the material of the sphere is 0.1 cal./sec.-cm.-°C. If the heat current is 10 cal./sec., calculate the temperature gradient dT/dr at the inner surface of the sphere and at a point 5 cm. from its center. Plot a graph to scale of this temperature gradient against distance out from the center of the sphere.

5. A metal ball of radius 2 cm. is covered uniformly with a coating of insulating material of thermal conductivity 0.00016 cal./sec.-cm.-°C. and of thickness 3 cm., and this in turn is covered uniformly with a coating of insulating material of thermal conductivity 0.0004 cal./sec.-cm.-°C. and of thickness 5 cm. The temperature of the surface of the ball is maintained at 130°C., and the temperature of the outer surface is maintained at 30°C. Calculate

 a. The heat current flowing radially outward through this sphere.

 b. The temperature at the outer surface of the first insulator.

6. A cylindrical steam pipe of outer radius 2 cm. carries steam at a temperature of 120°C. The pipe is covered uniformly with a coating of a thermal insulator of thermal conductivity 10^{-4} cal./sec.-cm.-°C. and of thickness 5 cm. The outer surface is at a temperature of 40°C.

 a. Set up the general equation for the temperature gradient transverse to the length of the pipe.

 b. Integrate this to obtain an expression for the heat current flowing transverse to the length of the pipe per centimeter of length.

 c. Calculate the value of this heat current.

7. Plot graphs to scale of the temperature gradient and the temperature in Prob. 6 as functions of the distance from the surface of the steam pipe.

8. A slab of a thermal insulator is 100 cm.² in cross section and 2 cm. thick and its thermal conductivity is 2×10^{-4} cal./sec.-cm.-°C. If the temperature difference between its opposite faces is maintained at 100°C. calculate the amount of heat in calories which flows through the slab in 1 day.

9. A furnace wall is made of two different layers, the inner of thickness 10 cm. and thermal conductivity 0.0004 cal./sec.-cm.-°C., the outer of thickness 20 cm. and thermal conductivity 0.002 cal./sec.-cm.-°C. The area of the wall is 1 meter^2. If the inner surface of the wall is maintained at a temperature of 600°C. and the outer surface 260°C., calculate:

    a. The heat current flowing through the wall in the steady state.

    b. The temperature at the joining surface.

10. A cubical tank has copper walls 0.95 cm. thick, its capacity is 10^6 cm.^{3} and the area of its inner surface is 6×10^4 cm.^{2}. The outside of the tank is kept at 0°C., and the tank is filled with water initially at 100°C. What is the initial rate of loss of heat of the water? What is its initial rate of decrease of temperature? What total heat will be lost by the water by the time it reaches 0°C.?

11. A solid steel rod 2 ft. long and 1 in. in diameter is surrounded by a cylindrical copper shell $\frac{1}{2}$ in. thick. One end of the compound rod is at 100°C. and the other at 0°C. If no heat escapes from the sides of the rod, find what fraction of the total heat current in the steady state is carried by each rod. The thermal conductivities of steel and copper are 0.11 and 0.95 cal./sec.-cm.°C., respectively.

12. Two concentric hollow spheres are made of iron and copper. The inner sphere (iron) has an inner radius of 10 cm. and an outer radius of 10.4 cm. The outer sphere (copper) has an inner radius of 10.4 cm. and an outer radius of 20 cm. The thermal conductivities of iron and copper are 0.16 and 0.95 cal./sec.-cm.-°C., respectively. The inner cavity is maintained at a temperature of 0°C. and the outer surface at 100°C.

Calculate the temperature at the boundary between the two metals, and calculate the heat current flowing across it.

CHAPTER XX

THERMODYNAMICS AND KINETIC THEORY OF AN IDEAL GAS

In this chapter we shall turn to a more detailed discussion of the properties of gases and to the application of the first law of thermodynamics to gaseous systems. We first consider the simplest case, that of an ideal or perfect gas. Such a gas approximates the behavior of a real gas for small densities and high temperatures. After the thermodynamic treatment of the ideal gas we shall develop the most elementary atomic theory of such gases.

130. Thermodynamic Definition of an Ideal Gas.—We have already pointed out that a perfect gas obeys the equation of state $pV = nRT$ exactly. This equation is not sufficient to define the gas completely, and we must consider an experiment called the *free expansion* of a gas. Suppose a gas expands from an initial volume V_0, initial pressure p_0, and initial temperature T_0 into a large volume V_1 with zero external pressure. Such an expansion is called a free expansion. In practice this process may be realized by breaking a flask of gas which is placed inside a large evacuated flask. We must take precautions to insulate the large flask thermally from the surroundings so that no appreciable quantity of heat flows into or out of the system. Since there is no work done on the gas as a whole by external forces, any temperature changes occurring in this process must be due to work done by internal forces. When such an experiment is carried out with real gases, it is observed that the temperature change of the gas is extremely small. *We demand of a perfect gas that there be no temperature change in a free expansion.*

This means that the internal energy of an ideal gas does not depend on the volume occupied by the gas but only on the temperature. Analytically, this fact may be written in the form

$$E = E(T); \qquad E \neq E(V) \tag{1}$$

Actually the results embodied in Eq. (1) can be deduced from the

337

laws of thermodynamics utilizing only the equation of state of an ideal gas

$$pV = nRT \tag{2}$$

Since we are not in a position to prove Eq. (1), we shall merely present it as part of the thermodynamic definition of an ideal gas. For real gases it is an experimental fact that the internal energy is very nearly a linear function of the temperature, and we shall postulate for an ideal gas that this is strictly true. As we shall see immediately, this implies that the heat capacity at constant volume of an ideal gas is constant.

131. Relation between C_p and C_v.—The first law of thermodynamics may be written in a special form for ideal gases. The state of a given amount of any ideal gas is specified if its volume and temperature are known. Then the pressure can be calculated from Eq. (2), and the temperature fixes the internal energy according to Eq. (1). If we heat one mole of a perfect gas at constant volume, the first law yields the fact that $dE = dQ$, *i.e.*, the heat added is equal to the increase of internal energy since there is no work done on the gas. Since, by definition,

$$C_v = \left(\frac{\partial Q}{\partial T}\right)_v = \left(\frac{\partial E}{\partial T}\right)_v$$

in general, and, since for a perfect gas the internal energy and hence its rate of change with temperature do not depend on the volume, we may equally well write for the ideal gas,

$$C_v = \frac{dE}{dT}$$

or

$$dE = C_v dT \tag{3}$$

In words, the total change in internal energy of an ideal gas during a small temperature change dT is equal to the heat capacity of the gas at constant volume times the change in temperature. *Equation* (3) *is true only for a perfect gas.* For other substances not satisfying Eq. (1), we must supplement Eq. (3) by a term which takes into account the change of internal energy due to a change in volume.

If we now substitute the expression for dE as given by Eq. (3) into the general expression of the first law of thermodynamics,

$$dE = dQ - p\,dV \tag{4}$$

it follows that

$$C_v dT = dQ - p\, dV \tag{5}$$

If in particular we heat our one mole of perfect gas at constant pressure, $dQ = C_p dT$ from the definition of C_p and there follows from Eq. (5)

$$(C_p - C_v)dT = p\, dV$$

in which p is constant. This may be rewritten as

$$C_p - C_v = p\left(\frac{dV}{dT}\right)_{p=\text{const.}} \tag{6}$$

Thus we see that the heat capacity of an ideal gas is greater at constant pressure than at constant volume, since the gas expands upon heating and $(dV/dT)_{p=\text{const.}}$ is a positive quantity, and work is done by the gas.

To evaluate the right-hand side of Eq. (6), we use the equation of state, Eq. (2), which for one mole is

$$pV = RT$$

so that by differentiation

$$\left(\frac{dV}{dT}\right)_{p=\text{const.}} = \frac{R}{p}$$

Inserting this into Eq. (6), it follows that

$$C_p - C_v = R \tag{7}$$

which is an important relation between the heat capacities of an ideal gas. Since we have considered one mole of the gas, the heat capacities refer to one gram-molecular weight of the gas and are called the *molal heat capacities* at constant pressure and constant volume, respectively.

132. Isothermal Changes for Ideal Gases.—During an isothermal process the temperature of the gas is kept constant, and for ideal gases Boyle's law is obeyed during such changes. We shall now calculate the work done by the ideal gas when it expands isothermally. We shall further imagine the gas to expand reversibly, *i.e.*, to expand so slowly that at each instant of time the gas is almost exactly in equilibrium and no kinetic energy is gained by the gas as a whole. Only in reversible changes may we justly assume that our equilibrium equations remain valid. Indeed, thermodynamic calculations deal exclusively with reversible or, as they are sometimes called, quasi-static processes, although the results may be applied to any process.

If the initial volume of the gas is V_1 and its final volume V_2, the work done by the gas is

$$W = \int_{V_1}^{V_2} p \, dV = nRT \int_{V_1}^{V_2} \frac{dV}{V} = nRT \ln \frac{V_2}{V_1} \qquad (8)$$

This work is equal to the shaded area in Fig. 126. During an isothermal compression an equal amount of work must be done on the gas.

133. Adiabatic Changes for Ideal Gases.—By an *adiabatic* expansion (or compression) is meant one in which the system is

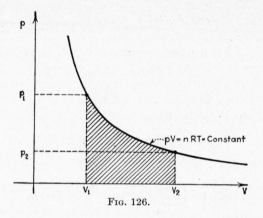

Fig. 126.

thermally insulated so that no heat enters or leaves the system. During such changes in a gas, the pressure, volume, and temperature all vary, but of course in such a way that the equation of state, Eq. (2), is satisfied at every point of the process. On the other hand, in the first law, $dQ = 0$, so that it becomes simply

$$dE = -p \, dV$$

for any adiabatic reversible process. For ideal gases we place $dQ = 0$ in Eq. (5) and it becomes

$$C_v dT + p \, dV = 0 \qquad (9)$$

If we consider one mole of an ideal gas, the equation of state

$$pV = RT$$

yields an expression for p which when inserted in Eq. (9) gives

$$C_v dT + \frac{RT\,dV}{V} = 0$$

or

$$\frac{dT}{T} + \frac{R}{C_v}\frac{dV}{V} = 0 \tag{10}$$

If we now integrate this equation we find

$$\ln T + \frac{R}{C_v}\ln V = \text{constant} \tag{11}$$

which may be written as

$$TV^{\frac{R}{C_v}} = \text{constant} \tag{12}$$

This relation between T and V exists throughout any reversible adiabatic change in an ideal gas. To calculate the relation between p and V during such changes, which we need to calculate the work done, we may replace T in Eq. (12) by its value in terms of p and V as given by the equation of state. It is, however, more convenient to take the logarithms of each side of the equation of state, obtaining

$$\ln p + \ln V - \ln T = \ln R$$

and, adding this to Eq. (11), there follows:

$$\ln p + \left(1 + \frac{R}{C_v}\right)\ln V = \text{constant} \tag{13}$$

From Eq. (7) we have

$$C_v + R = C_p$$

so that

$$1 + \frac{R}{C_v} = \frac{C_p}{C_v} = \gamma, \qquad \gamma > 1 \tag{14}$$

where γ denotes the ratio of the heat capacities of the gas.

Equation (13) then becomes

$$\ln p + \gamma \ln V = \text{constant}$$

or

$$pV^\gamma = \text{constant} \tag{15}$$

If we plot the curves given by Eq. (15), we get a family of curves as shown by the full lines in Fig. 127. The dotted curves are the isothermals. It is seen that the adiabatic curves have a steeper slope than the isothermals.

Let us calculate the work done by a gas during an adiabatic expansion. Since the temperature drops during such an expansion, we get less work done than in an isothermal expansion starting with the same initial conditions and ending in the same volume. This is indicated on the figure; the cross-hatched portion represents the work done in the adiabatic expansion and the

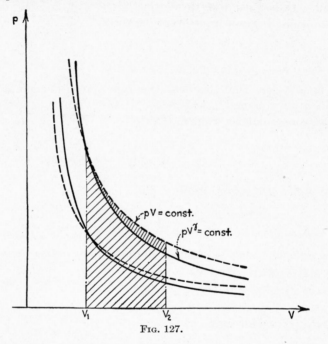

Fig. 127.

more heavily shaded area the added work obtained in the isothermal change specified above.

Since

$$pV^\gamma = C, \qquad p = CV^{-\gamma}$$

and

$$W = \int_{V_1}^{V_2} p\, dV = C \int_{V_1}^{V_2} V^{-\gamma} dV = \frac{C}{\gamma - 1}(V_1^{1-\gamma} - V_2^{1-\gamma})$$

and since

$$C = p_1 V_1^\gamma = p_2 V_2^\gamma$$

this may be written in the form

$$W = \frac{p_1 V_1 - p_2 V_2}{\gamma - 1} \tag{16}$$

Adiabatic changes occur when the change ensues so fast that there is not time for an appreciable amount of heat to escape from or to enter the system. Such is the case of an explosion in the cylinder head of an internal-combustion engine, or the case of the compression and rarefaction in a sound wave.

134. Isothermal and Adiabatic Compressibilities; Velocity of Sound.—In our study of the theory of elasticity we had defined the compressibility of a substance as

$$\kappa = -\frac{1}{V}\frac{dV}{dp}$$

It is now clear that this definition must be supplemented by a specification of the thermal conditions existing during the compression. Hence we define

$$\kappa_i = -\frac{1}{V}\left(\frac{dV}{dp}\right)_{T=\text{const.}} \tag{17}$$

as the *isothermal compressibility*, and

$$\kappa_a = -\frac{1}{V}\left(\frac{dV}{dp}\right)_{dQ=0} \tag{18}$$

as the *adiabatic compressibility*. Let us evaluate these quantities for a perfect gas. We have

$$V = \frac{nRT}{p}$$

so that, if T is constant,

$$\frac{dV}{dp} = -\frac{nRT}{p^2} = -\frac{V}{p}$$

and

$$\kappa_i = \frac{1}{p} \tag{19}$$

Similarly, during an adiabatic change,

$$V^\gamma = \frac{\text{constant}}{p}, \qquad V = cp^{-\frac{1}{\gamma}}$$

$$\frac{dV}{dp} = -\frac{1}{\gamma}cp^{-\frac{1}{\gamma}-1} = -\frac{1}{\gamma p}\left(cp^{-\frac{1}{\gamma}}\right) = -\frac{V}{\gamma p}$$

whence

$$\kappa_a = \frac{1}{\gamma p} \tag{20}$$

Let us use these compressibilities to calculate the velocity of sound in air, treating the latter as a perfect gas. In general we have for the velocity of sound in a gas,

$$\sqrt{\frac{1}{\kappa\rho}}$$

If the compressions and rarefactions were isothermal this would become

$$\sqrt{\frac{p}{\rho}}$$

whereas, if the changes were adiabatic, the velocity of sound would be

$$\sqrt{\frac{\gamma p}{\rho}}$$

We now compare the numerical values of these two expressions. The density of air at atmospheric pressure is 1.2 grams/liter $= 1.2 \times 10^{-3}$ grams/cm.^{3} and $p = 10^6$ dynes/cm.^{2}. Thus the isothermal velocity is

$$\sqrt{\frac{10^6}{1.2 \times 10^{-3}}} = \sqrt{\frac{10^{10}}{12}} = \frac{10^5}{3.5} = 2.86 \times 10^4 \text{ cm./sec.}$$

whereas the adiabatic velocity is ($\gamma = 1.4$ for air)

$$\sqrt{\gamma \frac{10^{10}}{12}} = \sqrt{\frac{1.4 \times 10^{10}}{12}} = 3.4 \times 10^4 \text{ cm./sec.} = 340 \text{ meters/sec.}$$

Since the measured value is about 340 meters/sec., it is clear that the propagation of sound in air is more nearly an adiabatic than an isothermal process.

135. Kinetic Theory of an Ideal Gas.—We have repeatedly made reference to the atomic structure of matter and have presented some qualitative results of this theory. At this point it becomes possible to carry out an elementary quantitative derivation of the gas laws on the basis of an atomic model. This derivation using a highly idealized picture of a gas will serve to illustrate the general nature of the atomic method. We start by constructing an atomic model of a gas, and indeed we shall first ask the question: What is the simplest conceivable picture of a gas in terms of atoms and molecules? Then, after investigating the behavior of such a gas, the next step is to refine the model employed and in this fashion to build up the atomic theory of gases which is given the name *kinetic theory of gases*. The ideas underlying the kinetic theory go back to D. Bernoulli (1738) and the development of these ideas is due largely to Clausius, Maxwell, and Boltzmann.

The simplest model of a gas is a collection of molecules which are small enough to be treated as mass points and which collide elastically with the walls of the vessel in which they are contained. We shall assume that the molecules exert no forces on each other. Consider the collision of one of these molecules with the wall of the container. If the molecule collides at an

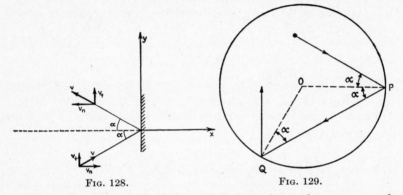

FIG. 128.   FIG. 129.

angle α with the normal, it will rebound at the same angle (Fig. 128). Since the speed of the molecule is unaltered by the collision, only the normal component of the velocity is changed. The initial normal component of momentum is $mv_n = mv \cos \alpha$. The final normal component of momentum is $-mv_n = -mv \cos \alpha$, so that the magnitude of the change of momentum of one molecule per collision is

$$2mv \cos \alpha$$

Consider a spherical container of radius r filled with the gas, and let us follow the behavior of one molecule. The distance covered by the molecule between two successive collisions with the walls (Fig. 129) is

$$PQ = 2r \cos \alpha$$

and hence the time between these collisions is

$$\Delta t = \frac{PQ}{v} = \frac{2r \cos \alpha}{v}$$

if v is the speed of the molecule.

The number of collisions of one molecule with the walls per unit time is then

$$Z = \frac{1}{\Delta t} = \frac{v}{2r \cos \alpha}$$

If there are ν molecules per unit volume the whole sphere contains $(4\pi r^3/3) \cdot \nu$ molecules which bombard the walls. On the average as many molecules strike an area ΔA of the walls as strike any other area of the same size. Thus the total number of molecules striking an element of area ΔA per unit time is

$$\frac{4\pi r^3}{3}\nu \cdot \frac{\Delta A}{4\pi r^2} \cdot Z = \frac{\nu v \Delta A}{6 \cos \alpha}$$

and, since the change of momentum of one molecule when striking the wall is $2mv \cos \alpha$, the average change of momentum per unit time for those molecules striking ΔA is

$$\frac{\nu v \Delta A}{6 \cos \alpha} \cdot 2mv \cos \alpha = \frac{2}{3}\nu \cdot \frac{mv^2}{2} \cdot \Delta A$$

Now this rate of change of momentum is equal in magnitude to the average force on the area ΔA due to the bombardment of the molecules, and hence the pressure of the gas is

$$\frac{\bar{F}}{\Delta A} = p = \frac{2}{3}\nu \cdot \frac{mv^2}{2} \tag{21}$$

so that the pressure of the gas depends only on the density ν and the kinetic energy of the molecules, and not on the containing vessel. If Avogadro's number is denoted by N, then in n moles of gas there are nN molecules, and, if the volume occupied by these n moles is V, we have for the number of molecules per unit volume

$$\nu = \frac{nN}{V} \tag{22}$$

Inserting this value of ν in Eq. (21), there follows

$$pV = n \cdot \frac{2}{3}N \cdot \frac{mv^2}{2} \tag{23}$$

If E is the energy of the gas, $\epsilon = mv^2/2$ the energy of a single molecule, and E_m is the energy of one mole, we may write

$$pV = \tfrac{2}{3}E = n(\tfrac{2}{3}N\epsilon) = \tfrac{2}{3}nE_m \tag{24}$$

If we compare this with the equation of state of an ideal gas

$$pV = nRT$$

we see that our picture leads to the correct equation of state provided we interpret the internal energy of the gas as kinetic energy of the molecules. Since there are no forces between the molecules, the total energy is simply the sum of the kinetic energies of the individual molecules and does not depend on the volume

A comparison of Eq. (24) with the equation of state shows that

$$RT = \tfrac{2}{3}E_m \tag{25}$$

i.e., the absolute temperature is proportional to the internal energy of the gas. This is in accord with the definition given by Eq. (1). Temperature then may be interpreted in the atomic picture as a measure of the kinetic energy of the gas molecules. Referred to one molecule, Eq. (25) becomes, on division by Avogadro's number N,

$$\epsilon = \frac{3}{2}\frac{R}{N}T = \frac{3}{2}kT \tag{26}$$

where k is called the *gas constant per molecule* or *Boltzmann's constant* and has the numerical value

$$k = \frac{R}{N} = \frac{8.31 \times 10^7}{6.06 \times 10^{23}} \text{ erg/degree} = 1.37 \times 10^{-16} \text{ erg/°Abs.}$$

Equation (26) shows that the average energy of a gas molecule is determined by the temperature. It can be shown that in an ideal gas (obeying Newtonian mechanics) at a temperature T each molecule possesses an average energy equal to $kT/2$ for each degree of freedom of its motion. *This law is called the equipartition of energy.* Thus a mass point has three degrees of freedom so that we expect the average energy per molecule to be $\tfrac{3}{2}kT$.

The molal heat capacity of our ideal gas at constant volume may now be calculated. It is

$$C_v = \frac{dE_m}{dT} = \frac{3}{2}R$$

or about 3 cal./mole-°C., and the molal heat capacity at constant pressure is

$$C_p = C_v + R = \tfrac{5}{2}R$$

leading to

$$\gamma = \frac{C_p}{C_v} = \frac{\tfrac{5}{2}R}{\tfrac{3}{2}R} = \frac{5}{3} = 1.67$$

Experimentally, this value is approximately found for monatomic gases like helium, but for air the measured value is about 1.4. We can understand this value by remembering that oxygen and nitrogen molecules are diatomic and by thinking of a molecule of these gases as two mass points mounted on the ends of a massless rod. Such a "dumb-bell" molecule has five degrees of freedom, three of translation and two of rotation, and hence, according to the equipartition law, should have an internal energy per mole equal to

$$E_m = 5\left(\frac{RT}{2}\right) = \frac{5}{2}RT$$

This gives

$$C_v = \tfrac{5}{2}R, \qquad C_p = \tfrac{7}{2}R,$$

whence

$$\gamma = \frac{C_p}{C_v} = \frac{7}{5} = 1.4$$

in good agreement with the measured value.

Let us calculate the average translational energy of a molecule at room temperature. We have

$$\epsilon = \tfrac{3}{2}kT = \tfrac{3}{2} \times 1.37 \times 10^{-16} \times 300 = 6 \times 10^{-14} \text{ erg}$$

and the corresponding velocity is obtained from

$$\frac{1}{2}mv^2 = \frac{3}{2}\frac{R}{N}T$$

Now $m = M/N$, where M is the molecular weight of the gas so that

$$v = \sqrt{\frac{3RT}{M}} \qquad (27)$$

For H_2, $M = 2$ so that

$$v = 1{,}900 \text{ meters/sec.}$$

and for O_2, $M = 32$ so that

$$v = \frac{1{,}900}{4} \cong 500 \text{ meters/sec.}$$

In our derivation of the preceding laws we have made some simplifying assumptions which must be briefly discussed. In the first place we have neglected entirely the collisions between molecules, and this rather artificial assumption simplifies the calculations enormously. These collisions must be assumed, to insure thermal equilibrium, and it turns out that a more exact and difficult calculation yields exactly the same results as our simple proof. Thus we are led to picture a gas as a horde of molecules dashing around in random directions, colliding with each other and with the walls with a kinetic energy proportional to the absolute temperature of the gas. Furthermore we have assumed that all the molecules have the same speed v at a given temperature. This assumption really endows the molecules with too much intelligence so that they all adjust themselves to the same velocity. One must assume that perfectly random laws govern the behavior of systems of molecules, and under such laws we should find that at a given temperature there are molecules with all possible velocities. Most of the molecules, however, possess roughly the same velocity. If we make a plot of the number of molecules per unit velocity range against the velocity v, we obtain the curve shown in Fig. 130.

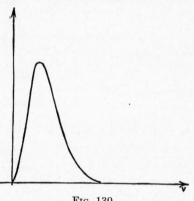

FIG. 130.

This is a probability curve and the distribution thus represented is called *a Maxwell velocity distribution*. Thus we must interpret the internal energy of a perfect gas as the average energy of the molecules. It is this average energy which obeys the equipartition law. Thus the square of the velocity given by Eq. (27) is the average of the squares of all the velocities, not the square of the average speed.

Problems

1. Starting from the equation of state of an ideal gas and the definitions of heat capacity, prove that the specific heat capacity of an ideal gas at constant volume is equal to

$$\frac{R}{M(\gamma - 1)}$$

where M is the molecular weight of the gas and γ the ratio of its heat capacities at constant pressure and at constant volume.

2. Two grams of nitrogen at 27°C. occupy a volume of 2 liters. If allowed to expand isothermally to four times its initial volume, calculate the final pressure of the gas and the heat energy added in the expansion.

3. In a container at a pressure of 2.00×10^6 dynes/cm.² at 0°C. are enclosed 3.2 grams of oxygen. If compressed isothermally until the pressure rises to 4.20×10^6 dynes/cm.², calculate the work in ergs done on the gas and the heat in calories given to, or given up by, the gas.

4. Derive a relation expressing the pressure of an ideal gas in terms of its temperature during an adiabatic process.

5. A monatomic ideal gas at 20°C. is suddenly compressed to one-tenth its original volume. Find its temperature after compression. Make the same calculation for a diatomic gas.

6. Prove that when an ideal gas expands adiabatically the work done by the gas equals $C_v(T_1 - T_2)$, where T_1 is the initial temperature of the gas, T_2 is the final temperature, and C_v the heat capacity of the gas at constant volume.

7. A gas initially at atmospheric pressure and 27°C. is enclosed in a cylinder with a movable piston. The gas is compressed isothermally to one-fourth its initial volume and is then allowed to expand adiabatically to its original volume. The final pressure of the gas is 0.4 atm.

a. Calculate the total change in internal energy of the gas per mole.

b. Calculate the ratio of heat capacities at constant pressure and volume for the gas.

8. Ten liters of air at 0°C. and atmospheric pressure are compressed isothermally to a volume of 2 liters and then allowed to expand adiabatically to a volume of 20 liters. Calculate the final temperature of the gas and the total work done on the gas. Take $\gamma = 1.40$.

9. Two-tenths gram of oxygen at atmospheric pressure and 27°C. is allowed to expand isothermally and reversibly until the pressure drops to 0.5 atm. Calculate:

a. The work done by the gas.

b. The heat absorbed by the gas.

c. The increase of internal energy of the gas.

10. Two moles of hydrogen at a pressure of 4 atm., volume of 8 liters, and temperature 200° Abs., are heated at constant volume until the pressure rises to 12 atm. and the temperature to 600° Abs. The hydrogen is then allowed to expand adiabatically to its initial pressure of 4 atm., the corresponding values of volume and temperature being 17.4 liters and 435° Abs.

a. Represent the processes above in the p-V plane.

b. Calculate the values of ΔE, ΔQ, and ΔW for the constant volume and the adiabatic processes. $(C_v = 5$ cal./mole $-$ °C.$; \gamma = 1.4.)$

11. Two and eight-tenths grams of nitrogen at 27°C. and at a pressure of 1 atm. is heated at constant pressure until its volume is doubled, then heated at constant volume until its pressure is doubled, and finally allowed to expand isothermally until its pressure drops to 1 atm.

Calculate the work done by the gas in each change, the heat absorbed or liberated, and the change in internal energy of the gas.

12. One mole of a monatomic ideal gas at 300° Abs. is subjected to three consecutive changes: (1) the gas is heated at constant volume until its temperature is 900° Abs.; (2) the gas is then allowed to expand isothermally until its pressure drops to its initial value; (3) the gas is then cooled at constant pressure until it returns to its original state.

a. Sketch a curve in the p-V diagram showing the above changes.

b. Calculate the total work done by the gas in the above changes, the total amount of heat transferred to or from the gas, and the total change in internal energy of the gas. (Express your answer in calories.)

13. A gas is undergoing isothermal compression in a cylinder fitted with a piston of area 100 cm.². At a given instant in the process the pressure of the gas is 10^6 dynes/cm.², and the piston is descending with a velocity v cm./sec. How much heat energy must be conducted through the cylinder walls per second for the compression to be isothermal at this instant? If the effective area of the walls is 240 cm.² and their thickness 1 cm. and if the temperature inside the cylinder is to be maintained only 0.1°C. above that outside, how large can v be? (1 joule = 0.24 cal.; heat conductivity of the walls = $\frac{1}{10}$ cal./sec.-cm.-°C.)

14. Three and two-tenths grams of oxygen is contained in a cylinder closed with a movable piston. Initially the pressure is 1 atm. and the volume is 1 liter. The gas is heated at constant pressure until the volume is doubled. Then it is heated at constant volume until the pressure is doubled. It is finally expanded adiabatically until the temperature drops to its initial value.

a. Draw a p-V diagram showing the stages of this process.

b. Calculate the heat added to, the work done by, and the change in internal energy of, the gas for each change. (Express your answer in calories.)

The molecular weight of oxygen is 32. $R = 8.31 \times 10^7$ ergs/°Abs. = 0.082 liter-atm./°Abs. $\cong$ 2 cal./°Abs. The molal heat capacity of oxygen at constant volume is 5 cal./°Abs.

15. Prove that the velocity of sound in air is proportional to the square root of the absolute temperature. Show that the proportionality constant is equal numerically to 2.01×10^3, if the velocity is expressed in centimeters per second and the temperature in Centigrade degrees on the Absolute scale.

16. If the velocity of sound in air at $T_0°$ Abs. is w_0, show that the velocity changes by an amount Δw due to an increase of temperature Δt given by

$$\frac{\Delta w}{w_0} = \frac{1}{2}\frac{\Delta t}{T_0}$$

From this show that the velocity of sound in air increases about 2 ft./sec. for each degree Centigrade rise in temperature.

17. Starting with a model of an ideal gas as a collection of mass points contained in a cubical box of side L, carry through a derivation of the equation of state. For this purpose assume that one-third of the mass points move back and forth along the x-axis, one-third along the y-axis, and one-third along the z-axis.

18. Calculate the average velocity of an argon atom at room temperature. At what temperature Centigrade is this velocity one-half its value at room temperature?

19. According to the Maxwellian distribution of velocities, the number of molecules having velocities lying between the velocity v and the velocity $v + dv$ is given by

$$\varphi(v) = 4\pi v^2 \left(\frac{m}{2\pi kT}\right)^{\frac{3}{2}} \nu e^{-\frac{mv^2}{2kT}}$$

times the velocity range dv. m is the mass of one molecule, k Boltzmann's constant, and ν the number of molecules per cubic centimeter. Make a graph of $\varphi(v)$ as ordinates vs. v as abscissas for hydrogen at 27°C. From this graph determine the velocity which is possessed by more molecules than any other velocity.

CHAPTER XXI

THE PROPERTIES OF REAL GASES

In this chapter we shall examine the behavior of real gases, and especially the behavior under the conditions under which they depart widely from the behavior of perfect gases. The latter, as we have seen, must always remain gaseous, *i.e.*, an increase of pressure at any temperature simply reduces the volume of the gas. Similarly, a reduction of temperature at constant pressure reduces the volume. In the case of real gases it is quite possible that an increase in pressure may produce condensation, *i.e.*, formation of the liquid, and further increase of pressure may, indeed, produce solidification. It is easy to see from the atomic picture why an ideal gas can never form a liquid. An ideal gas the internal energy of which does not depend on its volume is thought of as an assembly of atoms or molecules which exert no forces on each other. In order to account for the properties of liquids or solids we must demand that the molecules exert forces on one another so that the substance has internal potential as well as kinetic energy. The elastic properties of liquids and solids, and the free-surface and surface-tension phenomena of the former, are direct evidence for the existence of these forces.

136. Isotherms of a Real Gas.—Let us plot an isotherm of a real gas at such a temperature that condensation takes place. At low pressures and correspondingly large volumes the gas behaves very nearly like a perfect gas and satisfies Boyle's law, pV = constant. As the pressure is increased we reach a point A where liquid starts to form (Fig. 131). We now find that an attempt further to increase the pressure causes more liquid to form, and a decrease in volume takes place. The pressure does not increase but stays constant as long as liquid and gas are simultaneously present in the vessel. If we compress the mixture further, more and more liquid forms until all the gas has been changed to liquid and the liquid occupies the volume corresponding to the point B in Fig. 131. During this condensation process, heat is liberated and must be removed to keep the temperature constant. We shall discuss this evolution of heat in a later section. For the present we need only mention that this loss of heat energy of the system represents a decrease of the potential energy of the molecules. Careful experiments on the Joule effect, *i.e.*, free-expansion experiments, yield evidence for the existence of these attractive forces between the molecules of a gas. It is found that all gases cool down upon such a free expansion. This means that work must be done on the gas in pulling the molecules of the gas apart so that they fill a larger volume. Since no heat enters or leaves the system, the kinetic energy and

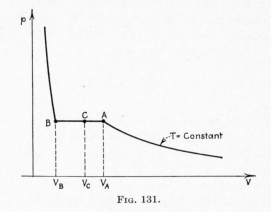

Fig. 131.

hence the temperature of the gas decrease. This cooling by free expansion is utilized in processes for the manufacture of liquid air.

137. Condensation Processes.—Let us examine the process of condensation more closely. During such a process, or more generally, whenever a liquid is in equilibrium with its vapor, *i.e.*, the gas, there exists a pressure of the vapor known as the *vapor pressure* of the liquid. This vapor pressure for a given substance depends only on the temperature. Imagine a liquid placed in an evacuated vessel maintained at a definite temperature. Evaporation of the liquid takes place and just enough liquid evaporates to build up the vapor pressure corresponding to the temperature at which the system is maintained.

Suppose, on the other hand, that we place an open vessel of liquid in a closed vessel in which there is a different gas from the vapor of a liquid such as air. The same evaporation process takes place as in an evacuated vessel and continues until the pressure of the vapor alone, the so-called *partial pressure* of the vapor, becomes equal to the vapor pressure corresponding to that temperature. The total pressure in the vessel is then the sum of the vapor pressure and the external pressure.* Thus a glass of water placed in a room evaporates until either the partial pressure of water vapor in the room equals the vapor pressure of water at the temperature of the room or until all the water evaporates. If enough water evaporates for the vapor pressure of water vapor to exist in the room at a given temperature, we say that the air is saturated with water vapor. When this state is reached, there is a definite concentration of water vapor in the air, usually measured in grams per liter, which we denote by C_s. The concentration of water vapor C in air measures the so-called *absolute humidity* at any temperature. The relative humidity at any temperature is defined as

$$\frac{C}{C_s} \times 100$$

and is measured in per cent. One hundred per cent relative humidity corresponds to a saturated state.

When a liquid is in equilibrium under the pressure of a foreign gas, *i.e.*, under an external pressure, we define the boiling point of the liquid at a given pressure as the temperature at which the vapor pressure of the liquid just equals the external pressure on the liquid. Thus we may write

$$T_B = f(p)$$

i.e., the boiling point of the liquid is a function of the external pressure, and it increases with increasing pressure.

We have already mentioned the fact that during a condensation process heat is liberated. The heat liberated per unit mass of the condensing gas is called the *latent heat of vaporization* of the substance. Similarly, when a liquid is vaporized, the latent heat of vaporization must be supplied per gram of the liquid to effect this vaporization process. This latent heat is a function of temperature, so that we may write

$$L = f(T)$$

---

* The law which states that in a mixture of gases the total pressure is the sum of the pressures which each constituent would exert if alone is known as *Dalton's law*. It is valid for comparatively low pressures.

An exactly similar evolution or absorption of heat occurs during the process of solidification or of melting. In this case we speak of the *latent heat of fusion* of a substance.

Finally, we must remember that the vapor pressure of a liquid is a function of the temperature, and it increases with increasing temperature. It can be shown that the change of vapor pressure

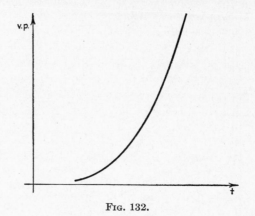

Fig. 132.

with temperature, as indicated in Fig. 132, is determined by the equation

$$\frac{dp}{dT} = \frac{L}{T\Delta v}$$

where L is the latent heat of vaporization and Δv is the change of specific volume in the transition liquid to vapor at the temperature T. This equation is known as the *Clausius-Clapeyron equation*. It cannot be integrated until the temperature dependence of L and Δv is known.

138. The Critical Point.—We have thus far confined our attention to the behavior of a real gas at one temperature and must now inquire into the question of the change of the isotherms as the temperature is changed. As the temperature is raised we find the isotherms retaining their general form, but with the important difference that the change of volume during condensation gets smaller and smaller. At a certain temperature there is no change of volume, and we can no longer distinguish between liquid and gas. This temperature is known as the *critical temperature*. At all higher temperatures no liquid can be formed no matter how much the pressure is increased. We can express these statements best by a graph (Fig. 133).

In this figure we have indicated the point known as the *critical point*. The corresponding pressure is called the *critical pressure*,

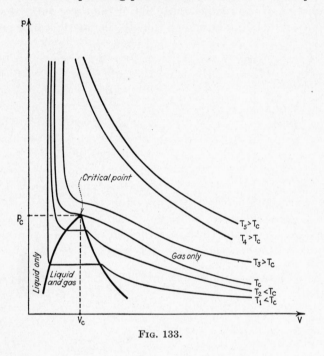

FIG. 133.

p_c, and the corresponding volume the *critical volume, V_c*. For 1 gram of CO_2 we have the following values

$$p_c = 73 \text{ atm.}$$
$$v_c = 128.4 \text{ cm.}^3$$
$$T_c = 304°\text{Abs.} \cong 31°\text{C.}$$

Furthermore, we have divided the pressure-volume diagram into three regions corresponding to the existence of only gas, liquid and gas, and liquid alone.

To illustrate the liquid-solid transition we draw a complete isotherm at a temperature where liquid-gas and liquid-solid may coexist (Fig. 134).

139. Constant-volume Changes.—To illustrate the interpretation of the isothermal curves, let us consider the changes which occur at constant volume. All such changes carry us on a vertical line in the p-V diagram.   Suppose we have a liquid in equilibrium with its vapor at temperature T in a closed vessel of volume V_1 greater than the critical volume V_c.   If we heat this liquid at constant volume, we move from the isothermal T to isothermals corresponding to higher temperatures along the vertical dotted line through V_1 in Fig. 135, and from this we find that the liquid evaporates forming more and more gas until we reach the temperature corresponding to the isothermal passing through D. At this point, all the liquid has disappeared and we have only gas.

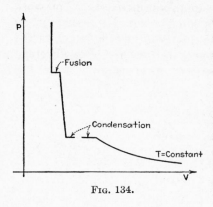

Fig. 134.

Further heating increases the pressure of the gas. If, however, we start with our liquid and gas in a vessel of volume V_2 less than V_c, we find that upon raising the temperature the gas condenses and when the point E is reached all the vapor has

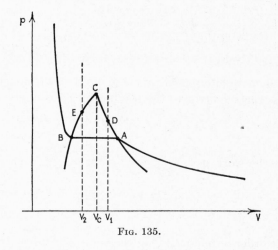

Fig. 135.

disappeared and the vessel is full of liquid. Further heating increases the pressure and temperature of the liquid.

The process of evaporation from an atomic viewpoint consists of the faster moving molecules of the liquid escaping through the free surface of the liquid.   Only those molecules fast enough to overcome the attraction of the remaining molecules ever get out of the liquid. As heat is added to the liquid more and more molecules acquire kinetic energies great enough to allow their escape, and hence the rate of evaporation increases. The work done by the attractive forces holding a liquid together on an escaping molecule is equal to the change of kinetic energy of the molecule and is the increase of potential energy of the system. This work is the heat of vaporization. As an example, water has a latent heat of vaporization

$$L \cong 500 \text{ cal./gram at } 100°C.$$

In ergs per cubic centimeter this is about

$$500 \text{ cal./cm.}^3 = 2 \times 10^{10} \text{ ergs/cm.}^3$$

Now let p_i be the pressure which would produce the same force per unit area on the molcules at the surface as the attractive forces of the other molecules do. We call this pressure the *internal pressure* of the liquid. If there are ν molecules per cubic centimeter, in a layer of liquid at the surface of area ΔA and thickness δ there are

$$\nu \Delta A \, \delta \text{ molecules}$$

The force acting on these molecules due to the internal pressure is $p_i \times \Delta A$, and the force on one of these molecules is $\dfrac{p_i \times \Delta A}{\nu \delta \Delta A} = \dfrac{p_i}{\nu \delta}$. The work done in moving one of these molecules from the bottom face of this surface layer to the top face is accordingly

$$\frac{p_i}{\nu \delta} \times \delta = \frac{p_i}{\nu}$$

and hence the work per cubic centimeter is

$$\frac{p_i}{\nu} \times \nu = p_i = 2 \times 10^{10} \text{ ergs/cm.}^3 = 2 \times 10^{10} \text{ dynes/cm.}^2$$

$$\cong 20,000 \text{ atm.}$$

This is the order of magnitude of the enormous internal pressures of liquids.

140. Kinetic Theory of Real Gases; Van der Waals' Equation. There are two major improvements which we must make in our elementary atomic theory of a gas. In the first place we must make a correction in our theory for the finite volume of the gas molecules, and secondly we must introduce the molecular inter-action forces without which no explanation of the formation of a liquid may be obtained.

According to the equation of state of an ideal gas it is possible to make the volume of the gas as small as we like by increasing the pressure sufficiently.   In the case of real molecules the volume of the gas must approach a finite value instead of zero as the pressure gets infinitely great.   Thus we may write

$$V \to b \qquad \text{as} \qquad p \to \infty$$

so that we must replace V by $V - b$ in the equation of state of the ideal gas.

The attractive forces cause the gas to behave as if it were subjected to an additional pressure, an internal pressure p_i similar to but much smaller than that in a liquid.   Thus we must replace p in the ideal-gas equation by $p + p_i$, and, including the volume correction, this becomes

$$(p + p_i)(V - b) = nRT$$

The internal pressure p_i increases as the density of the gas increases.   Consider the molecules near the surface of the container.   The attractive force on one molecule there increases proportional to the density of the gas since there are proportion-ally more molecules exerting this force.   The total force on all the molecules near the surface is again proportional to the density due to the proportionate increase of the number of molecules near the surface.   Thus

$$p_i \sim \rho^2$$

and, since the density varies inversely as the volume for a given mass of gas, we may write

$$p_i \sim \frac{1}{V^2} \qquad \text{or} \qquad p = \frac{a}{V^2}$$

Thus our corrected equation of state becomes

$$\left(p + \frac{a}{V^2}\right)(V - b) = nRT$$

which is known as *Van der Waals' equation*

Plotting an isotherm we obtain Fig. 136. The portions of the curve X, Y are unstable physically since they represent the case of decreasing volume and decreasing pressure. According to the second law of thermodynamics, which we shall next briefly discuss, we must draw the line 1,2,3 so that the two shaded areas

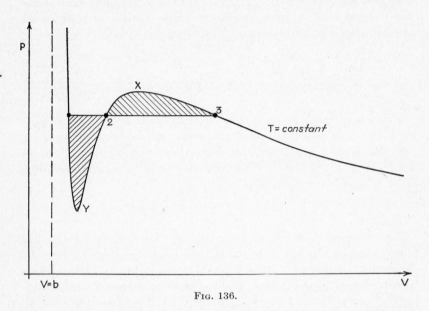

Fig. 136.

are equal in order to represent the behavior of a real substance, and thus we find the type of isotherm experimentally observed.

Van der Waals' equation is only an approximation to the real equation of state, but further refinements of this theory would take us beyond the scope of this book and we shall content ourselves with this second approximation to the real state of affairs.

Problems

1. The specific volume of steam at 100°C. and atmospheric pressure is 1,640 cm.³, and the latent heat of vaporization of water is 536 cal./gram under these conditions.

a. Calculate the work done on 1 cm.³ of water as it changes from liquid to gas at 100°C. and atmospheric pressure.

b. Calculate the increase of internal energy of this amount of water during boiling.

2. How much heat in calories is necessary to change 1 gram of ice at −10°C. to steam at 120°C. at atmospheric pressure? The specific heat capacity of ice is 0.50 cal./gram-°C. and that of steam at constant pressure is 0.48 cal./gram-°C.

3. The concentration of water vapor in air when the latter is saturated is given by the table

Temperature, °C.	Concentration, Grams/Cubic meter
−10	2.15
0	4.84
10	9.33
20	17.12
30	30.04
40	50.63

When the air in a room at 25°C. is cooled to 5°C., water starts to condense out of the air. Calculate the relative humidity in the room. Plot a graph of the above data and interpolate. (The temperature at which the water starts to condense is known as the *dew point*.)

4. A piece of ice at 0°C. falls from rest into a lake of water at 0°C., and 0.1 per cent of the ice is melted. Calculate the height through which the ice falls. The latent heat of fusion of ice is 80 cal./gram.

5. A copper bar 15 cm. long and of 6.0 cm.² cross section is placed with one end in a steam bath and the other in a mixture of ice and water at atmospheric pressure. The sides of the bar are thermally insulated. How much ice melts in 2 min.? How much steam condenses in this time? The thermal conductivity of copper is 0.90 cal./cm.-sec.-°C.

6. A copper vessel weighing 60 grams contains 250 grams of water and 10 grams of ice at 0°C. Dry steam at 100°C. is condensed in this water until the temperature of the mixture is 30°C. Calculate the final weight of the calorimeter and its contents. The specific heat capacity of copper is 0.09 cal./gram-°C.

7. A copper calorimeter weighing 100 grams contains 150 grams of water and 8 grams of ice at 0°C. A 100-gram piece of lead at a temperature of 200°C. is dropped into the calorimeter. Calculate the final temperature of the mixture.

8. A mixture of ice and water stands in a calorimeter. How much steam at 100°C. must be condensed to melt 200 grams of ice?

9. One pound of water, when boiled at 212°F. and atmospheric pressure, becomes 26.8 ft.³ of steam. The latent heat of vaporization at this temperature is 970 B.t.u./lb. (1 B.t.u. = 778 ft.-lb.)

  a. Compute the external work done in the process, in foot-pounds.

  b. Compute the increase in internal energy of the water, in B.t.u.

10. A 2-kg. steel shell at temperature 200°C. and velocity 400 meters/sec. is fired into an iceberg at 0°C. How much ice melts due to this cause? (Specific heat of steel = 0.10.)

11. A 200-gram block of ice at −40°C. is placed in 100 grams of water at 5°C. What happens? Find the resulting temperature.

12. A sheet of ice 1 cm. thick has frozen over a pond. The upper surface of the ice is at $-20°C$. At what rate is the thickness of the sheet of ice increasing?

13. The specific volume of a liquid such as water is extremely small compared with the specific volume of the vapor. If one neglects the former compared with the latter, the Clausius-Clapeyron equation becomes

$$\frac{dp}{dT} = \frac{L}{Tv_s}$$

where v_s is the specific volume of the water vapor. Assuming that the latter is determined by the equation of state of an ideal gas and that the latent heat L is constant, independent of temperature, integrate this equation to find a relation between the vapor pressure of water vapor and the temperature.

14. Solve Prob. 13 for water vapor where

$$L = 764 - 0.6T \text{ cal./gram}$$

where T is Absolute temperature. Calculate the vapor pressure of water vapor at 80°C. (The vapor pressure of water vapor at 100°C. is 1 atm.)

15. Discuss with the help of a diagram the constant-pressure changes in a real gas:

a. When the pressure is above the critical pressure.

b. When the pressure is below the critical pressure.

16. A cylinder contains water vapor at 200°C. and at atmospheric pressure. Heat is taken from the vapor steadily until the temperature falls to $-10°C.$, while the pressure is kept constant by reducing the volume. Sketch a curve showing the approximate relation between volume and temperature.

17. An open vessel contains 500 grams of ice at $-20°C.$, and heat is imparted to the vessel at the constant rate of 1,000 cal./min. for 100 min. Plot a curve showing elapsed time as abscissas and temperature as ordinates, assuming the vessel gives no heat to surrounding bodies.

CHAPTER XXII

THE SECOND LAW OF THERMODYNAMICS

The law of conservation of energy as expressed in the first law of thermodynamics places heat energy on an equal footing with all other forms of energy. In so doing many processes are pronounced possible which do not happen in reality. Heat energy is a unique form of energy, and this uniqueness which places definite restrictions on the processes which may occur in nature forms the basis for the second law of thermodynamics.

A few examples may help to clarify the above statements. A rotating flywheel left to itself will gradually slow down and stop. During this process the bearings are heated, and according to the first law of thermodynamics the loss of kinetic energy of the wheel is just equal to the heat supplied to the surroundings in the process of stopping the wheel. Such a process is very usual and common, but no one has ever seen a flywheel at rest suddenly start rotating, gaining kinetic energy while the bearings get cooler. This seemingly absurd process would not violate the first law as we need only require that the heat energy lost is gained by the wheel in the form of kinetic energy of rotation. As another example, consider the changes which occur when a stone falls off a roof. Upon hitting the ground its kinetic energy is turned into heat. The reverse process in which a stone lying on the ground at rest suddenly jumps up to the roof while the ground cools off is one which might occur according to the first law but which never happens. The reader can supply innumerable further examples.

In all these processes which result in an evolution of heat, energy is conserved, but one has the feeling that something has been lost. The internal energy of a piece of metal is not so available for doing work as the kinetic energy of this piece of metal when it is in motion. The quantitative formulation of the second law of thermodynamics consists of laying down a measure for this degradation or loss of availability of energy.

141. Reversible and Irreversible Processes.—Before we proceed further with our discussion of the second law, we must carefully discriminate between *reversible* and *irreversible* processes. A process is said to be reversible or quasi-static when it occurs so slowly that, at any point of the change, equilibrium conditions prevail. Our equilibrium equations then describe the state of the system at each instant of time. An example may help to clarify the distinction between reversible and irreversible changes. Let us consider the adiabatic expansion of a gas from a volume V_1, pressure p_1 to a volume V_2. Suppose the gas is initially in a flask of volume V_1 which is connected by means of a stopcock to an evacuated flask, so that the total volume of both flasks is V_2. If we open the stopcock, the gas rushes from one flask to the other, turbulence ensues, and eventually thermal equilibrium within the gas is attained. No external work has been done by the gas and we have a typically irreversible process. The total energy of the expanded gas is equal to the energy of the compressed gas, but there has been a definite loss of the ability of the gas to perform work due to this irreversible expansion.

On the other hand, let us suppose that the gas is initially contained in a metal cylinder which is thermally insulated and which is fitted with a tight frictionless piston. If we now allow the expansion to proceed very slowly by keeping the external pressure on the piston only infinitesimally less than the pressure of the gas, the moving piston may do work and indeed the maximum amount of work attainable in such an adiabatic expansion is obtained by this reversible expansion.

142. The Carnot Cycle.—We may now give a verbal statement of the second law. One of the formulations given by Lord Kelvin is as follows: *There is no natural process the **only** result of which is to cool a heat reservoir and do work as exemplified by raising a weight.* Another statement we shall expand on in some detail is: *Heat energy cannot be transformed into work with 100 per cent efficiency by a heat engine which carries a substance called the working substance through a cyclic process.*

By a cyclic process we mean a series of changes of the working substance such that it is returned at the end to its initial state. We shall now investigate the efficiency of such a thermodynamic engine, which we shall imagine as perfectly free from friction and in which all the changes occur reversibly. In so doing we shall get an upper limit to the efficiency of a real engine. As our working substance we choose an ideal gas and carry this gas through a cycle known as a *Carnot cycle*. This process is to take place as follows: Our gas initially of volume V_1, pressure p_1, and temperature T_1 is allowed to expand reversibly and isothermally to a volume V_2 and pressure p_2. During this process an amount of heat Q_1 is absorbed by the gas from a heat reservoir at the temperature T_1. Next we allow a reversible adiabatic expansion to a volume V_3, pressure p_3, and temperature T_2 lower than T_1. The gas is then compressed isothermally at this temperature T_2 to a volume V_4, pressure p_4, and during this compression it gives up a quantity of heat Q_2 to a heat reservoir at the lower temperature T_2. Finally an adiabatic reversible compression returns the

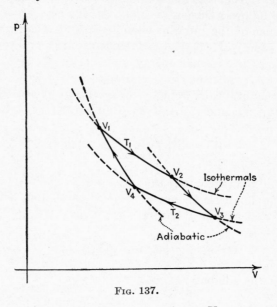

FIG. 137.

gas to its original state, *i.e.*, to a volume V_1, pressure p_1, and temperature T_1.

The net result of this cycle has been to absorb a quantity of heat Q_1 at a temperature T_1, give off a quantity of heat Q_2 at a temperature T_2, and the gas does a total amount of work W on its surroundings. The efficiency of this engine is then the ratio of the work done by the gas to the heat energy taken in at the higher temperature T_1. Of course the cycle may be repeated as many times as desired.

We next make a diagram of such a cycle on a p-V plot (Fig. 137). Now the work done by the gas in the isothermal expansion is

$$W_{12} = nRT_1 \ln \frac{V_2}{V_1} \tag{1}$$

and, during the isothermal compression, it is

$$W_{34} = nRT_2 \ln \frac{V_4}{V_3} \tag{2}$$

The work done by the gas in the adiabatic expansion $V_2 \rightarrow V_3$ is equal to the work done *on* the gas in the adiabatic compression $V_4 \rightarrow V_1$, so that there is no contribution to the total work done by the gas from the adiabatic processes. We see this most easily as follows: During an adiabatic change, work is done at the expense of the internal energy of the gas only. Since the internal energy of a perfect gas depends only on its temperature, the changes in internal energy going from T_1 to T_2 and back from T_2 to T_1 must be equal and opposite.

Thus the total work done by the gas in the cycle is obtained by adding Eqs. (1) and (2), and this sum may be written as

$$W = nR\left(T_1 \ln \frac{V_2}{V_1} - T_2 \ln \frac{V_3}{V_4}\right) \tag{3}$$

We shall now show that the ratios V_2/V_1 and V_3/V_4 are equal. During an adiabatic change there exists a relation between temperature and volume given by

$$TV^{\frac{R}{C_v}} = \text{constant}$$

Thus, for the adiabatic expansion,

$$T_1 V_2^{\frac{R}{C_v}} = T_2 V_3^{\frac{R}{C_v}} \tag{4}$$

and, for the adiabatic compression,

$$T_1 V_1^{\frac{R}{C_v}} = T_2 V_4^{\frac{R}{C_v}} \tag{5}$$

Dividing Eq. (4) by Eq. (5) there follows:

$$\frac{V_2}{V_1} = \frac{V_3}{V_4}$$

which equality we set out to prove.

Thus Eq. (3) may be written in the form

$$W = nRT_1 \ln \frac{V_2}{V_1}\left(1 - \frac{T_2}{T_1}\right) \tag{6}$$

There remains now only the task of calculating Q_1, the heat absorbed from the reservoir at the higher temperature T_1 during the isothermal expansion. During this expansion $dE = 0$, so that the first law yields

$$dQ_1 = p\,dV$$

or

$$Q_1 = \int_{V_1}^{V_2} p\,dV = nRT_1 \int_{V_1}^{V_2}\frac{dV}{V} = nRT_1 \ln \frac{V_2}{V_1} \tag{7}$$

Dividing Eq. (6) by Eq. (7), there follows for the efficiency of our ideal engine

$$\text{Efficiency} = \frac{W}{Q_1} = \frac{T_1 - T_2}{T_1} \tag{8}$$

Thus we see that the efficiency is always less than 100 per cent and that it depends only on the two operating temperatures T_1 and T_2. It turns out to be generally true for any working substance carried reversibly in a Carnot cycle that Eq. (8) gives the efficiency of the conversion of heat into mechanical work. Of course, in a real engine the efficiency of conversion will be less than that given by Eq. (8) since the latter is derived for ideal conditions which may never be exactly realized in practice. Thus we may write

$$\text{Efficiency} \leq \frac{T_1 - T_2}{T_1} \tag{9}$$

as the efficiency of any heat engine which converts heat energy into work by carrying a working substance in a cyclic process between the temperatures T_1 and T_2.

143. Entropy.—There is an elegant and important formulation of the second law of thermodynamics which we must briefly mention although we can but indicate its utility. We postulate that there is a quantity which we call the *entropy of a body* which, like the internal energy, depends only on the state of the body. It is defined as follows: If during an infinitesimal *reversible* change an amount of heat dQ is *absorbed* by a body, the increase of entropy dS of the body is equal to the heat absorbed divided by the temperature at which this change occurs. Thus

$$dS = \frac{dQ}{T} \tag{10}$$

and the second law then may be formulated in the statement that in any isolated system every change which takes place is accompanied by an increase of entropy of the system, or at best by a zero change in entropy. The entropy of an isolated system can never decrease.

It must be emphasized that Eq. (10) holds *only* for reversible changes. Thus, in our example of the irreversible adiabatic expansion of a gas, there is an increase of entropy of the gas although no heat is absorbed. On the other hand, in a reversible adiabatic change the change of entropy is zero.

We shall as a last example show how this formulation of the second law works for the Carnot cycle. All the changes are reversible so that we may use Eq. (10) to calculate the change of entropy. Since the working substance is carried through a cycle back to its initial state, the sum of all the changes of entropy of the working substance is zero. This follows from the fact that the entropy depends only on the state of the body.

During the isothermal expansion, we have

$$(\Delta S)_1 = \int \frac{dQ}{T_1} = \frac{1}{T_1} \int dQ = \frac{Q_1}{T_1}$$

where Q_1 is the total heat absorbed at the constant temperature T_1. During the adiabatic changes there is no change of entropy since $dQ = 0$, and they are reversible changes.

During the isothermal compression,

$$(\Delta S)_2 = \int \frac{dQ}{T_2} = \frac{1}{T_2} \int dQ = -\frac{Q_2}{T_2}$$

if Q_2 is the heat given off (the negative of the absorbed heat) at T_2. Thus we must have, according to the second law,

$$\frac{Q_1}{T_1} - \frac{Q_2}{T_2} = 0 \tag{11}$$

To attain our former result we must use the first law. Since in the cycle the change of internal energy of the working substance is zero, we must have

$$Q_1 - Q_2 - W = 0 \tag{12}$$

Solving for Q_2, we obtain

$$Q_2 = Q_1 - W$$

so that Eq. (11) becomes

$$\frac{Q_1}{T_1} - \frac{Q_1}{T_2} + \frac{W}{T_2} = 0$$

or

$$\frac{W}{T_2} = Q_1\left(\frac{1}{T_2} - \frac{1}{T_1}\right)$$

whence there follows that

$$\frac{W}{Q_1} = 1 - \frac{T_2}{T_1} = \frac{T_1 - T_2}{T_1} \tag{13}$$

which is identical with Eq. (8). In this proof we have not used the properties of an ideal gas so that it is more general than the one previously given.

Problems

1. One mole of a monatomic ideal gas at pressure p, volume V, is heated at constant pressure until its volume is doubled and then heated at constant volume until its pressure is doubled. Sketch the path followed in a diagram in the p-V plane. Calculate the heat absorbed and the work done on the gas in both parts of the process, and from this find the change in internal energy of the gas.

2. Carry out the same calculation as in Prob. 1, except that the gas is first heated at constant volume until the pressure is doubled and then heated at constant pressure until the volume is doubled. Show that the change in internal energy is the same as in Prob. 1. Is the total heat absorbed the same as in Prob. 1? Explain.

3. Carry the mole of ideal gas in Prob. 1 from its initial to its final state by first letting it expand isothermally until its volume is doubled and then carrying it to the final state by a process at constant volume. Make the same calculations as in Prob. 1.

4. Carry the mole of ideal gas in Prob. 1 from its initial to its final state by first compressing it isothermally until its pressure is doubled and then carry out a constant-pressure process to reach the final state. Make the same calculations as in Prob. 1.

5. Repeat Prob. 3 with an adiabatic instead of isothermal expansion for the first process.

6. Repeat Prob. 4, using an adiabatic instead of isothermal compression for the first process.

7. One mole of a substance is heated reversibly from a temperature T_1 to a temperature T_2 (*a*) at constant pressure, and (*b*) at constant volume. Show that the changes of entropy are

$$(a) \quad \Delta S = \int_{T_1}^{T_2} C_p \, dT / T$$

$$(b) \quad \Delta S = \int_{T_1}^{T_2} C_v \, dT / T$$

Calculate the increases of entropy per mole of an ideal monatomic gas heated reversibly from 0° to 300°C.

8. Show that the entropy per mole of an ideal gas is given by

$$S = \int \frac{(C_v \, dT + p \, dV)}{T}$$

Using the ideal-gas equation to express p/T in terms of V, integrate this expression. Show that, when S = constant, the relation obtained is identical with the relation between temperature and volume for an adiabatic process.

9. Consider a mole of a monatomic ideal gas carried from a volume V, pressure p to a volume $2V$, pressure $2p$ by the processes described in Probs. 1 to 6. Calculate the entropy change in several of these processes, and show that it does not depend on the particular process.

10. *a.* A Carnot engine, whose high-temperature reservoir is at 127°C., takes in 100 cal. at this temperature in each cycle and gives up 80 cal. to the low-temperature reservoir in each cycle. Find the temperature of the latter reservoir.

b. A Carnot engine, whose low-temperature reservoir is at 7°C., has an efficiency of 40 per cent. It is desired to raise this value to 50 per cent. By how much must the temperature of the high-temperature reservoir be increased?

APPENDIX

TABLES OF PHYSICAL CONSTANTS

DENSITIES
(grams/cm.^{3})

Substance	Density	Substance	Density
Aluminum	2.7	Ethyl alcohol at 0°C	0.81
Brass	8.6	Benzene at 0°C	0.90
Copper	8.9	Water at 0°C	1.00
Gold	19.3	Ether at 0°C	0.74
Ice at 0°C	0.92	Glycerin at 0°C	1.26
Iron	7.8	Air at 0°C.; 76 cm	1.3×10^{-3}
Lead	11.3	Argon at 0°C.; 76 cm	1.8×10^{-3}
Nickel	8.8	CO_2 at 0°C.; 76 cm	2.0×10^{-3}
Platinum	21.4	He at 0°C.; 76 cm	0.18×10^{-3}
Silver	10.5	H_2 at 0°C.; 76 cm	9×10^{-5}
Steel	7.8	Ne at 0°C.; 76 cm	9×10^{-4}
Tin	7.3	N_2 at 0°C.; 76 cm	1.25×10^{-3}
Zinc	7.1	O_2 at 0°C.; 76 cm	1.4×10^{-3}
Mercury	13.6		

THERMAL CONDUCTIVITIES
k (cal./cm.-sec.-°C.)

Substance	k	Substance	k
Aluminum	0.5	Lead	0.08
Brass	0.26	Mercury	0.02
Copper	0.95	Steel	0.11
Glass	0.002	Silver	1.0
Gold	0.7	Tin	0.15
Iron	0.16	Water	0.0013
Ice	0.005	Zinc	0.26

THERMAL EXPANSION COEFFICIENTS

Linear coefficient α [(°C.)$^{-1}$]		Volume coefficient β [(°C.)$^{-1}$]	
Aluminum	2.3×10^{-5}	Alcohol	101×10^{-5}
Brass	1.9×10^{-5}	Glass	2.5×10^{-5}
Copper	1.7×10^{-5}	Mercury	18×10^{-5}
Gold	1.4×10^{-5}	Water	37×10^{-5}
Iron	1.1×10^{-5}		
Lead	2.9×10^{-5}		
Platinum	0.9×10^{-5}		
Quartz	0.057×10^{-5}		
Silver	1.9×10^{-5}		
Steel	1.3×10^{-5}		
Tin	2.2×10^{-5}		

SPECIFIC HEAT CAPACITIES
c (cal./gm.-°C.)

Alcohol	0.6	Iron	0.11
Aluminum	0.22	Lead	0.03
Brass	0.09	Mercury	0.03
Copper	0.09	Silver	0.06
Glass	0.17	Tin	0.05
Gold	0.03	Water	1.0
Ice	0.49	Zinc	0.09

ELASTIC CONSTANTS

	Young's modulus		Poisson's ratio σ	Torsion modulus	
	E(lb./in.^{2})	E(dynes/ cm.^{2})		μ(lb./in.^{2})	μ(dynes/ cm.^{2})
Aluminum	10×10^6	7×10^{11}	0.33	3.4×10^6	2.4×10^{11}
Copper	16×10^6	12×10^{11}	0.34	6×10^6	4.2×10^{11}
Steel	30×10^6	20×10^{11}	0.28	11.8×10^6	8.2×10^{11}

Compressibility
(Atmospheres)$^{-1}$

Alcohol	95×10^{-6}
Ether	170×10^{-6}
Mercury	3.9×10^{-6}
Water	49×10^{-6}

Surface Tension

α (dynes/cm.)
at room temperature

Alcohol.............	22
Ether...............	16
Mercury............	500
Soap solution........	26
Water..............	72

Coefficients of Viscosity

η (dyne-sec./cm.^{2})
at room temperature

Glycerin............	11
Water..............	0.01
Heavy oil...........	4
Air.................	180×10^{-6}
Mercury............	0.015

Miscellaneous Constants

Gravitational constant...... 6.66×10^{-8} c.g.s. units

Ice point (absolute scale).... 273.18 °Abs.

g........................ 980.7 cm./sec.^{2}

joules/calorie............. 4.185

Avogadro's number........ 6.06×10^{23} per mole

Boltzmann's constant....... 1.37×10^{-16} erg/°Abs.

Latent heat of fusion of water 80 cal./gm.

Latent heat of vaporization
of water................ 536 cal./gm.

Gas constant R........... 8.31×10^7 ergs/°Abs. =
0.082 liter-atm./°Abs. =
1.99 cal./°Abs.

Velocity of sound in air at
20°C .... 1,130 ft./sec. = 344 meters/sec.

Atmospheric pressure....... 76 cm. of Hg = 14.7 lb./in.^{2}
$\cong 10^6$ dynes/cm.^{2}

INDEX

A

Abscissas, axis of, 11
Absolute humidity, 355
Absolute reference system, 53, 123
Absolute system of units, 61ff.
Absolute temperature scale, 310–311
Accelerated reference system, 124
Acceleration, angular, 26, 43
  average, 15
  central and tangential, 42
  of gravity, 62
    altitude variation, 212ff.
    latitude variation, 125
  instantaneous, 21
  in particle plane motion, 35, 37ff.
Acoustic waves, velocity of, 285ff.
Action, at a distance, 54
  and reaction, 51–52
Adiabatic changes for ideal gases, 340ff.
Adiabatic compressibility, 343
Amplitude, simple harmonic motion, 111
  wave, 281
Angle of contact, 229
Angular acceleration, 43
  average and instantaneous, 26
Angular coordinate, 39
Angular frequency, 111
Angular harmonic motion, 191ff.
Angular impulse–angular momentum theorem, 199
Angular momentum, 196
  conservation of, 198
Angular motion, 25ff.
Angular position, 25
Angular velocity, 43
  average, 26
  of a particle, 39
  as a vector, 194ff.

Archimedes' principle, 223–224
Atomic method in physics, 321ff.
Atomic structure of matter, 218
Atwood's machine, 82, 187
Avogadro's number, 346
Avogadro's principle, 218
Axis of rotation, instantaneous, 177ff.

B

Ballistic pendulum, 104
Beats, 295ff.
Bernoulli, 345
Bernoulli's principle, 239ff.
  applications of, 241
Body forces, 220
Boiling point, 355
Boltzmann, 345
  gas constant of, 347
Boyle's law, 309
B.t.u., 325
Bubbles, excess pressure in, 230–231
Bulk modulus, 271
Buoyant force, 223

C

Calorie, gram, 325
Calorimeter, water, 327
Capillary rise, 228–229
Carnot cycle, 365ff.
  efficiency of, 368
Center, of gravity, 154
  of mass, 131ff.
    motion of, 133
  of oscillation, 192–193
  of percussion, 199–200
Centigrade temperature scale, 307
Central acceleration, 42
Circular motion, 38ff.
Clausius, 345

Clausius-Clapeyron equation, 356
Coefficient, of friction, 55
  of linear expansion, 314
  of restitution, 106*ff.*
  of surface expansion, 314
  of surface tension, 226*ff.*
  of thermal conductivity, 330
  of torsional stiffness, 194
  of viscosity, 246
  of volume expansion, 310
Collisions of particles, 106*ff.*
  elastic, 107
  energy loss in, 109
  inelastic, 107
Components of vectors, 33
Compressibility, 270*ff.*
  adiabatic and isothermal, 343
Compression, simple, 261*ff.*
Condensation, 354*ff.*
Conduction of heat, 330
Conjugate points of a physical pendulum, 193
Conservation, of angular momentum, 198
  of energy, general principle of, 323
  of mechanical energy, 94–95
  of momentum, 75*ff.*
Conservative forces, 92
Constrained motion, 71*ff.*
Contact, angle of, 229
Contact forces, 54
Continuity, equation of, 237–238
Convection of heat, 330
Coordinate, angular, 39
Coordinate systems, dynamical equivalence of, 123
Coordinates, origin of, 8
  of a particle, 9
Critical point, pressure, temperature, and volume, 356–357
Critical velocity, 251–252
Curvature, radius of, 249
Cyclic process, 324, 365

D

Dalton's law of partial pressures, 355
Deformable bodies, 217*ff.*
  definition of, 7

Degrees of freedom, 8–9
  of rigid bodies, 146*ff.*
Densities, table of, 373
Density, definition of, 135
Dew point, 362
Dilation, volume, 266
Discharge rate, 238
Displacement, of a particle, 9
  in a plane, 35
Dissipative forces, 92
Divisions of physics, 1*ff.*
Doppler effect, 297
Drops, formation of, 228
Dynamical measure of force, 61*ff.*
Dynamical stability, 202
Dynamics, definition of, 7
Dyne, 62

E

Ear, sensitivity of, 295
Efficiency of ideal thermodynamic engine, 368, 370
Elastic bodies, forced vibrations and resonance of, 294*ff.*
Elastic collisions, 107
Elastic constants, 269
  table of, 374
Elastic deformation, 257
Elastic solids, equilibrium of, 257*ff.*
Elasticity, 217
  dynamics of, 278*ff.*
Energy, conservation of, 94–95, 323
  equipartition of, 347
  internal, 323
  loss of, in collisions, 109
  of a particle, kinetic, 89
    mechanical, 94
    potential, 91
Energy relations for rigid-body rotation, 172*ff.*
Entropy, 368–370
Equation, of continuity, 237–238
  of motion, 17
  of state, 308
    of ideal gas, 311
Equilibrium, of fluids, 220
  of a particle, 55*ff.*

Equilibrium, of rigid bodies, 147*ff*.
  thermal, 305
Equipartition of energy, 347
Equipotential surfaces, 95*ff*., 210
Erg, 89
Excess pressure in bubbles, 230–231
Expansion, of gases, 308*ff*.
  linear coefficient of, 313
  surface coefficient of, 314
  as temperature-measuring device, 307
  volume coefficient of, 310

F

Fahrenheit temperature scale, 307
Field of force, 208*ff*.
  intensity of, 208
First law of thermodynamics, 323*ff*.
Flow, lines and tubes of, 237
Fluid dynamics, 235*ff*.
Fluid flow, stationary or steady, 236
Fluids, equilibrium of, 220
Force, action at a distance, 49
  buoyant, 223
  concept of, 48*ff*.
  contact, 49
  dynamical measure of, 61*ff*.
  field of, 208*ff*.
  of friction, 55
  gravitational unit of, 54
  linear restoring, 114
  lines of, 208
  static measure of, 53–54
Forced harmonic motion, 116*ff*.
Forced vibrations, 117, 294*ff*.
Forces, conservative, 92
  dissipative, 92
  moments of, 147*ff*.
  surface, 258
  surface and body, 220
  work done by, 87*ff*.
Fourier's theorem, 280
Free expansion of a gas, 337
Free surface of liquids, 224–225
Free vibrations, 117
Frequency of simple harmonic motion, 111

Friction, coefficients of static and sliding, 55
  role of, in rolling of rigid bodies, 181–182
Frictional force, 55
Fusion, latent heat of, 356

G

Galileo, 3
  principle of, 48
Gas constant, per molecule, 347
  universal, 312
Gradient, 210
Gram, mass, 51
  weight, 63
Graphs of motion, 11*ff*.
Gravitation, Newton's law of, 208
Gravitational constant, 208
Gravitational potential, 211
  of a sphere, 211–212
Gravitational system of units, 62
Gravitational unit of force, 54
Gyration, radius of, 168
Gyroscope, motion of, 200*ff*.

H

Heat, atomic picture of, 322
  concept of quantity of, 306
  mechanical equivalent of, 325
  steady flow of, 330
Heat capacities, 325
  of ideal gas, 347
  relation between, for ideal gas, 338
Heat capacity, molal, 339
Heat conduction, 330*ff*.
Heat current, 331
Hooke's law, 114, 268
  for principal axes, 270
Horsepower, 98
Humidity, absolute and relative, 355
Hydraulic press, 222–223
Hydraulics, 236
Hydrodynamics, 235*ff*.
Hydrostatics, 217*ff*.
  law of equilibrium, 220

I

Ideal gas, adiabatic changes of, 340*ff.*
  adiabatic compressibility of, 343
  equation of state of, 338
  isothermal changes of, 339–340
  isothermal compressibility of, 343
  kinetic theory of, 344*ff.*
  relation of specific heats, 338
  thermodynamic definition of, 337
  velocity of sound in, 344
Impulse, of a force, 78
  of restitution, 106
  of a torque, 199
Impulse-momentum theorem, 78
Inelastic collisions, 107
Inertia, concept of, 47*ff.*
  moment of (*see* Moment of inertia)
Initial conditions, 22
  for linear motion, 65
  for plane motion, 68–69
  for simple harmonic motion, 113
Instantaneous axis of rotation, 177*ff.*
Intensity of a force field, 208
Interference of waves, 295*ff.*
Internal energy, 323
  of an ideal gas, 337, 347
Internal pressure, of a gas, 360
  of a liquid, 359
Irreversible processes, 365
Isochors, 309
Isolated systems, 75
Isothermal changes of ideal gas, 339–340
Isothermal compressibility, 343
Isotherms, 309
  of a real gas, 353*ff.*

J

Joule, 325
Joule effect, 354

K

Kelvin, 365
  temperature scale, 311
Kepler's law, 206

Kinematics, definition of, 7
Kinetic energy, of a particle, 89
  of a rigid body, 181
  in rotation, 173
  of a system of particles, 140*ff.*
Kinetic theory, of ideal gases, 344*ff.*
  of real gases, 359*ff.*

L

Laminar flow, 246
Latent heat, of fusion, 356
  of vaporization, 355
Latitude, variation of *g* with, 125
Length, measurement of, 4*ff.*
Linear expansion coefficient, 313
Linear motion, graphical description of, 9*ff.*
Linear restoring force, 114
Lines, of flow, 237
  of force, 208
Liquid, free surface of, 224–225
  internal pressure of, 359
  surface tension of, 225*ff.*
Lissajous figures, 121*ff.*
Longitudinal strain, 265
Longitudinal waves, 278
  velocity of, 285*ff.*

M

Macroscopic methods in physics, 320–321
Mass, center of, 131*ff.*
  concept of, 49*ff.*
  measure of, 50–51
Material bodies, classification of, 6*ff.*
Maxwell, 345
Maxwell velocity distribution, 349, 352
Mean solar day, 6
Measurement, of length, 4*ff.*
  of time, 6
Mechanical energy, conservation of, 94–95
  of a particle, 94
Mechanical equivalent of heat, 325
Mechanics, definition of, 3
  divisions of, 7

Microscopic method in physics (*see* Atomic method in physics)
Modes of vibration, of closed pipes, 292
of open pipes, 291
Modulus of elasticity, compression or bulk, 271
torsion or shearing, 269
Young's or stretch, 269
Molal heat capacity, 339
Moment of inertia, 164
calculation of, 165*ff.*
about parallel axes, 169*ff.*
Moments, of forces, 147*ff.*
of vectors, 195
Momentum, 49
angular, 196
conservation of, 75*ff.*
Motion, equations of, 17*ff.*
Newton's law of, 51–52
periodic, 110
quantity of, 49
rotatory, 110
simple harmonic, 110
vibratory, 110

N

Natural frequencies of organ pipes, 291–292
Newton, 3
law of gravitation, 208
laws of motion, 51–52
for plane motion, 67*ff.*
Nodal lines and surfaces, 299
Nodes, pressure, 289
velocity, 290
Normal stress, 259
Nutation of a gyroscope, 202

O

Orbit, equation of, 69
Ordinates, axis of, 11
Organ pipes, closed, 292
open, 291
Oscillation, center of, 192–193
Overtones, 291

P

Partial pressure, 355
Pascal, paradox, 224
principle, 220
Pendulum, ballistic, 104
physical, 191*ff.*
simple, 104, 119*ff.*
torsion, 193*ff.*
Percussion, center of, 199–200
Perfect gas (*see* Ideal gas)
Periodic motion, 110
Periodic waves, 280*ff.*
Phase, changes in reflection of waves, 290
of simple harmonic motion, 111
Physical constants, tables of, 373*ff.*
Physical pendulum, 191*ff.*
conjugate points of, 193
Physical quantities, definitions of, 4
Physics, divisions of, 1*ff.*
Pitot tube, 244
Plane motion, initial conditions for, 68–69
Newton's laws for, 67*ff.*
of rigid bodies, 146
Planetary motion, 206*ff.*
Poiseuille's law, 248
Poisson's ratio, 265
Potential, gravitational, 211
of a sphere, 211–212
Potential energy, 91*ff.*
Pound, force, 54, 63
mass, 51
Power, 97–98
Precession of a gyroscope, 200*ff.*
Pressure, 219
changes perpendicular to streamlines, 249*ff.*
independence of surface orientation in fluids, 220
nodes, 289
resistance, 251
variation with depth, 222
Principal axes, Hooke's law for, 270
of stress and strain, 270
Principle of superposition, 280–281

Projectile, motion of, 69*ff.*
  range of a, 70
Proper frequencies, 298–299
  of organ pipes, 291–292
Proper functions, 298–299

Q

Quantity, of heat, concept of, 306
  of motion, 49
Quasi-static process, 340

R

Radiation of heat, 330
Radius, of curvature, 249
  of gyration, 168
Real gases, isotherms of, 353*ff.*
  kinetic theory of, 359*ff.*
Réaumur temperature scale, 307
Reference systems, 8*ff.*
Reflection, of waves, phase changes
    in, 290
  and transmission of waves, 292*ff.*
Relative humidity, 355
Resonance, 116*ff.*, 294*ff.*
  role in hearing, 295
Restitution, coefficient of, 106*ff.*
  impulse of, 106
Reversible processes, 339, 365
Reynolds number, 252
Rigid bodies, 7
  combined translation and rotation
      of, 175*ff.*
  degrees of freedom of, 146*ff.*
  equilibrium of, 147*ff.*
  kinetic energy of, 181
    in rotation, 173
  plane motion of, 146
  rolling of, 175–176
  rotation about fixed axis, 162*ff.*
  translation of, 160*ff.*
Rolling and sliding, 183*ff.*
Rolling rigid bodies, 175–176
  instantaneous axis for, 177*ff.*
Rotation, effect of earth's on *g*, 123*ff.*
  of a rigid body, fixed axis, 162*ff.*
    energy relations for, 172*ff.*

S

Second law of thermodynamics,
    364*ff.*
Shear, simple, 263*ff.*
Shearing modulus, 269
Shearing stress, 259
Sidereal day, 6
Simple compression or tension,
    strains in, 264*ff.*
  stresses in, 261*ff.*
Simple harmonic motion, 110
  amplitude, frequency and phase
      of, 111
  initial conditions for, 113
Simple harmonic waves, 280*ff.*
Simple pendulum, 104, 119*ff.*
Simple shear, strains in, 265*ff.*
  stresses in, 263*ff.*
Simple torsion, 272*ff.*
Sliding friction, 55
Slope of a curve, 14
Slug, 62
Sound waves, velocity of, 285*ff.*
Specific heat capacities, 326
  ratio of, 341, 348
  table of, 374
Specific volume, 312
Spring balance, 54
Stability of gyroscopic precession,
    202
Standing waves, 288*ff.*
Static friction, 55
Static measure of force, 53–54
Stationary fluid flow, 236
Steady-state motion, 117
Stiffness coefficient, 114
Stokes's law, 249
Strain, 264*ff.*
  general analysis of, 266
  longitudinal and transverse, 265
  principal axes of, 270
  in simple compression and tension,
      264*ff.*
  in simple shear, 265*ff.*
Streamlines, 237
Stresses, 257*ff.*
  components of, 258